P9-DFV-383

STRUCTURE OF MATTER SERIES

MARIA GOEPPERT MAYER

*Advisory Editor*

# THE CALCULATION OF ATOMIC STRUCTURES

# THE CALCULATION OF ATOMIC STRUCTURES

Based on lectures given under the auspices of the

William Pyle Philips Fund
of Haverford College
1955

by
DOUGLAS R. HARTREE
John Humphrey Plummer Professor of Mathematical Physics
in the University of Cambridge, England
and Philips Visitor at Haverford College

New York · JOHN WILEY & SONS, Inc.
London · CHAPMAN & HALL, Ltd.
1957

Library of Congress Catalog Card Number: 57-5916

PRINTED IN THE UNITED STATES OF AMERICA

To the memory of my father,

WILLIAM HARTREE

in recollection of our happy cooperation

in work on the calculation of atomic structures.

# PREFACE

Judging by the enquiries I have had during the past four years for results of calculations of atomic structures and for information on methods of carrying out such calculations, there seems to have been a revival of interest recently in this subject. Without evidence of such interest, I would hardly have ventured to choose it as the subject for a series of lectures which I was invited to give as a Philips Visitor to Haverford College in the early part of the spring semester of 1955, since much of the material for such a series dates from before the war, and might now seem somewhat old-fashioned. However, that material has never been collected, except in a rather condensed form in a review article (*Reports on Progress in Physics*, **11**, 113, 1948), and very little information was given there on practical methods for carrying out the calculations. Further, there has been some recent work in the subject, and the rapid development, since the war, of automatic digital calculating machines, and of methods of programming for them, promises to make practicable many calculations in this field which would be impracticable without the assistance that such machines provide.

These lectures at Haverford were later repeated at Princeton University, and this book follows the lectures closely. It is intended for those who want to know about, or to carry out, quantitative calculations of atomic structure; aspects of atomic theory, however elegant or profound, which do not contribute to a practicable procedure for carrying out such calculations would be out of place here.

The reader is expected to have some familiarity with the general ideas and results of wave mechanics up to the theory of the hydrogen atom. In Chapter 1, sections 1.5 to 1.8 summarize, for reference and as a reminder, some of the relevant terminology and some of the properties of Schrödinger's equation and its solutions which will be required in later chapters; the reader requiring a fuller discussion of this equation and its solutions should consult a standard text on wave mechanics; the reader with fuller previous knowledge could omit these sections. The first two sections of Chapter 9 summarize similarly some relevant properties of Dirac's relativistic wave equation.

Chapters 2 and 3 are concerned with the derivation of the equations for the structure of an atom in the approximation expressed by the term "self-consistent field," either with or without exchange. These chapters involve some fairly elaborate algebra; the reader who is prepared to take for granted the equations to be solved, without deriving them or following how they are derived, but wants to get to grips with the practical problem of solving them, can omit the detailed algebra of these two chapters and go on to Chapters 4, 5, 6, and 7.

I have been concerned here with methods for the calculation of atomic structures, rather than with the results of such calculations for particular atoms. Such results are only relevant when, as in Chapter 7, those already calculated for one atom can be used to assist the calculations for another. For this reason, results already published have not been reproduced here; a reference list for such results is given in Appendix 1 and in a previous tabulation there quoted. On the other hand, in Appendix 2 are given some tables of results in a form that has been found convenient as providing a starting point for calculations for other atoms; these have not been published previously.

Further, my experience has been that enquirers for results of calculations of atomic structure usually require the results of the best approximation which can be both represented and applied simply, if not something better. So the emphasis is deliberately on means of obtaining such results. However, in some contexts a rougher approximation may be adequate, and I have mentioned at the end of Chapter 1 and in Chapter 7 some methods that could be used for this purpose.

One method of improving on the approximation of the "self-consistent field" is that developed by Dr. S. F. Boys, which has a great advantage that its practical application is not restricted to the lightest atoms, as are some other methods. The theory of this method involves some algebra much more elaborate than that of Chapters 3 and 6, and to develop the theory and give enough practical information to enable the reader to carry out calculations of his own on these lines would have increased the size of this book considerably, as well as going way outside the range of the lectures on which it is based. I have therefore done little more than give references to the papers of Boys and others who have worked with him, so that those interested shall know where to find an account of this method.

I wish to express my warmest thanks to the board of managers of Haverford College and to Professor L. C. Green for the invitation to go to Haverford College as a Philips Visitor, and for their assistance in providing for the secretarial help necessary in preparing the copy for this book. And equally I wish to thank Professor A. G. Shenstone and the managers of the Higgins Trust of Princeton University for the opportunity of working for a time at the Palmer Physical Laboratory at Princeton as a Higgins Visiting Professor. And I am glad to take this opportunity to express, on behalf of my wife and myself, our appreciation of the kindness and friendliness we found throughout the period of our stay at Haverford and at Princeton.

I also wish to thank Miss Norma Sedgewick for her accurate and expert typing of the copy for this book, and for her clear and precise writing in of the many formulae, often elaborate; and also Professor L. C. Green of Haverford College and Professor J. A. Wheeler of Princeton for several interesting discussions and valuable comments.

D. R. HARTREE

*Cavendish Laboratory*
*Cambridge University*
*October 1956*

# CONTENTS

# 1. INTRODUCTION

## 1.1. SEVEN STEPS IN THE DEVELOPMENT OF ATOMIC THEORY

There have been seven main steps in the development of atomic theory up to the point at which it is possible to carry out quantitative calculations (albeit approximate) of atomic structures. Most of these steps are so familiar today that they are part of our normal thinking, and are almost taken for granted. But they were large steps into the unknown at the time they were taken, and needed insight and imagination. A summary of them will be a convenient starting point for a discussion of means of carrying out such calculations.

The first was the discovery of the electron by Thomson in 1897, and his recognition of the electron as a component in the structure of all matter. For a good many years the configuration of the positive charge in an atom was a matter of dispute, until the second main step, the discovery of the atomic nucleus by Rutherford. From a study of the scattering of $\alpha$ particles by atoms, Rutherford showed that the positive charge, and the main part of the mass, of an atom is concentrated in a region, the atomic nucleus, very small compared to the size of the whole atom. This accounted, among other things, for the backward scattering of $\alpha$ particles, a phenomenon described by Rutherford as being as surprising as it would be if an artillery shell, fired at a piece of paper, occasionally bounced back from it. But it raised other difficulties. On classical mechanics, no static configuration of the electrons in an atom would be stable, and, if they were moving, they would radiate energy and the whole electronic system would collapse onto the nucleus; moreover, this collapse would take place not in a long time of the order of geological time, but in a very short time of the order of $10^{-8}$ seconds.

This discrepancy led to the third step, Bohr's postulate of the "stationary states" of an atomic system, states that are nonclassical in three respects; first, they are nonradiating although the electrons may be in accelerated relative motion; second, they are discrete, and, third, they have "a peculiar stability, so that it is impossible either to add energy to or to remove energy from the atom except by a process of transition of the atom into another of these states."[1] The most direct experimental evidence for these states was provided by the work on controlled electron collisions with atoms, by Frank and Hertz and others.

[1] Bohr, *The Theory of Spectra and Atomic Constitution*, p. 62, Cambridge (1922).

All these three steps were concerned with general atomic theory. The next, more specifically related to the qualitative description of atomic structure and later to quantitative calculations of it, was also due to Bohr. This was the concept that the general features of the structure of a many-electron atom could be represented, at least to a good approximation, by regarding each electron as being in a stationary state in the field of the nucleus and of the charge distribution of the other electrons. This will be discussed further in § 1.9 below.

The fifth step (which came later in the historical development of the subject, but which it is convenient to mention at this stage) was the formulation by Goudsmit and Uhlenbeck of the concept of electron spin. This is considered further in § 1.7.

The sixth step was Pauli's formulation of what is called the "exclusion principle" which states, in terms of Bohr's concept of each electron being in a stationary state in the field of the nucleus and of the other electrons, that not more than one electron can occupy each of these stationary states.

The last step was Schrödinger's formulation of the system of mechanics known as "wave mechanics," a synthesis of Hamilton's formal analogy between mechanics and optics and of de Broglie's concept of wave systems associated with material particles, a concept that has now become familiar through the phenomena of electron diffraction and their applications.

## 1.2. WHY CALCULATE ATOMIC STRUCTURES?

The spectra absorbed by atoms, or emitted by them when they are stimulated, have long been recognized as providing the key to the understanding of atomic structure if we only knew how to interpret them. The first step in this interpretation was provided by Bohr's two postulates: one concerning the existence of stationary states, and the second the relation between transitions between such states and the radiation absorbed or emitted in such transitions.

In the years immediately following Bohr's formulation of these postulates, the main interest in any atomic theory was first, did it account for the existence of stationary states, and second, did it account quantitatively for their energies? And then, did it also give an account of other atomic properties such as dimensions, electrical polarizability, scattering of X rays and its variation with angle? And one of the purposes of atomic structure calculations in those times was to try to provide answers to these questions.

Now, however, the system of quantum mechanics used in the calculation of atomic structures is well established within its range of application, and its limitations are known, and the main interest in the calculation of atomic structures is the provision of results from which other atomic properties can be evaluated, for use in the study of other physical phenomena, such as transition probabilities, molecular and solid-state properties, and X-ray and neutron scattering.

The evaluation of transition probabilities is important for application in astrophysics. All we know about a star is what we can deduce from the light we receive from it, and this has three main properties, (i) the direction from which it comes, (ii) its amount, and (iii) its kind—broadly, its color, and, in more detail, its spectrum. Our knowledge of the structure of a nebula or of the outer layers of a star depends largely on a study of its spectrum, and for this the wavelengths and transition probabilities of various lines in the spectra of various elements in various states of ionization are required. Thus there is a close link between atomic physics and astrophysics. The wavelengths can be obtained by laboratory experiments much more accurately than they can be calculated, but transition probabilities, except for some neutral atoms, are not usually observable, and calculation is the only means of determining them.

This book is concerned only with the calculation of the outer, electronic, structure of atoms, not at all with the structure of the nucleus. For the present purpose the nucleus is regarded as a point charge, and its mass is regarded as so large, compared with the aggregate mass of the electrons, that the nucleus can be regarded as fixed.

## 1.3. ATOM AND SOLAR SYSTEM

An atom, with its electrons circulating round a central, relatively massive, nucleus, is often compared, descriptively, with the solar system, with its planets circulating round the relatively massive central sun. But, from the point of view of quantitative calculations, the differences are more marked than the similarities. These are:

(i) Different systems of mechanics have to be used for the two systems: classical dynamics for the solar system, and some form of quantum mechanics for the atom.

(ii) The mutual forces between the planets are always small compared with the force on each due to the sun; in an atom the mutual interactions of the electrons are not small compared with the attraction of the nucleus.

(iii) The solar system is nearly plane, the atom is more nearly spherically symmetrical.

Of these, (ii) is particularly important. In the solar system, it is a good approximation to take each planet separately as acted on by the sun only, and to treat the mutual interactions as small perturbations. For an atom, not highly ionized, the aggregate force exerted on one electron by the others may be comparable to the attraction of the nucleus, especially when that electron is in the outer regions of the atom. The total force on the electron may be a tenth or less of that due to the nucleus, and to treat it as in the field of the nucleus alone provides no useful approximation at all; this would apply whether the appropriate system of mechanics were classical or quantum. We shall see later that, in trying to do quantitative work on the structure of a many-electron atom, we have to be content with approximations. This quantitative difference from the situation in the solar system means that from the beginning we have to think in terms of quite other approximations than those that have been so successful in working out the dynamics of the solar system.

The following are two aspects of the first difference, (i) above, between an atom and the solar system. The motion of a member of the solar system, say Mars, is not affected by whether we look at it—or more strictly whether we see it—and we can imagine ourselves observing it continuously as it moves along its orbit. But an electron in an atom is vitally affected by whether we observe it or not. The only entities in the physical world are matter and radiation; these are the only tools we have for studying their own properties, and these properties themselves put restrictions on what we can observe about matter, radiation, and their interaction. These restrictions are not due to limitations of technique, such as difficulties of making slits $10^{-8}$ cm wide, or lenses for X rays; they are inherent in the basic properties of matter and radiation. We may significantly consider ideal experiments which are not inconsistent with these restrictions, but it is not significant to consider what might happen in any ideal experiment which does violate them.

For an electron in an atom, one consequence of these properties is that, if we use a means of observation fine enough to determine the position of an electron to an accuracy of the order of $10^{-8}$ cm (and nothing coarser would give results of any interest), the reaction on the electron would drive it right out of the atom. Hence we could not, even ideally, keep continuous observation on an electron in an atom; the concept of an electron "orbit" in an atom, as a continuum of successively observable positions like the orbit of the moon or of a planet, is not a significant concept.

The second point is that two electrons are not only similar but quite indistinguishable; although in our analysis we may regard the electrons as labeled (say as electron 1, electron 2, · · ·) to keep count of them, we cannot physically attach such labels to them, or distinguish them in any other way such as painting them red, green, blue, · · · And if in an ideal experiment we could simultaneously observe the positions of two or more electrons in an atom, we could not say that electron 1 was at $\mathbf{r}_1$, electron

2 at $\mathbf{r}_2, \cdots$; all we could say is that there is *an* electron at $\mathbf{r}_1$, *an* electron at $\mathbf{r}_2, \cdots$; whereas we can identify the members of the solar system even if we do not keep them under continuous observation.

## 1.4. ATOMIC UNITS

In quantitative work on atomic structure and properties, it is convenient to regard physical quantities as measured in terms of a system of units such that absolute constants, such as the charge and rest mass of the electron, disappear from the formulae used, and the numerical evaluation of these formulae does not require the use of large positive or negative powers of 10.

The following natural atomic units form a convenient set:

Unit of mass $= m_0$, the rest-mass of the electron,
Unit of charge $= |e|$, the magnitude of the charge on the electron,
Unit of length $= a_{(\mathrm{H})} = h^2/4\pi^2 m_0 e^2$, the radius of the first Bohr orbit of the hydrogen atom.

Consistently with these, we have

Unit of energy $= e^2/a_{(\mathrm{H})}$, the mutual potential energy of two unit charges at unit distance apart. This has the value $4\pi^2 m_0 e^4/h^2$, which is *twice* the ionization energy of the normal state of the hydrogen atom.

Roughly, the unit of length is $0.53 \cdot 10^{-8}$ cm, and the unit of energy is 27 electron volts.[2]

In any consistent system of measures, $a_{(\mathrm{H})} = h^2/4\pi^2 m_0 e^2$, and $hc/2\pi e^2$, which is a dimensionless quantity, has a value close to

$$hc/2\pi e^2 = 137. \tag{1}$$

Hence in units in which the measures of $a_{(\mathrm{H})}$, $m_0$, and $e$ are all unity, that of $h/2\pi$ must also be unity, and the measure of the velocity of light $c$ is 137. The fact that this is considerably greater than unity is important to our subject for two reasons. First, relativistic effects arising from the variation of mass with velocity, etc., are of order $v^2/c^2$. For an atom of atomic number $N$, velocities (in atomic units) are of order $N$; so relativistic effects are of order $(N/137)^2$, and therefore are small for light atoms. Second, on classical theory the electromagnetic mass of the electron, regarded as a charged sphere of radius $b$, is $\beta e^2/c^2 b$ (where $\beta$ is a

[2] For more accurate values, see J. W. M. DuMond and E. R. Cohen, *Revs. Mod. Phys.*, **25**, 691 (1953). An advantage in working in atomic units is that the results are not affected by revisions of the values of $a_{(\mathrm{H})}$, etc.

coefficient of order of magnitude 1, depending on the distribution of electricity assumed); if the mass of the electron is wholly electromagnetic, then

$$b = \beta e^2/m_0c^2,$$
$$a_{(\mathrm{H})}/b = (h^2/4\pi^2me^2)/(\beta e^2/m_0c^2) = (hc/2\pi e^2)^2/\beta = (137)^2/\beta;$$

also the measure of the rest energy of the electron $m_0c^2$ in atomic units is

$$\frac{m_0c^2}{4\pi^2m_0e^4/h^2} = \left(\frac{hc}{2\pi e^2}\right)^2 = (137)^2.$$

The fact that $b/a_{(\mathrm{H})}$ is small compared with 1 means that it is a good approximation in this context to treat the electron as a point charge; the question of the constitution (if any) of the electron can be separated as a separate problem, and we do not have to cope with quantum electrodynamics as part of the problem of atomic structure.

The above atomic units will be assumed in the remainder of this book, but it should be mentioned that another choice of units is sometimes used in contexts in which energies of order $m_0c^2$ are involved. These are defined by $m_0 = 1$, $c = 1$, $h/2\pi = 1$; then

Unit of length $= a_{(\mathrm{H})}/137$,
Unit of charge $= (137)^{1/2}|e|$,
Unit of energy $= m_0c^2 =$ rest energy of electron.

It should be noted that, in these units, the unit of charge is *not* $|e|$; one consequence of relation (1) is that it is not possible to choose a set of units so that the measures of $c$, $h/2\pi$, and $e^2$ are all unity.

### 1.5. SCHRÖDINGER'S EQUATION FOR AN ELECTRON

The purpose of this section and the following one is to summarize, for reference and as a reminder, some properties of Schrödinger's equation and its solutions which will be required later. These will be quoted without proof; for proofs, the reader should refer to any standard text on wave mechanics.

For a stationary state, of energy $E$, of an electron in a conservative field of force in which its potential energy is $V(r)$, Schrödinger's equation, in atomic units, is

$$\nabla^2\psi + 2(E - V)\psi = 0. \tag{1}$$

Another way of writing this is

$$(-\tfrac{1}{2}\nabla^2 + V)\psi = E\psi,$$

or

$$H\psi = E\psi, \tag{2}$$

where $H$ is short for the operator, $H = -\frac{1}{2}\nabla^2 + V$, the "Hamiltonian" of the system in a quantum-mechanical sense.

For a solution representing a stationary state, $\psi$ must tend to 0 as $r \to \infty$, and the values of $E$ for which equation (1) has a solution, finite and single-valued throughout all space, with this property $\psi \to 0$ as $r \to \infty$, form a discrete set and are the energies of the stationary states. In the context with which we are concerned, $V$ tends to a constant as $r \to \infty$, and the usual convention is to take this constant as the zero of $V$; then the values of $E$ for the stationary states are negative, and the way in which $\psi \to 0$ for large $r$ is expressed roughly by $\exp[-(-2E)^{1/2}r]$, and $\int \psi^2 d\tau$ converges as $r \to \infty$.

If $\psi$ is any solution of (1), then so is any constant multiple of $\psi$; if this constant is such that $\int \psi^2 d\tau = 1$, $\psi$ is said to be "normalized." Two solutions $\psi_m$ and $\psi_n$ of (1) for *different* energy values $E_m$, $E_n$ have the property

$$\int \psi_m \psi_n d\tau = 0, \tag{3}$$

which is expressed by calling them "orthogonal." A set of functions mutually orthogonal, and each one normalized, is called an "orthonormal set"; these relations are expressed concisely by

$$\int \psi_m \psi_n d\tau = \delta_{mn}, \tag{4}$$

$\delta_{mn}$ (known as the "Kronecker $\delta$") standing for the set of numbers

$$\begin{aligned} \delta_{mn} &= 1 \quad \text{when} \quad n = m \\ &= 0 \quad \text{when} \quad n \neq m. \end{aligned} \tag{5}$$

If $\psi_{m_1}$ and $\psi_{m_2}$ are two solutions of equation (1) for the *same* value $E_m$ of $E$, it does not follow from equation (1) alone that they are orthogonal. However, since they are both solutions of equation (1) with the same value of $E$, it follows that any linear combination $A\psi_{m_1} + B\psi_{m_2}$ is also a solution of equation (1) with the same value of $E$, and, from this set of linear combinations, two mutually orthogonal functions can be selected—and indeed this can be done in an infinite number of ways. Further, from any such pair of orthogonal solutions of (1), any other solution for the same value of $E$ can be constructed by linear combination. Similarly, if there are more than two solutions $\psi_{m_1}, \psi_{m_2} \cdots \psi_{m_j}$ for the same value $E_m$ of $E$. Hence it is no restriction to suppose that the solutions of equation (1) form an orthonormal set.

Since the Hamiltonian operator $H$ in equation (2) is real, this equation by itself imposes no need ever to use complex solutions of equation (1). For, if $\psi = \psi_1 + i\psi_2$ is a complex solution of (1), then $\psi_1$ and $\psi_2$ separately are solutions of (1); then either $\psi_2$ is a constant multiple of $\psi_1$, when a constant complex factor can be taken out by writing

$$\psi = (1 + i\beta)\psi_1,$$

where $\psi_1$ is real, or $\psi_1$ and $\psi_2$ are distinct *real* solutions of (1), with the same energy value $E$. However, we shall see later that there are reasons why it may be convenient to adopt complex functions as the standard solutions of this equation (see end of § 1.6).

### 1.6. CENTRAL-FIELD WAVE FUNCTIONS

Consider an electron in a field in which its potential energy is $V(r)$, *not* necessarily the potential energy $-N/r$ in the Coulomb field of a point charge $N$. Such a field is not physically attainable; nevertheless as the basis for a quantitative treatment of atomic structure the results are more useful than those for the special and restricted case of a Coulomb field. The results for a Coulomb field have some peculiar and unrepresentative properties, such as that expressed by the term "$l$ degeneracy" which will be explained later; it will be recalled that also, in the classical mechanics of orbits in a central field, the Coulomb field has some peculiar properties, such as that any bounded orbit joins up to form a closed curve, whereas in almost any other central field a closed orbit is an exceptional case.

For an electron in a central field, the wave equation [§ 1.5(1)], in atomic units is

$$\nabla^2\psi + 2[E - V(r)]\psi = 0. \tag{1}$$

It is convenient to use spherical polar coordinates and to write

$$\nabla^2\psi = \frac{1}{r}\frac{\partial^2}{\partial r^2}(r\psi) + \frac{1}{r^2}\Omega\psi,$$

where $\Omega$ involves $\theta$, $\partial/\partial\theta$, and $\partial/\partial\phi$ only; there is no need, for our present purposes, to write it out in full. Then (1) becomes

$$\left\{\frac{\partial^2}{\partial r^2} + 2[E - V(r)]\right\}(r\psi) + \frac{1}{r^2}\Omega(r\psi) = 0. \tag{2}$$

Correspondingly Laplace's equation

$$\nabla^2 u = 0 \tag{3}$$

becomes

$$\frac{\partial^2}{\partial r^2}(ru) + \frac{1}{r^2}\Omega(ru) = 0. \tag{4}$$

Now the solutions of equation (4), separable in $r$ on the one hand and $(\theta, \phi)$ on the other, are

$$ru = r^{l+1}S_l(\theta, \phi), \tag{5}$$

where $S_l(\theta, \phi)$ is a function of direction only, satisfying the equation

$$\Omega S_l + l(l+1)S_l = 0; \tag{6}$$

and to each such separable solution of equation (4) there is a corresponding solution of equation (2) having the same variation with direction, say

$$r\psi = P(r)S_l(\theta, \phi), \tag{7}$$

where $P(r)$ is a function of the radius $r$ only, and is a solution of the equation

$$\left\{\frac{d^2}{dr^2} + 2[E - V(r)] - \frac{l(l+1)}{r^2}\right\} P(r) = 0, \tag{8}$$

with the conditions, for a stationary state,

$$P(0) = 0, \quad P(r) \to 0 \quad \text{as} \quad r \to \infty. \tag{9}$$

The function $P(r)$ is called the "radial wave function." If it is normalized, in the sense that

$$\int_0^\infty P^2(r)\, dr = 1, \tag{10}$$

then $P^2(r)\, dr$ measures the probability of the electron being found between radii $r$ and $r + dr$; that is, $P^2(r)$ is a measure of probability per unit *radius*, not per unit *volume*. Correspondingly the radial variation of the wave function $\psi$ is not $P(r)$ but $P(r)/r$.

From the theory of Laplace's equation it is known that the only solutions of equation (6) that are finite and single-valued over the whole sphere are those for which $l$ is integral. Thus we are only concerned with solutions equation of (8) for integral values of $l$. For a fixed value of $l$, this equation has a whole set of solutions satisfying the conditions (9); these are distinguished by a numerical label whose general value is usually written $n$, taking integral values, in order of $E$ increasing, from $n = l + 1$ for the lowest state for each value of $l$. When it is necessary to specify the $(nl)$ values for a radial wave function, they will be indicated by writing this function $P(nl; r)$; numerical values of $l$ are conventionally indicated by small letters, as follows:

| Values of $l$: | 0 | 1 | 2 | 3 | 4 | 5 · · · |
|---|---|---|---|---|---|---|
| Indicated by: | $s$ | $p$ | $d$ | $f$ | $g$ | $h$ · · · |

Equation (8) for this radial wave function $P(r)$ is just the same as that for a particle in one dimension ($r \geqslant 0$ only) in a field in which its potential energy is

$$V'(r) = V(r) + l(l+1)/2r^2. \tag{11}$$

This has a close analog in classical mechanics. The energy equation of a particle in a central field is

$$\tfrac{1}{2}m(\dot{r}^2 + r^2\dot{\theta}^2) + V(r) = E; \tag{12}$$

the moment of momentum is

$$mr^2\dot{\theta} = L \tag{13}$$

and is constant. Use of formula (13) to eliminate $\dot{\theta}$ from equation (12) gives

$$\tfrac{1}{2}m\dot{r}^2 + V(r) + L^2/2mr^2 = E,$$

which is the energy equation for a particle in one dimension in a field in which its potential energy is

$$V'(r) = V(r) + L^2/2mr^2. \tag{14}$$

Now the relation (11) is in atomic units, and applies to an electron for which $m = 1$ in these units; so for an electron the expressions (11) and (14) are identical if $L^2$ (in atomic units) has the value $l(l+1)$. This corresponds to the fact that the quantum values of $L^2$ for a particle in a central field are indeed the values of $l(l+1)$ for integral values of $l$.

For a given value of $l$, equation (6) for $S_l(\theta, \phi)$, the variation of the wave function with direction, has $(2l+1)$ linearly independent solutions, finite and single-valued over the sphere. The corresponding solutions $u = r^l S_l(\theta, \phi)$ of Laplace's equation (3) are the solutions that are homogeneous polynomials of degree $l$ in $(x, y, z)$; for example, for $l = 0$, 1, and 2 the following are such solutions

$$l = 0,\quad S_0(\theta, \phi) = 1; \qquad l = 1,\quad rS_1(\theta, \phi) = \begin{cases} x \\ y; \\ z \end{cases}$$

$$l = 2,\quad r^2S_2(\theta, \phi) = \begin{cases} xy \\ yz \\ zx \end{cases} \text{and} \begin{Bmatrix} x^2 - y^2 \\ 2z^2 - x^2 - y^2 \\ = 3z^2 - r^2 \end{Bmatrix}. \tag{15}$$

The energies $E$ of the stationary states, given by solution of equation (8) subject to the condition (9), depend on the value of $l$, but not on the particular $S_l(\theta, \phi)$ function occurring in formula (7). This occurrence of a number of stationary states with the same energy is a consequence of the spherical symmetry of the force field, and is known as $m$ degeneracy. [For the particular case of a Coulomb field, the energy values of the stationary states (excluding the lowest) are also common to different values of $l$; this is known as $l$ degeneracy, and is a special and peculiar property of a Coulomb field.]

In the absence of a magnetic field, the Hamiltonian operator $H$ is real, and, as mentioned in § 1.4, it is not *necessary* to use complex wave functions at all. However, it is often *convenient* to use such functions because a convenient and easily visualized way of removing the $m$ degeneracy is to impose an external constant magnetic field. The force on an electron in a magnetic field is velocity-dependent, and so cannot be expressed by a contribution to $V(r)$ in the wave equation (1). However, this equation can be extended to include terms representing such forces; one consequence is that the Hamiltonian $H$ and the wave functions for the stationary states in a magnetic field are complex; the radial variation of $\psi$ is unaffected but the angular variation is given by the following linear combinations of the solutions (15):

$$l = 0, \quad S_0(\theta, \phi) = 1; \qquad l = 1, \quad rS_1(\theta, \phi) = \begin{cases} x \pm iy; \\ z \end{cases}$$

$$l = 2, \quad r^2S_2(\theta, \phi) = \begin{cases} (x \pm iy)^2 \\ (x \pm iy)z \\ 3z^2 - r^2. \end{cases}$$

These are also the most convenient standard solutions of equation (6) to adopt when using spherical polar coordinates, for the $\phi$ variation is now of the form exp $(im\phi)$ where $m$ is an integer in the range $|m| \leq l$, and this simplifies any $\phi$ integrations that have to be carried out; also the variation exp $(im\phi)$ has a simple physical interpretation, in terms of a wave system rotating about the $z$ axis.

### 1.7. ELECTRON SPIN

There are three main lines of evidence for electron spin. These will be summarized briefly here.[3]

The first is the gyromagnetic effect. On classical mechanics, there is a general result relating the magnetic moment produced by electrons moving in orbits to their moment of momentum; namely,

$$\text{(Magnetic moment)/(Moment of momentum)} = \tfrac{1}{2}e/mc. \qquad (1)$$

On quantum mechanics, only the component of moment of momentum in one direction is observable at one time; also only the component magnetic moment in the direction of an applied field is observable. But relation (1) is still valid on the understanding that it refers to observable

[3] For a survey of the experimental evidence and of the kinds of experiment that provide it, see E. C. Stoner, *Magnetism and Matter*, Methuen (1938).

components of the magnetic moment and moment of momentum in the same direction. The observed value for many substances is close to

$$(\text{Magnetic moment})/(\text{Moment of momentum}) = 1 \cdot e/mc, \qquad (2)$$

indicating that the magnetism of these substances arises from something other than moving electrons.

The second phenomenon is the result of the experiment known as the Stern–Gerlach experiment. A beam of neutral atoms is passed through a gap between magnetic pole pieces shaped so as to give a strongly inhomogeneous magnetic field. In a uniform magnetic field, a magnetic dipole experiences a couple but no resultant force; in a nonuniform field it experiences a force. It is found that a beam of neutral sodium or neutral silver atoms is split into two in this field, indicating that there are two (and only two) distinct states, with different values of the magnetic moment.

Now the ten-electron $Na^+$ core can be expected to have the same structure as neutral Ne which, from all evidence from spectra as well as of experiments of this kind, is a spherically symmetrical structure, nondegenerate and with no magnetic moment; so it would be expected that the stationary states of neutral Na would be represented to a good approximation by the set of states of a single electron ("valence electron") in the central field of the $Na^+$ core; and this does account for the gross structure of the set of terms derived from analysis of the spectrum. However, the lowest term is an $s$ term, which for a point electron in a central field is nondegenerate and so should give only one state in a magnetic field, whereas the splitting of the beam in the Stern–Gerlach experiment indicates the existence of two distinct states.

The third phenomenon is the fine structure of the spectra arising from the transitions of a single electron in the field of a spherically symmetrical core, as illustrated by the pair of D lines of sodium, and more particularly the Zeeman effect in these spectra. Analysis of the Zeeman effect in the spectrum of neutral sodium shows that the ($3s$) term, and indeed each ($ns$) term, has two states instead of the one state of an $s$ term which would be expected for a point electron in a central field (this agrees with the result of the Stern–Gerlach experiment), each ($np$) term has six states instead of three, and in general each term has *just twice* as many distinct states as would be expected of a point electron. This count of the number of states is really the strongest of these three lines of evidence, as it shows that the electron has a further degree of freedom beyond those expressing its position in space. Moreover it shows that, however the fourth coordinate is represented, the behavior of this degree of freedom is such that it has *just two* distinct states in a magnetic field.

The gyromagnetic effect shows that with the fourth coordinate, which indicates the configuration of the electron as far as this fourth degree of freedom is concerned, is associated a moment of momentum and a magnetic moment; the term "spin coordinate" is used to express the intrinsic moment of momentum associated with this coordinate. The most convenient "spin coordinate" to take is one component (conventionally the $z$ component) of the intrinsic moment of momentum or "spin" of the electron itself. On quantum mechanics only one component of a moment of momentum is determinable in any one observation, and the observable values differ by unity (in atomic units).

For an electron, with just two distinct spin states, the values of this spin coordinate $s$ are $\pm \frac{1}{2}$, and the wave function can be written either as a single function of the four variables $(x, y, z, s)$, of which the fourth has only two discrete values, or as a pair of functions of $(x, y, z)$ only, say $\psi_+(x, y, z)$ and $\psi_-(x, y, z)$, one referring to the value $s = +\frac{1}{2}$ of the spin coordinate and the other to the value $s = -\frac{1}{2}$.

For light atoms, the effect of electron spin on the variations of $\psi$ with $(x, y, z)$ is small. The effect of electron spin on the energy of a state is called "spin-orbit interaction," and the order of magnitude of this is illustrated by the separation of the D lines of sodium; this separation is a spin effect, and is about 1 part in 1000 of the wavelength itself. The effect on the wave functions themselves will be of the same order of magnitude. If this effect on the wave functions is neglected, the wave function, as a function of $(x, y, z, s)$, separates into a product $\psi(x, y, z)\chi(s)$. Since the spin coordinate $s$ only takes two values, the function $\chi(s)$ can hardly have a "wave" character, but from the manner of its occurrence it is called a "spin wave function." The experimental fact that the spin has *just two* distinct states in a magnetic field means that, in this approximation neglecting spin-orbit interaction, there are *just two* distinct spin wave functions $\chi(s)$, and this is almost the only property of them that we shall need to use.

If $\chi_{\text{I}}(s)$ and $\chi_{\text{II}}(s)$ are any two distinct functions of $s$, any other function can be expressed as a linear function of $\chi_{\text{I}}(s)$ and $\chi_{\text{II}}(s)$; we shall suppose the standard functions chosen so as to be orthonormal, but shall not need to know anything further about them.

## 1.8. MANY-PARTICLE SYSTEMS IN WAVE MECHANICS

For two interacting particles, the force on particle 1 depends not only on its position $\mathbf{r}_1$, but also on the position vector $\mathbf{r}_2$ of the other particle, and vice versa, and so we cannot represent the behavior of each particle separately by a function of its coordinates only. A system of two particles in space has to be represented by a *single* function of the position vectors $\mathbf{r}_1$ and $\mathbf{r}_2$ of the two particles, and *not* by *two* functions, each a function of the position of a single particle. Further, neither particle separately has constant energy; it is only the system of the two particles together that has a stationary state of constant energy. It is rather easy to forget this, for, as we shall see, a common approximation in the theory of a many-electron atom is to regard each electron as being in a stationary state in the field of the nucleus and of the remainder of the electrons; and the terminology and notation based on this approximation is so widely and freely used, both in qualitative arguments and in quantitative work concerning many-electron atoms, that familiarity with it makes it easy to forget that it is only an approximation. The symbol $\Psi$ will be used here to distinguish a wave function of a many-particle system, regarded as a function of the positions and spin coordinates of all the particles of the system, from a wave function $\psi$ of a single particle.

Consider first a conservative system of two particles of masses $m_1$ and $m_2$, and let the total potential energy of the system when the particles are at $\mathbf{r}_1$ and $\mathbf{r}_2$, respectively, be $V(\mathbf{r}_1, \mathbf{r}_2)$. Then, for a stationary state of the system of two particles, of total energy $E$, the extension of Schrödinger's equation is (in atomic units)

$$\left[-\frac{1}{2m_1}\nabla_1^2 - \frac{1}{2m_2}\nabla_2^2 + V(\mathbf{r}_1, \mathbf{r}_2)\right]\Psi(\mathbf{r}_1, \mathbf{r}_2) = E\Psi(\mathbf{r}_1, \mathbf{r}_2). \quad (1)$$

In general, the potential energy $V(\mathbf{r}_1, \mathbf{r}_2)$ will be a sum of three contributions, one depending on the position $\mathbf{r}_1$ of particle $m_1$ only, another on $\mathbf{r}_2$ only, and the third on the relative positions of the two particles, say

$$V(\mathbf{r}_1, \mathbf{r}_2) = V_1(\mathbf{r}_1) + V_2(\mathbf{r}_2) + V_{12}(\mathbf{r}_1 - \mathbf{r}_2). \quad (2)$$

If $V_{12} \equiv 0$, then $-\partial V/\partial \mathbf{r}_1$, which is the force acting on particle $m_1$ when it is at $\mathbf{r}_1$, is independent of $\mathbf{r}_2$; that is, it is independent of where the particle $m_2$ is. This is what we mean by saying that there is no interaction between the particles. In this case equation (1) is separable; it has solutions of the form

$$\Psi(\mathbf{r}_1, \mathbf{r}_2) = \psi_1(\mathbf{r}_1)\psi_2(\mathbf{r}_2), \quad (3)$$

and constant energy values $E_1$ and $E_2$ can be ascribed to the particles individually. Further, for such a product wave function the relative probabilities of finding $m_1$ in different regions of space is independent of the position of $m_2$, as would be expected of noninteracting particles.

On the other hand, if $V_{12} \neq 0$, then $-\partial V/\partial \mathbf{r}_1$, which is the force on $m_1$, depends on $\mathbf{r}_2$ as well as on $\mathbf{r}_1$, which is what we mean by saying that the particles interact. Then equation (1) has no solution of the form (3); the individual particles do not have definite constant energies; and the probability of $m_1$ being in different regions of space depends on $\mathbf{r}_2$.

For a system of many electrons ($m = 1$ in atomic units) the corresponding extension of Schrödinger's equation is

$$H\psi = E\psi, \tag{4}$$

where

$$H = -\tfrac{1}{2}\Sigma_j \nabla_j^2 - \Sigma_j(N/r_j) + \Sigma'_{ij}(1/r_{ij}), \tag{5}$$

the $'$ in $\Sigma'_{ij}$ meaning that the sum is over all pairs ($j \neq i$), each pair being counted *once*; that is, over all $i$, and for each $i$ over all $j > i$. The first term in $H$ is the term which in quantum mechanics takes the place of the kinetic energy in classical mechanics; the second term is the potential energy of the electrons in the field of the nucleus; the third is the contribution to the potential energy from the mutual interactions between the electrons.

From all the solutions of equation (4), considerations of symmetry select a small group as being physically significant. Let $\Psi_0$ be a solution of equation (4) with energy $E = E_0$, and consider the effect on $\Psi_0$ of interchanging the space-and-spin coordinates of one of the electrons with those of another. The interchange of coordinates of electrons $i$ and $j$ can be expressed formally by an operator $\mathscr{P}_{ij}$ applied to the function $\Psi_0$; for example, $\mathscr{P}_{12}$ is the operator such that, for any values of $a$, $\alpha$, $b$, $\beta$, the value of the function $\mathscr{P}_{12}\Psi_0$ for the coordinate values $r_1 = a$, $s_1 = \alpha$, $r_2 = b$, $s_2 = \beta$ is the same as the value of the function $\Psi_0$ for the coordinate values $r_1 = b$, $s_1 = \beta$, $r_2 = a$, $s_2 = \alpha$, the positions and spin coordinates of the other electrons being the same in both cases.

The Hamiltonian operator $H$ given by (5) is unaltered by such an interchange of coordinates of two electrons; hence, if $\Psi_0$ is a solution of equation (4) for energy $E = E_0$, then so is $\mathscr{P}_{ij}\Psi_0$ for any $(i, j)$. If the energy value $E_0$ is nondegenerate, then, apart from an arbitrary multiplying constant, $\Psi_0$ is the *only* solution of equation (4) for $E = E_0$ (this is what is meant by calling the energy value $E_0$ nondegenerate); hence, in this case $\mathscr{P}_{ij}\Psi_0$ must be a constant multiple (perhaps depending on $i$ and $j$) of $\Psi_0$; that is,

$$\mathscr{P}_{ij}\Psi_0 = c_{ij}\Psi_0,$$

$c_{ij}$ being a constant number; then

$$\mathscr{P}_{ij}(\mathscr{P}_{ij}\Psi_0) = c_{ij}\mathscr{P}_{ij}\Psi_0 = (c_{ij})^2\Psi_0. \tag{6}$$

But the effect on any function of interchanging the values of two variables and then again interchanging the values of those same variables is to reproduce the original function. Hence,

$$\mathscr{P}_{ij}(\mathscr{P}_{ij}\Psi_0) \equiv \Psi_0. \tag{7}$$

Hence, from (6), $(c_{ij})^2 = 1$, so that $c_{ij} = \pm 1$. A function $\Psi_0$ for which $c_{ij} = +1$, so that $\mathscr{P}_{ij}\Psi_0 = +\Psi_0$, is called "symmetrical" with respect to interchange of coordinates of electrons $i$ and $j$, or shortly "symmetrical in $i$ and $j$"; and one for which $c_{ij} = -1$, so that $\mathscr{P}_{ij}\Psi_0 = -\Psi_0$, is called "antisymmetrical" with respect to this interchange.

If, however, the energy value $E_0$ is degenerate, then $\mathscr{P}_{ij}\Psi_0$, though a solution of equation (4) with $E = E_0$, is not necessarily a constant multiple of $\Psi_0$. However, if it is not, then neither of the functions $\Psi_0 + \mathscr{P}_{ij}\Psi_0$ and $\Psi_0 - \mathscr{P}_{ij}\Psi_0$ is identically zero, and both of them are solutions of equation (4). The first is symmetrical and the second is antisymmetrical in $i$ and $j$, and the unsymmetrical solutions $\Psi_0$ and $\mathscr{P}_{ij}\Psi_0$ can be regarded as linear combinations of the symmetrical and antisymmetrical solutions. Thus equation (4) has a set of solutions symmetrical in $i$ and $j$ and a set antisymmetrical in $i$ and $j$, and other solutions, if any, are linear combinations of these.

Equation (4) may have solutions symmetrical in some pairs of values of $(i, j)$ and antisymmetrical in others. However,

Only those solutions of equation (4) that are antisymmetrical in *all* pairs of electrons are physically significant. (8)

Such a solution is called just "antisymmetrical." The statement (8) is the wave-mechanical form of Pauli's exclusion principle. This principle was originally stated in terms of the approximation in which each electron was regarded as in a stationary state in the field of the nucleus and of the remainder of the electrons; the form (8) is more general, and does not involve this approximation.

Thus, in the calculation of the structure of a many-electron atom we are concerned with the determination of antisymmetrical solutions of equation (4) with $H$ given by (5).

### 1.8.1. THE NECESSITY FOR APPROXIMATION IN CALCULATIONS OF ATOMIC STRUCTURES

For an atom or ion of $q$ electrons, the equation to be solved is a non-separable partial differential equation in $3q$ variables (for example, for neutral Fe, $q = 26$, 78 variables). Even for the two-electron system of neutral helium this equation has no exact formal solution in finite terms. One way of representing a solution quantitatively would be by a table of its numerical values, but an example will illustrate that such a table would be far too large ever to evaluate, or to use if it were evaluated. Consider, for example, the tabulation of a solution of equation § 1.8(4) for one stationary state of neutral Fe. Tabulation has to be at discrete values of the variables, and 10 values of each variable would provide only a very coarse tabulation, but even this would require $10^{78}$ entries to cover the whole field; and even though this might be reduced to, say, $5^{78} \approx 10^{53}$ by use of the symmetry properties of the solution, the whole solar system does not contain enough matter to print such a table. And, even if it could be printed, such a table would be far too bulky to use. And all this is for a single stationary state of a single stage of ionization of a single atom.

This example shows that in order to have wave functions in forms that are practicable to calculate, to tabulate, and to use so as to evaluate other atomic properties, it is not only desirable but also quite necessary to have recourse to approximations. The question now is: What approximation is simple enough for such calculations to be practicable, and at the same time not too crude for the results of such calculations to furnish a useful approximation?

## 1.9. THE SEPARABLE WAVE-FUNCTION APPROXIMATION

The approximation that has been most widely used is one in which each electron is regarded as being in a stationary state in the field of the nucleus and of the other electrons. This approximation is several years older than wave mechanics itself. It is implied in Bohr's early descriptive treatment of X-ray and the simpler optical spectra of atoms, and of the periodic system of the elements;[4] and the first formulation of Pauli's exclusion principle was expressed in terms of this approximation. In X-ray spectra, the interpretation of the line-emission spectra as being due to transitions of single inner electrons between their various quantum states is only significant in an approximation in which one thinks that there *are* these states to be occupied by single electrons. And Pauli's exclusion principle in the form that each such state can be occupied by at most one electron also implies that one is thinking in terms of an approximation in which there are such states.

In wave mechanics, this approximation is represented by a product wave function

$$\Phi = \psi_\alpha(1)\psi_\beta(2) \cdots \psi_\pi(p). \tag{1}$$

Here $(\alpha, \beta, \cdots, \pi)$ are labels of the various one-electron wave functions, each of which is thought of as occupied, and $(1, 2, \cdots, p)$ are labels of the electrons, $j$ standing for the space-and-spin coordinates of electron $j$. The symbol $\Phi$ is used in (1) rather than $\Psi$; the capital letter is used to indicate a function of the coordinates of all the electrons, and $\Phi$ to indicate

[4] See particularly N. Bohr, *Theory of Spectra and Atomic Constitution*, Essay III, "The structure of the atom and the periodic system of the elements", Cambridge (1922).

that it is not intended or implied that this function can be a solution of equation § 1.8(4), but on the contrary it is recognized that the function $\Phi$ is, at best, only an approximation to such a solution.

For such an approximate wave function $\Phi$, $|\psi_\alpha(j)|^2$ gives the average charge density resulting from the presence of electron $j$ in wave function $\psi_\alpha$, and this suggests that each one of these functions $\psi_\alpha, \psi_\beta, \cdots, \psi_\pi$ should be determined as a solution of Schrödinger's equation for one electron in the field of the nucleus and of the total average charge distribution of the electrons in the *other* wave functions. In such a treatment, the field of the average electron distribution derived from the wave functions $\psi_\alpha, \psi_\beta, \cdots, \psi_\pi$ must be the same as the field used in evaluating these wave functions. This aspect has led to the term "self-consistent field" for the atomic field so determined.[5]

The approximate wave function (1) does not conform to Pauli's principle; the one-electron wave functions $\psi_\alpha, \psi_\beta, \cdots, \psi_\pi$ are not obliged to be all different, and even if, as a further condition, the restriction were imposed that they shall be all different, the resulting function $\Phi$ still would not conform to Pauli's principle in the form stated in § 1.8(8). This can be satisfied by taking, as an approximate wave function $\Phi$, a determinant of one-electron wave functions:

$$\Phi = \begin{vmatrix} \psi_\alpha(1) & \psi_\alpha(2) & \cdots & \psi_\alpha(p) \\ \psi_\beta(1) & \psi_\beta(2) & \cdots & \psi_\beta(p) \\ \cdots & \cdots & \cdots & \cdots \\ \psi_\pi(1) & \psi_\pi(2) & \cdots & \psi_\pi(p) \end{vmatrix}. \tag{2}$$

Expanded, such a determinant consists of a sum of terms, each representing a permutation of the electrons $1, 2, \cdots, p$ among the wave functions $\alpha, \beta, \cdots, \pi$; all such permutations are included, and each term has coefficient $\pm 1$. Thus this function $\Phi$ represents a situation in which there is one electron in each one-electron wave function, but we cannot assign any one electron to any one wave function, all permutations of the electrons among the wave functions $\psi$ being equally probable.

Since such a determinant is unaltered by replacement of $\psi_\beta$ by $\psi_\beta + A\psi_\alpha$, for any constant $A$, it is no restriction to suppose the $\psi$'s to be orthogonal. Furthermore, normalization of the $\psi$'s only introduces a constant multiplying factor which disappears in the applications we are going to make. Hence it is no restriction to suppose that the $\psi$'s form an orthonormal set.

[5] D. R. Hartree, *Proc. Cambridge Phil. Soc.*, **24**, 89 (1927).

For atoms, it is usual to take the one-electron wave functions $\psi$ to be of central-field type:

$$\psi_\alpha(j) = (1/r_j)P(n_\alpha l_\alpha; r_j)S(l_\alpha, m_\alpha; \theta_j, \phi_j)\chi(s_j). \tag{3}$$

Then wave functions $\psi_\alpha$, $\psi_\beta$ *not* of the same $l$, $m$ and spin are orthogonal through the properties of the spherical harmonic functions $S$ or of the spin functions, and, in order to ensure orthogonality of all the functions $\psi_\alpha, \psi_\beta, \cdots, \psi_\pi$, it is only necessary to impose the condition

$$\int_0^\infty P(nl; r)P(n'l; r)\, dr = 0 \qquad \text{for} \quad n' \neq n \tag{4}$$

on the set of wave functions for each separate value of $l$.

In a central field, there are $2(2l + 1)$ wave functions (3) with any specified $(nl)$, formed by $(2l + 1)$ different functions $S$, and two different spin functions $\chi$. A set of wave functions $\psi$, with the same $(nl)$, in the determinant (2), is called a "group" or "$(nl)$ group"; if all the $2(2l + 1)$ functions with the same $(nl)$ occur, the group is called "complete." Most atomic structures consist (in this approximation) of complete groups only, or of complete groups and a few electrons in one or two incomplete groups, seldom more except perhaps in excited states.

A group of $q$ $(nl)$ wave functions is written $(nl)^q$, and qualitatively the structure of an atom, in this approximation, is specified by the number of occupied wave functions in each of the different $(nl)$ groups. For example, the normal state of neutral Mn ($N = 25$) has the structure

$$\text{Mn:} \quad (1s)^2(2s)^2(2p)^6(3s)^2(3p)^6(3d)^5(4s)^2.$$

Such a statement of the number of occupied wave functions in each $(nl)$ group is said to specify a "configuration" of the atomic system.

Delbrück[6] has shown that, if we adopt the approximation of separable wave functions at all, then for a configuration of complete groups the use of central-field wave functions is required by the spatial symmetry of the atom as a whole. A configuration of complete groups gives a $^1S$ state, and such a state is nondegenerate. It follows that its wave function is isotropic, in the sense that its value for any values of $\mathbf{r}_1, \mathbf{r}_2, \cdots$ is unaffected if the whole wave function is rotated, as a rigid body, relative to the frame of reference; for, if such a rotation transformed a wave function $\Psi_0$ into a different function, $\Psi_1$, of $\mathbf{r}_1, \mathbf{r}_2, \cdots$, $\Psi_0$ and $\Psi_1$ would be two different solutions of the wave equation for the same energy; and this would conflict with the nondegenerate property of a $^1S$ state. Delbrück showed that the transformation properties of the spherical

[6] M. Delbrück, *Proc. Roy. Soc.*, **129**, 686 (1930).

harmonics under a rotation are just such as to give the determinant (2) this isotropic property, provided the one-electron wave functions are of central-field type.

For a configuration of complete groups, each one-electron wave function of each $(nl)$ group appears in the determinant (2). But for a configuration that includes an incomplete $(nl)$ group, a single determinant (2) can only include a selection of the $2(2l + 1)$ different wave functions of the $(nl)$ group. Let us write $A$ for the set of one-electron wave functions $\psi_\alpha, \psi_\beta, \cdots, \psi_\pi$, and $\Phi_A$ for a determinant (2) constructed from the set $A$ of wave functions $\psi$; and consider, for example, the normal configuration $(1s)^2(2s)^2(2p)^2$ of neutral $C$. There are six different $(2p)$ wave functions, but only two of them can be included in the set $A$ of wave functions $\psi$ in any one determinant. There are altogether 15 such determinants, corresponding to the $\frac{1}{2} \cdot 6 \cdot 5 = 15$ ways in which a pair of $(2p)$ wave functions can be chosen from 6 distinct functions.

For a configuration including a single $(nl)^q$ incomplete group, the appropriate wave function for an atomic state, in the approximation we are considering, may be a linear combination of determinants

$$\Phi = \Sigma_A C_A \Phi_A,$$

the sum being over all sets $A$ containing $q$ $(nl)$ wave functions. The treatment of configurations containing incomplete groups is considered in Chapter 6.

The greater part of this book is concerned with the theory and practical procedure of calculating atomic wave functions on this approximation (expressed by the term "self-consistent field with exchange"), or in a simplified version of it ("self-consistent field without exchange," see § 3.9) which, for heavy atoms, is the best that has been found practicable without the assistance of an automatic digital calculating machine. The last chapter (Chapter 10) gives an outline of various attempts which have been made, mainly for quite light atoms, to improve on this approximation.

As mentioned in the preface, it seems that most users of atomic wave functions require the best functions that are available, provided they are not too complicated and are easy to use, and would like better ones. However, in some contexts rougher approximations may be adequate. Some such approximations, such as the use of scaling procedures, or of analytic wave functions with screening parameters given by Slater's rules,[7] are mentioned in Chapter 7. There they are considered primarily from the point of view of providing the initial estimates required in a self-consistent field calculation. However, if the results of using such an

[7] J. C. Slater, *Phys. Rev.*, **36**, 57 (1930); also *Quantum Theory of Matter*, appendix 13, McGraw-Hill, New York (1951).

approximation are regarded as accurate enough for some particular application, they can be used as they stand. Almost any approximation will give fair to good results for the inner wave functions of an atom, but some calculation beyond use of the approximations mentioned in Chapter 7 will usually be required to give good approximations to the outer wave functions.

# 2. THE VARIATION PRINCIPLE

## 2.1. STATIONARY STATES OF A PARTICLE IN ONE DIMENSION

For the derivation of approximate wave functions, there is an important general theorem in quantum mechanics known as the variation principle. In this context it seems both more important and more general than perturbation theory. For perturbation theory is only applicable to a system with a potential energy function $V$ when there is a neighboring potential energy function $U$ for which solutions of the wave equation can be obtained, whereas application of the variation principle is independent of such a restriction. And, further, the results of perturbation theory for time-constant perturbations can be derived from the variation principle as special cases.

To exhibit the variation principle in the simplest case, it will first be derived for a particle in a conservative field in one dimension, and later extended.

The wave equation for the stationary states of such a particle is

$$H\psi = E\psi, \tag{1}$$

where

$$H = -\frac{1}{2m}\frac{d^2}{dx^2} + V(x). \tag{2}$$

Let the solutions, satisfying the two-point boundary conditions $\psi = 0$ at $x = a$, $x = b$, be $\psi_n$, with energies $E_n$; that is,

$$H\psi_n = E_n\psi_n. \tag{3}$$

Consider the quantity

$$E' = \int_a^b \phi\, H\phi\, dx \Big/ \int_a^b \phi^2\, dx, \tag{4}$$

where $\phi(x)$ is a function of $x$, twice differentiable with respect to $x$ and satisfying the two-point boundary conditions on $\psi$, but not necessarily a solution of equation (1), and inquire how the value of $E'$ depends on the function $\phi(x)$. [Note that $E'$ is not a function of $x$; it depends on the way in which $\phi(x)$ varies with $x$ over the whole range of $x$; such a relation is expressed by calling $E'$ a "functional" of $\phi(x)$.] If $\phi(x)$ does happen to be the wave function $\psi_n$ of a stationary state, then $E'$ has the energy value $E_n$ of that state; thus $E'$ is related to energy values, and this is why the symbol $E$ is used for it; the prime is used as a reminder that, if the expression (4) is evaluated for a function $\phi$ other than a wave function of a stationary state, then $E'$ is not in general an energy of such a state (though it will often be an approximation to such an energy).

It will be necessary, both here and in other contexts later, to have a notation for the difference between the values, for the *same* value of $x$ (or of $\mathbf{r}$), of two *different* functions of $x$ (or of $\mathbf{r}$). Such a difference will be indicated by $\Delta$, whereas $\delta$ will be used for a difference between the values of the *same* function of $x$ at two *different* values of $x$ (see Fig. 2.1).

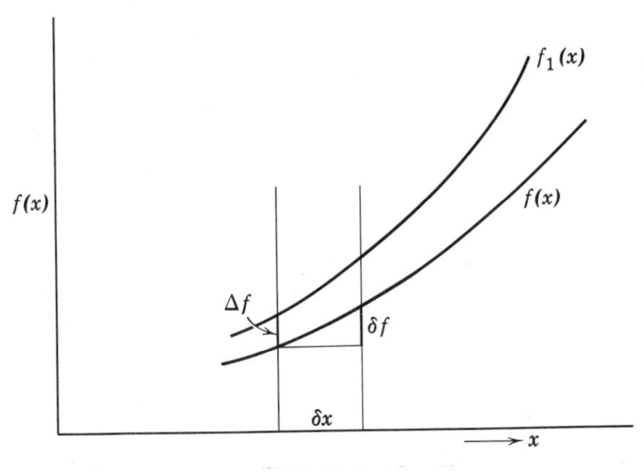


Fig. 2.1.

We shall also need, both here and later, a result related to the standard formula for integration by parts in elementary calculus and almost as useful. If $u$ and $v$ are any twice-differentiable functions of $x$, we have the identity

$$\frac{d}{dx}\left(u\frac{dv}{dx} - v\frac{du}{dx}\right) = u\frac{d^2v}{dx^2} - v\frac{d^2u}{dx^2}, \tag{5}$$

and hence, by integration between limits $x = a$ and $x = b$ and rearrangement of terms,

$$\int_a^b u\frac{d^2v}{dx^2}\,dx = \left|u\frac{dv}{dx} - v\frac{du}{dx}\right|_a^b + \int_a^b v\frac{d^2u}{dx^2}\,dx \tag{6}$$

(which can alternatively be obtained by two integrations by parts). In particular, if $u$ and $v$ are zero at both ends of the range (and $du/dx$, $dv/dx$ are finite there)

$$\int_a^b u\frac{d^2v}{dx^2}\,dx = \int_a^b v\frac{d^2u}{dx^2}\,dx. \tag{7}$$

(This does *not* imply that the integrands of these integrals are equal over the whole range; it is a special relation between the values of the integrals over this particular range *only*.)

Consider now the quantity $E'$ evaluated for two different functions $\phi(x)$ and $\phi_1(x) = \phi(x) + \Delta\phi(x)$, neither necessarily a solution of equation (1). Let $E' + \Delta E'$ be written for the quantity obtained by substituting $(\phi + \Delta\phi)$ for $\phi$ in (4); that is,

$$E' + \Delta E' = \int_a^b (\phi + \Delta\phi)\, H(\phi + \Delta\phi)\, dx \Big/ \int_a^b (\phi + \Delta\phi)^2\, dx, \tag{8}$$

and $E'$ is given by formula (4).

The simplest way of arranging the algebra to get the result required is to multiply formula (8) by $\int(\phi + \Delta\phi)^2\, dx$, and then subtract $E'\int(\phi + \Delta\phi)^2\, dx$ from both sides. The result is

$$\left[\int_a^b (\phi + \Delta\phi)^2\, dx\right] \Delta E' = \int_a^b (\phi + \Delta\phi)(H - E')(\phi + \Delta\phi)\, dx \tag{9}$$

$$= \int_a^b \phi(H - E')\phi\, dx + \int_a^b \phi(H - E')\Delta\phi\, dx + \int_a^b \Delta\phi(H - E')\phi\, dx + \int_a^b \Delta\phi(H - E')\Delta\phi\, dx. \tag{10}$$

In this expression, the first term is zero because $E'$ is given by formula (4). The second term is

$$\int_a^b \phi \left\{-\frac{1}{2m}\frac{d^2}{dx^2} + [V(x) - E']\right\} \Delta\phi\, dx = \int_a^b \phi \left(-\frac{1}{2m}\frac{d^2}{dx^2}\right) \Delta\phi\, dx + \int_a^b \phi[V(x) - E']\Delta\phi\, dx. \tag{11}$$

Since $\phi$ and $\Delta\phi$ are both zero at $x = a$, $x = b$, it follows from the relation (7) that the first term here has the same value as

$$\int_a^b \Delta\phi \left(-\frac{1}{2m}\frac{d^2}{dx^2}\right) \phi\, dx,$$

and, in the second term in formula (11), $[V(x) - E']$ is a multiplying factor simply, so that the order of the factors can be changed without altering the integrand at any value of $x$, and so without altering the integral. Hence the second term in the expression (10) is equal to the third, and altogether

$$\left[\int_a^b (\phi + \Delta\phi)^2\, dx\right] \Delta E' = 2\int_a^b \Delta\phi(H - E')\phi\, dx + \int_a^b \Delta\phi(H - E')\, \Delta\phi\, dx. \tag{12}$$

From this we can draw two conclusions:

First, *if* $\phi$ *is* a solution of equation (1), say $\phi = \psi_n$, so that $E' = E_n$ from formula (4), and $(H - E')\phi = (H - E_n)\psi_n = 0$ since $\psi_n$ is a solution of equation (1) with energy $E = E_n$, then, from formula (12),

$$\left[\int_a^b (\psi_n + \Delta\phi)^2\,dx\right] \Delta E' = \int_a^b \Delta\phi(H - E_n)\,\Delta\phi\,dx; \tag{13}$$

that is

$$\Delta E' = O(\Delta\phi)^2. \tag{14}$$

Second, *if* $\Delta E' = O(\Delta\phi)^2$ for every $\Delta\phi$, then, from formula (12),

$$\int_a^b \Delta\phi(H - E')\phi\,dx = 0$$

for every $\Delta\phi$ (twice differentiable and satisfying the two-point boundary conditions on $\psi$), and hence

$$(H - E')\phi = 0$$

for all $x$.

That is: (i) *if* $\phi$ is a solution of equation (1), *then* $E'$ is stationary, in the sense that $\Delta E' = 0$ to first order in $\Delta\phi$, for any variation $\Delta\phi$; hence, if $\phi$ is an approximation to $\psi_n$, then $E'$ calculated from formula (4) is a better approximation to $E_n$ than $\phi$ is to $\psi_n$; for example, if $\phi$, as an approximation to $\psi_n$, is good to 1 per cent, $E'$ as an approximation to $E_n$ may be expected to be good to roughly 0.01 per cent.

And (ii) *if* $E'$ is stationary, in the above sense, for any variation $\Delta\phi$ from a function $\phi$, *then* this $\phi$ is a solution $\psi_n$ of equation (1), and the stationary value of $E'$ is the corresponding value of $E_n$.

For the normal state there is a further result. Let $\psi_k$ be the normalized solutions of equation (1), which form an orthonormal set. In the expression (13) for $\Delta E'$, suppose $\Delta\phi$ expanded in terms of these functions

$$\Delta\phi = \Sigma_k a_k \psi_k. \tag{15}$$

Then

$$(H - E_n)\,\Delta\phi = \Sigma_k a_k (H - E_n)\psi_k = \Sigma_k a_k (E_k - E_n)\psi_k,$$

since $H\psi_k = E\psi_k$. Then

$$\Delta\phi(H - E_n)\,\Delta\phi = \Sigma_j a_j \psi_j \Sigma_k a_k (E_k - E_n)\psi_k.$$

Since different subscripts have been used to indicate the two summations, we can write this:

$$\Delta\phi(H - E_n)\,\Delta\phi = \Sigma_{jk} a_j a_k (E_k - E_n)\psi_j\psi_k,$$

and then

$$\begin{aligned}\int \Delta\phi(H - E_n)\,\Delta\phi\,dx &= \Sigma_{jk} a_j a_k (E_k - E_n) \int \psi_j \psi_k\,dx \\ &= \Sigma_{jk} a_j a_k (E_k - E_n)\delta_{jk},\end{aligned}$$

since the $\psi_k$'s form an orthonormal set. In the summation over $k$, the coefficient $\delta_{jk}$ of $a_j a_k(E_k - E_n)$ is zero unless $k = j$, when it is 1; hence

$$[\int(\psi_n + \Delta\phi)^2\,dx]\Delta E' = \int \Delta\phi(H - E_n)\,\Delta\phi\,dx = \Sigma_j a_j^2(E_j - E_n). \quad (16)$$

If $n = 0$ (normal state), all terms of the sum (16) are positive, and the integral on the left is also positive, so that $\Delta E'$ is positive. Hence the value of $E'$ for the normal state is an *absolute minimum*.

### 2.1.1. E′ AS A LAGRANGE PARAMETER

We have seen two aspects of the quantity

$$E' = \int \phi H \phi\,dx / \int \phi^2\,dx. \quad (1)$$

One is simply the value of this ratio of integrals for any function $\phi$, and the second is an approximation to the energy of a stationary state if $\phi$ is an approximation to the wave function for that state. A third aspect of this quantity is obtained if the variation principle is put in another form.

The stationary values $E'$ of the ratio (1) are also the stationary values of the integral $I = \int_a^b \phi H \phi\,dx$ if this is evaluated, not for *all* twice-differentiable functions $\phi$, but only for such functions $\phi$ as satisfy the normalization condition:

$$N \equiv \int_a^b \phi^2\,dx = 1. \quad (2)$$

For any variation $\Delta\phi$ of $\phi$,

$$\Delta I = 2\int_a^b (\Delta\phi)\,H\phi\,dx, \qquad \Delta N = 2\int_a^b (\Delta\phi)\phi\,dx,$$

and the stationary values of $I$, conditional on $N = 1$, can be obtained[1] by forming $\Delta I - \lambda\,\Delta N$, where $\lambda$ is a constant multiplier as yet undetermined (called a "Lagrange multiplier" or "undetermined multiplier") and requiring that the resultant expression shall be zero for *all* $\Delta\phi$, unrestricted by the condition $\int_a^b \phi\,\Delta\phi\,dx = 0$. This gives

$$\int_a^b \Delta\phi(H - \lambda)\phi\,dx = 0,$$

so that $\phi$ and $\lambda$ together must satisfy the equation

$$(H - \lambda)\phi = 0. \quad (3)$$

[1] See, for example, R. Courant, *Differential and Integral Calculus*, vol. 2, ch. 7, sec. 2, subsec. 6(*b*), Blackie (1936).

Unless $\lambda$ is a characteristic value of equation § 2.1(1), equation (3) has no solution satisfying the boundary conditions on $\phi$, other than the solution $\phi \equiv 0$ which certainly does not fit the restrictive condition (2) imposed on the functions $\phi$ contemplated in the present argument. Hence the values of the Lagrange multiplier $\lambda$, for which the conditional stationary value problem ($I$ stationary subject to $N$ constant) has a solution, are the energy values of the stationary states. Also the stationary property of $I$ subject to $N =$ constant means that, if $\phi$ is not a solution of (3), $\lambda = I = \int_a^b \phi\, H\phi\, dx$ is still an approximation to the corresponding Lagrange multiplier $\lambda$.

## 2.2. PARTICLE IN THREE DIMENSIONS

For a particle in a conservative field in three dimensions, the wave equation is

$$H\psi = E\psi, \tag{1}$$

where, now,

$$H = -\frac{1}{2m}\nabla^2 + V(\mathbf{r}). \tag{2}$$

For real functions $\phi$, not necessarily solutions of equation (1), let

$$E' = \int \phi\, H\phi\, d\tau / \int \phi^2\, d\tau, \tag{3}$$

where $\phi$ is now a function of position $\mathbf{r}$, and $d\tau$ stands for a volume element and integration is over all space; and consider how the value of $E'$ depends on the function $\phi(\mathbf{r})$.

The algebra is the same as for a particle in one dimension, with $\int \cdots d\tau$ substituted for $\int \cdots dx$, as far as § 2.1(10) inclusive. Now, however, $H$ contains

(i) The differential operator $\nabla^2$.
(ii) The function $[V(r) - E']$ which is a multiplying factor in the integrand.

It is a standard result of vector analysis that, if $S$ is a closed surface enclosing a volume $\tau$, and, on $S$, $\mathbf{n}$ is a unit vector normal to $S$ drawn outwards from the volume $\tau$ (see Fig. 2.2), then

$$\int u\, \nabla^2 v\, d\tau = \int (u\, \nabla v - v\, \nabla u) \cdot \mathbf{n}\, dS + \int v\, \nabla^2 u\, d\tau; \tag{4}$$

this is the three-dimensional analog of formula § 2.1(6). If we restrict the functions $\phi$ for which we evaluate $E'$ to functions that tend to zero fast enough as $r \to \infty$ for the integral over the sphere at infinity to vanish, then it follows from formula (4) that $\int \phi\, \nabla^2(\Delta\phi)\, d\tau = \int \Delta\phi\, \nabla^2\phi\, d\tau$, and the remainder of the argument is the same as for a particle in one dimension.

As already mentioned in § 1.6, it is never necessary to use complex wave functions in dealing with solutions of the wave equation for stationary states in a conservative field, though it is often convenient to do so. If

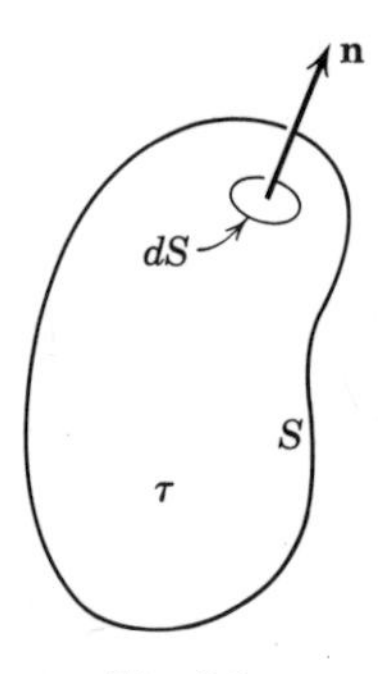


Fig. 2.2.

$\phi$ stands for a complex wave function and $\phi^*$ for its complex conjugate, the quantity corresponding to (3) is

$$E' = \int \phi^* H\phi \, d\tau / \int \phi^* \phi \, d\tau, \tag{5}$$

and has a similar stationary property, that, *if* $\phi$ is a solution of equation (1), then $E'$ is stationary for any small variation $\Delta\phi$ (which may itself be complex).

If $E'$ is stationary, then (to first order in $\Delta\phi$)

$$\int [\Delta\phi^*(H - E')\phi + \Delta\phi(H - E')\phi^*] \, d\tau = 0 \tag{6}$$

for all $\Delta\phi$. Here $\Delta\phi$, $\Delta\phi^*$ are not independent variations, and so we cannot immediately deduce from (6) that

$$(H - E')\phi = 0, \qquad (H - E')\phi^* = 0. \tag{7}$$

However

$$\Delta\phi = \Delta u + i \, \Delta v,$$
$$\Delta\phi^* = \Delta u - i \, \Delta v,$$

where $\Delta u$ and $\Delta v$ are real and are independent variations; hence formula (6) can be written

$$\int [\Delta u(H - E')(\phi + \phi^*) - i \, \Delta v(H - E')(\phi - \phi^*)] \, d\tau = 0$$

for all $\Delta u$, $\Delta v$. Hence

$$(H - E')(\phi + \phi^*) = 0, \qquad (H - E')i(\phi - \phi^*) = 0.$$

Hence the real functions $\phi + \phi^*$ and $i(\phi - \phi^*)$ are both solutions of equation (1), and relations (7) follow.

### 2.3. MANY-PARTICLE SYSTEMS IN COORDINATE SPACE

The wave functions $\Psi$ for the stationary states of a many-particle system under conservative forces satisfy a wave equation $H\Psi = E\Psi$ in which the Hamiltonian operator $H$ contains terms $-(1/2m)\nabla_i^2$ for the separate particles and a potential energy function which is a factor multiplying $\Psi$. Let $E'$ be defined by

$$E' = \int \Phi\, H\Phi\, d\tau / \int \Phi^2\, d\tau \qquad \text{for real functions } \Phi \qquad (1)$$

$$= \int \Phi^*\, H\Phi\, d\tau / \int \Phi^*\Phi\, d\tau \qquad \text{for complex functions } \Phi, \qquad (2)$$

the integrations being now over the coordinate space of the system. This quantity has the same stationary properties as has the corresponding quantity for a particle in one and in three dimensions. The proof follows that for a particle in three dimensions and will not be given in detail.

The property of $E'$, defined by formulae (1) or (2), that it is an absolute minimum for the normal state of the system, provides a useful criterion for comparing approximations to the wave function for the normal state, without knowing the exact solution of the wave equation to which they *are* approximations. One wave function can be regarded as a "better" approximation to the normal state if it gives a lower value of $E'$. In this sense "better" means "better for the calculation of the total energy of the whole atomic system"; other approximations might be better for calculation of other atomic properties, but in most instances the only test is the empirical one of agreement with observed values; and, since one of the purposes of the calculation of atomic structures is to provide data for the evaluation of atomic properties not accessible to direct observation, this test is not generally available. No one criterion can give a full specification of the goodness of an approximate wave function, for different features of the wave function are important in different applications; for example, the van der Waals attractive forces between two inert-gas atoms at a large separation from each other, and the repulsive forces between them at a smaller separation, depend primarily on the behavior of the wave function for large $r$, whereas hyperfine structure separations depend primarily on the behavior of the wave function in the immediate neighborhood of the nucleus. However, the total energy criterion seems at present the most generally useful one;[2] as already

[2] For a discussion of other criteria see H. M. James and A. S. Coolidge, *Phys. Rev.*, **51**, 860 (1937); R. E. Williamson, *Phys. Rev.*, **62**, 538 (1942).

mentioned, it can be applied without knowledge of the wave function $\Psi$ to which an approximate function $\Phi$ *is* an approximation.

### 2.4. TWO WAYS OF USING THE VARIATION PRINCIPLE TO DERIVE APPROXIMATE WAVE FUNCTIONS

There are two ways of using the variation principle to derive approximate wave functions $\Phi$. The first way is to consider a class of functions $\Phi$ of specified analytical form, containing *parameters* whose "best" values, in the sense of the variation principle, are to be determined by making $E'$ stationary with respect to these parameters, when $\Phi$ is restricted to the class of functions of the particular form adopted. For example, for the normal state of the helium atom we may consider the class of functions

$$\Phi = e^{-k(r_1+r_2)} \tag{1}$$

with different values of $k$, or the class of functions

$$\Phi = e^{-(k_1r_1+k_2r_2)} + e^{-(k_2r_1+k_1r_2)} \tag{2}$$

with different values of $k_1$ and $k_2$. We know (or can verify by substitution in the wave equation) that the solution $\Psi$ of Schrödinger's equation is certainly *not* of either of these forms. Nevertheless we can ask what is the "best" approximation, in the sense of the variation principle, among functions of the form (1), or among functions of the form (2). Application of the variation principle gives a nonlinear algebraic expression in the parameters in the trial wave function, to be minimized. This minimization may often be carried out by solution of a finite number of *algebraic equations*, possibly nonlinear, for the finite number of these *parameters*.

If the trial wave function includes only a few parameters, then, except for systems of a few electrons, only a rough approximation is to be expected unless a fortunate choice of the class of approximate functions has been made. On the other hand, if the trial wave function includes many parameters, with the intention of improving the approximation, determination of the "best" values of them all simultaneously may be a difficult and lengthy process.

The second way of using the variation principle is to consider a class of functions $\Phi$ constructed in a specified manner out of arbitrary *functions* of the variables of the problem, these *functions* to be determined so as to minimize $E'$. For example, for the normal state of the helium atom we may consider the class of functions

$$\Phi = \psi(r_1)\psi(r_2) \tag{3}$$

without imposing any restriction on the form of the function $\psi(r)$. Again, we know that the solution of the wave equation is certainly *not* of this form; nevertheless, we can ask, among functions of the general form (3), what function $\psi(r)$ gives the "best" approximation in the sense of the variation principle? Application of the variation principle to such functions $\Phi$ leads to *differential equations* for the unknown *functions* such as $\psi(r)$ in formula (3) (in the case of (3) there is only a single unknown function).

## 2.5. THE SEPARABLE WAVE FUNCTION APPROXIMATION FOR THE NORMAL STATE OF HELIUM

The simpler approximations for a two-electron system, (1) and (3) of § 2.4, form almost the only cases for which the algebra can be written out shortly and yet fully enough for the steps to be followed in detail. Since they provide a simple case of an argument of a kind to be used later, but only given in outline, they are considered in some detail here.

Since much of the algebra is the same whether the algebraic form of the function $\psi(r)$ in § 2.4(3) is specified or left unspecified, the first part of the algebra is carried out for the more general case; and since, to anticipate, the most convenient function in terms of which to work is not $\psi$ but $r\psi$, we will adopt the form

$$\Phi = P(r_1)P(r_2)/r_1r_2 \tag{1}$$

for the approximate wave function. Since the value of

$$E' = \int\Phi\, H\Phi\, d\tau / \int\Phi^2\, d\tau \tag{2}$$

is unaffected by multiplication of $\Phi$ by any constant factor, it is no restriction to suppose the radial wave functions $P(r)$ normalized to

$$\int_0^\infty P^2\, dr = 1, \tag{3}$$

and to simplify the algebra it will be supposed that they are so normalized. This condition on the function $P(r)$ must be remembered when we come to evaluate the variation $\Delta E'$ in $E'$ for a variation $\Delta P$ in $P$; if we are to use for $E'$ a formula derived on the basis of $P$ being normalized, the variation in $P$ must be made conditional on $P$ remaining normalized. The calculation now has two main stages, one concerned with the derivation of the formula for $E'$ in terms of the function $P(r)$ and the other with the application of the variation principle to this expression for $E'$.

If $d\omega$ is an element of solid angle (apex at the origin), the volume element of coordinate space is

$$d\tau = d\tau_1\, d\tau_2 = r_1{}^2 r_2{}^2\, dr_1\, dr_2\, d\omega_1\, d\omega_2. \tag{4}$$

In the denominator of the expression (2) for $E'$, the integrations over $r_1, r_2, \omega_1, \omega_2$ separate, and give

$$\int\Phi^2\,d\tau = \int P^2(r_1)\,dr_1\int P^2(r_2)\,dr_2\int d\omega_1\int d\omega_2 = 1\cdot 1\cdot(4\pi)\cdot(4\pi) = (4\pi)^2. \quad (5)$$

The Hamiltonian operator for the two-electron system is

$$H = \underbrace{-\tfrac{1}{2}(\nabla_1^2+\nabla_2^2)}_{\text{K.E.}} \underbrace{-(2/r_1)-(2/r_2)}_{\substack{\text{P.E. of electrons}\\ \text{in field of}\\ \text{nucleus}}} + \underbrace{(1/r_{12})}_{\substack{\text{Mutual}\\ \text{P.E. of}\\ \text{electrons}}}. \quad (6)$$

If $f(r)$ is a function of $r$ only, the most convenient form for $\nabla^2 f$ is $\dfrac{1}{r}\dfrac{d^2}{dr^2}(rf)$.

Hence

$$\nabla_1^2\Phi = \frac{1}{r_1}\frac{\partial^2}{\partial r_1^2}(r_1\Phi) = \frac{1}{r_1r_2}P''(r_1)P(r_2), \qquad \nabla_2^2\Phi = \frac{1}{r_1r_2}P(r_1)P''(r_2),$$

and so

$$\begin{aligned} r_1^2r_2^2\Phi H\Phi = &-\tfrac{1}{2}P(r_1)[P''(r_1)+(4/r_1)P(r_1)]P^2(r_2)\\ &-\tfrac{1}{2}P(r_2)[P''(r_2)+(4/r_2)P(r_2)]P^2(r_1)+(1/r_{12})P^2(r_1)P^2(r_2). \end{aligned} \quad (7)$$

In $\int\Phi\,H\Phi\,d\tau = \int r_1^2r_2^2\Phi\,H\Phi\,dr_1\,dr_2\,d\omega_1\,d\omega_2$, the first two terms in the integrand (7) depend on the radial coordinates only; the integrations over $r_1, r_2, \omega_1, \omega_2$ again separate, and each of these terms gives a contribution

$$-\frac{1}{2}\int_0^\infty P(r)\left[P''(r)+\frac{4}{r}P(r)\right]dr\cdot(4\pi)^2 \quad (8)$$

to $\int\Phi\,H\Phi\,d\tau$ in (8); the $(4\pi)^2$ factor arises from the integrations over $\omega_1, \omega_2$. The first term in formula (7) gives a contribution (8) in which the integral is over $r_1$, whereas the second term gives a corresponding integral over $r_2$; however, for any given function $P(r)$ these integrals have the same value. Hence altogether the contribution to $E'$ from these terms in formula (7) is $2I$ where

$$I = -\frac{1}{2}\int_0^\infty P(r)\left[P''(r)+\frac{4}{r}P(r)\right]dr. \quad (9)$$

The third term in formula (7) gives a contribution to $E'$ of amount

$$F_0 = \frac{1}{(4\pi)^2}\int\frac{1}{r_{12}}P^2(r_1)P^2(r_2)\,dr_1\,dr_2\,d\omega_1\,d\omega_2 \quad (10)$$

$$= \int\frac{1}{r_{12}}\frac{P^2(r_1)}{4\pi r_1^2}\frac{P^2(r_2)}{4\pi r_2^2}\,d\tau_1\,d\tau_2 = \int\frac{P^2(r_1)}{4\pi r_1^2}\left[\int\frac{1}{r_{12}}\frac{P^2(r_2)}{4\pi r_2^2}\,d\tau_2\right]d\tau_1. \quad (11)$$

This is the mutual potential energy of two spherically symmetrical distributions of charge, each of volume density

$$\rho = P^2(r)/4\pi r^2 \tag{12}$$

or of radial density (charge per unit radius) $4\pi r^2\rho = P^2$. Consider now the integral over $\tau_2$ in formula (11), for a fixed value of $r_1$. This integral depends on $r_1$ and is

$$V(r_1) = \int \frac{1}{r_{12}} \frac{P^2(r_2)}{4\pi r_2{}^2} d\tau_2, \tag{13}$$

which is the potential at $r_1$ due to a spherically symmetrical charge distribution with volume density given by (12). This potential satisfies the equation

$$\nabla^2 V = -4\pi\rho = -P^2/r^2. \tag{14}$$

Since the charge distribution $\rho$ is spherically symmetrical, $V$ is a function of $r$ only, and consequently $\nabla^2 V = \dfrac{1}{r}\dfrac{d^2}{dr^2}(rV)$; so, if we write

$$V(r) = Y(r)/r, \tag{15}$$

equation (14) becomes

$$d^2Y/dr^2 = -P^2/r. \tag{16}$$

Thus, for any value of $r_1$, the integral over $\tau_2$, in square brackets in formula (11), is $Y(r_1)/r_1$. Hence the integrations over $r_1$ and $\omega_1$ now separate, and give for the integral (10) the value

$$F_0 = \int_0^\infty P^2(r) \frac{1}{r} Y(r)\, dr, \tag{17}$$

and altogether

$$E' = 2I + F_0. \tag{18}$$

(*i*) *Analytic Wave Functions.* The simplest analytic wave function is given by

$$P(r) = re^{-\frac{1}{2}kr} \tag{19}$$

where $k$ is a parameter to be determined by evaluating the integrals $I$ and $F_0$ in terms of $k$ from formulae (9), (16), and (17), from these results finding how $E'$ depends on $k$, and applying the variation principle to determine the "best" value of $k$. A factor $\frac{1}{2}$ is included in the exponent since the integrals $I$ and $F_0$ all involve $P^2$ or $PP''$.

The function $P(r)$ given by formula (19) is not normalized, whereas, in deriving the expressions for the integrals $I$ and $F_0$, it has been supposed that $P(r)$ is normalized. For the function (19), $\int_0^\infty P^2\, dr = \frac{2}{k^3}$, so that the corresponding normalized function is given by

$$P^2(r) = \tfrac{1}{2}k^3 r^2 e^{-kr}. \tag{20}$$

For this function, the values of $\int_0^\infty PP''\, dr$ and $\int_0^\infty \frac{4}{r} P^2\, dr$ are obtained by elementary integration, and are

$$\int_0^\infty PP''\, dr = -\frac{1}{4}k^2, \qquad \int_0^\infty \frac{4}{r} P^2\, dr = 2k, \tag{21}$$

whence

$$2I = \tfrac{1}{4}k^2 - 2k.$$

Equation (16) for $Y(r)$ becomes

$$Y'' = -\tfrac{1}{2}k^3 r e^{-kr}. \tag{22}$$

From formula (13) it follows that $V$ is finite at the origin and is $O(1/r)$ at infinity, so $Y(0) = 0$ and $Y(r)$ remains finite at infinity. These conditions determine uniquely the two integration constants in the two-fold integration of (22) to give $Y$. The result is

$$Y = 1 - (1 + \tfrac{1}{2}kr)e^{-kr},$$

and evaluation of the integral (16) gives $F_0 = 5k/16$, and finally

$$E' = \tfrac{1}{4}k^2 - 2k + \tfrac{5}{16}k = \tfrac{1}{4}k^2 - \tfrac{27}{16}k. \tag{23}$$

The stationary value of $E'$ as a function of $k$ occurs when $\frac{1}{2}k = \frac{27}{16}$. Hence, of functions of the form (19) with different values of $k$, the "best" approximation, in the sense of the variation principle, to the wave function of the normal state of neutral helium is given by

$$P(r) = re^{-27r/16} = re^{-[2-(5/16)]r}.$$

In this approximation, we think of each electron as being in a screened hydrogen-like wave function, and the number (5/16) in the exponent here represents, in this approximation, the effect, on the wave function of one electron, of the screening of the nucleus by the other electron.

The corresponding value of $2E'$ is $-(27/16)^2 = -5.695$; this is the total energy, in this approximation, of the two-electron system in Rydbergs (1 Rydberg = ionization energy of the hydrogen atom = $\frac{1}{2}$ atomic unit of energy). The observed value is $-5.807$. In these units, the ionization energy of $He^+$ is 4; hence in this approximation, that of neutral He is $(27/16)^2 - 4 = 1.695$.

(*ii*) *No Restriction on Form of* $P(r)$. Instead of specifying that we want the "best" function $P(r)$ of a specified analytical form, we may inquire for the "best" approximation of the form (1) without restriction on the form of $P(r)$. The algebra is the same as far as formula (18), but now we have to express $\Delta I$ and $\Delta F_0$ in terms of a general variation $\Delta P(r)$ of $P(r)$.

If in formula (9) $P(r)$ changes by $\Delta P(r)$, the first-order change of $I$ is

$$\Delta I = -\frac{1}{2}\int_0^\infty \Delta P(r)\left(\frac{d^2}{dr^2}+\frac{4}{r}\right)P(r)\,dr - \frac{1}{2}\int_0^\infty P(r)\left(\frac{d^2}{dr^2}+\frac{4}{r}\right)\Delta P(r)\,dr.$$

By § 2.1(7), these integrals are equal, so that

$$\Delta I = -\int_0^\infty \Delta P(r)\left(\frac{d^2}{dr^2}+\frac{4}{r}\right)P(r)\,dr. \tag{24}$$

From formula (10), the first-order variation of the integral $F_0$ is

$$\Delta F_0 = \frac{1}{(4\pi)^2}\int\frac{1}{r_{12}}[2P(r_1)\Delta P(r_1)P^2(r_2)+P^2(r_1)2P(r_2)\Delta P(r_2)]dr_1\,dr_2\,d\omega_1\,d\omega_2. \tag{25}$$

In the first term here, integration over $r_2$, $\omega_2$ gives

$$\int\frac{1}{r_{12}}P^2(r_2)\,dr_2\,d\omega_2 = \int\frac{1}{r_{12}}\frac{P^2(r_2)}{r_2{}^2}\,d\tau_2 = 4\pi\,V(r_1) = \frac{4\pi\,Y(r_1)}{r_1};$$

the integrations over $r_1$, $\omega_1$ now separate, and give, as the contribution of this term to $F_0$,

$$\int_0^\infty \Delta P(r_1)\,2P(r_1)\frac{1}{r_1}\,Y(r_1)\,dr_1.$$

The second term in the expression (25) gives a similar integral over $r_2$, which has the same value. Hence altogether

$$\Delta F_0 = 4\int_0^\infty \Delta P(r)\frac{1}{r}\,Y(r)\,P(r)\,dr, \tag{26}$$

and finally

$$\begin{aligned}\Delta E' &= 2\Delta I + \Delta F_0\\ &= -2\int_0^\infty \Delta P(r)\left[\frac{d^2}{dr^2}+\frac{4}{r}-\frac{2Y(r)}{r}\right]P(r)\,dr.\end{aligned} \tag{27}$$

In deriving the formula for $E'$ in terms of the radial wave functions $P(r)$, it has been supposed, to simplify the algebra, that these functions are normalized, and formula (27) for $\Delta E'$ holds only for those variations $\Delta P(r)$ for which $(P + \Delta P)$ remains normalized. Thus, in applying the variation principle we must require $\Delta E'$ to be zero, not for *all* variations

$\Delta P(r)$, but only for those variations subject to the condition $\Delta \int P^2 \, dr = 0$, or $2\int_0^\infty P \, \Delta P \, dr = 0$.

This condition can be incorporated by forming the quantity

$$E'' = E' + \lambda \int_0^\infty P^2 \, dr,$$

where $\lambda$ is a constant multiplier ("Lagrange multiplier"; compare § 2.1.1) whose value is undetermined at this stage of the argument, and requiring that $\Delta E'' = 0$ for all variations $\Delta P$, unconditionally. Then $P$ is given by

$$\left[\frac{d^2}{dr^2} + \frac{4}{r} - \frac{2Y(r)}{r} - \lambda\right] P = 0, \tag{28}$$

where $Y(r)$ is related to the solution of this equation by

$$d^2 Y/dr^2 = -P^2/r$$

[see equation (16)].

In this case, these are just the equations that would be written down from the more descriptive "self-consistent field" approach (see § 1.9) without reference to the variation principle. Their solution can be evaluated by the methods explained in § 5.1–5.4. The calculation has been carried out and the results tabulated.[3, 4]

## 2.6. THE VARIATION PRINCIPLE FOR EXCITED STATES

The results (i) and (ii) of § 2.1 apply to any excited state as well as to the normal state. However, for excited states the stationary value of $E'$ may not be a minimum; for some variations $\Delta\phi$, $\Delta E'$ may be positive and for others negative, so that the criterion given in § 2.3 for comparing approximations to the normal state is not applicable. Also it is possible that, in the restricted class of functions among which a wave function for an excited state is being sought, there is none that gives a stationary value of $E'$ in the neighborhood of the energy of the excited state sought, and then the attempt to find an excited state might only produce a poor approximation to the normal state.

If the wave functions of all states with energy *less* than $E_n$ were known, and the functions $\phi_n$ among which an approximation to $\psi_n$ is being sought were restricted to be orthogonal to all states of lower energy, the stationary value of $E'$ for the class of functions $\phi_n$ so restricted would be a minimum. For let

$$\Delta\phi = \phi_n - \psi_n = \Sigma_k a_k \psi_k$$

[3] D. R. Hartree, *Proc. Cambridge Phil. Soc.*, **24**, 111 (1927).

[4] W. S. Wilson and R. B. Lindsay, *Phys. Rev.*, **47**, 681 (1935).

[see § 2.1(15)]. The $\psi_k$ form an orthogonal set, so that, if $\phi_n$ is orthogonal to all $\psi_j$ for which $E_j < E_n$, then $a_j = 0$ for $E_j < E_n$, and there are no negative terms in the sum § 2.1(16).

However, the wave functions for the lower states will only be known approximately, and so the condition that $\phi_n$ should be orthogonal to all states of lower energy cannot be applied strictly, and insistence on orthogonality to what are only approximations to the wave functions for lower states may lead to a worse approximation for the excited state than would be obtained if this condition were not imposed.

Thus neither of the two courses, either omitting or insisting on orthogonality to the approximate wave functions for the lower states, seems entirely satisfactory. In practice, it seems possible to obtain useful approximations to wave functions for excited states without formally applying a condition of orthogonality to lower states.

This difficulty does not arise when the excited state is necessarily orthogonal to the lower states for reasons of parity, spatial symmetry of the wave functions, or (if spin-orbit interaction is neglected), from considerations of the spin wave functions involved. For example, it would not occur in the case of the $(1s)(2s)\ {}^3S$ state or the $(1s)(2p)\ {}^1P$ or ${}^3P$ states of neutral He.

## 2.7. ANALYTIC WAVE FUNCTIONS

As already mentioned in § 2.4, one way of using the variation principle to obtain approximate wave functions is to restrict the class of functions, among which a search is to be made for the "best" approximation, to functions of specified analytical form containing parameters whose values are to be determined by appeal to the variation principle. A simple example of this procedure, as applied to the normal state of the helium atom, has been considered in § 2.5(i); some other examples are considered in Chapter 10.

Similarly for a many-electron atom we may adopt, for the approximate wave function of the whole atom, a determinant of wave functions of central-field type (see § 1.9) with the additional restriction that the radial wave functions shall be of specified analytical form, such as products of polynomials and exponentials, or sums of terms of the form

$$a_n r^n e^{-\alpha_n r} \tag{1}$$

Tables for assisting the determination of analytic wave functions consisting of terms of the form (1) have been evaluated by Morse, Young, and Haurwitz, and by others.[5] Most work on analytic wave functions has

[5] P. M. Morse, L. A. Young, and E. S. Haurwitz, *Phys. Rev.*, **48**, 948 (1935); L. Coldberg and A. M. Clogston, *Phys. Rev.*, **56**, 696 (1939); W. E. Duncanson and G. A. Coulson, *Proc. Roy. Soc. Edinburgh*, **62**, 37 (1944).

been done for the lighter atoms; for configurations with more than three or four $(nl)$ groups, the number of parameters required to obtain a good approximation becomes rather large. Even for the lighter atoms it may be found necessary, in order to limit the numbers of parameters to be determined, to be content with a rather rough approximation. For example, in some work on analytic wave functions, a scaled hydrogen-like $(2p)$ wave function has been taken, whereas (see Chapter 7) this is not a good approximation for atoms, not highly ionized, in which the $(2p)$ group is the outermost group. And a similar comment applies, much more strongly, to the use of a hydrogen-like $(3d)$ wave function for atoms, not highly ionized, in which the $(3d)$ group is the outermost; Fig. 7.7 illustrates how far from hydrogen-like the $(3d)$ wave function of such an atom can be.

Because of these practical limitations on analytic wave functions, the main part of this book is concerned with the evaluation of approximate atomic wave functions without the restriction to particular analytical forms.

For some applications, however, analytic wave functions may be more convenient than wave functions specified by tables. Löwdin[6] has developed a method for analyzing a wave function given by a table into a sum of terms of the form (1), and has shown that, by the use of a relatively small number of such terms, good approximations can be obtained to wave functions calculated without the restriction to functions of particular analytical forms.

[6] P. O. Löwdin, *Phys. Rev.*, **90**, 120 (1952).

# 3. CONFIGURATIONS OF COMPLETE GROUPS

## 3.1. THREE STAGES IN THE CALCULATION OF ATOMIC STRUCTURES

We are concerned with evaluating atomic structures in the approximation in which each electron is regarded as in a stationary state in the field of the nucleus and the average charge distribution of the other electrons. This approximation is represented by an approximate wave function $\Phi$ which, for a configuration of complete groups, is a single determinant of one-electron wave functions $\psi$. Further, each of these one-electron wave functions is taken to be of central-field type. We wish to find the radial wave functions $P(nl; r)$ in these functions $\psi$ so that the quantity

$$E' = \int \Phi^* H\Phi \, d\tau / \int \Phi^*\Phi \, d\tau \tag{1}$$

is stationary with respect to variations in these radial wave functions.

The determination of the radial wave functions has three main stages. These are, first, the derivation of the expression for $E'$ in terms of the radial wave functions; second, the derivation of the equations for the radial wave functions from the expression for $E'$, and, third, the solution of these equations. The first two stages are illustrated, in a particularly simple case, by the example of the normal state of helium considered in § 2.5; they are considered for the general case of a configuration of complete groups in the present chapter. The third stage is the subject of Chapter 5.

Configurations containing one or more incomplete groups are considered in Chapter 6; the first stage, the derivation of the expression for $E'$, is in some cases different, but the second and third stages are the same.

## 3.2 ALGEBRAICAL PRELIMINARIES TO THE MANIPULATION OF DETERMINANT WAVE FUNCTIONS

For an atom or ion with $p$ electrons, the determinant

$$\Phi = \begin{vmatrix} \psi_1(1) & \psi_1(2) & \cdots & \psi_1(p) \\ \psi_2(1) & \psi_2(2) & \cdots & \psi_2(p) \\ \cdots & \cdots & \cdots & \cdots \\ \psi_p(1) & \psi_p(2) & \cdots & \psi_p(p) \end{vmatrix}, \tag{1}$$

written out in full, would comprise $p!$ terms (for example 28!, that is about $10^{30}$, terms for the $Cu^+$ ion); and in $E'$ we are concerned with expressions involving the product of two such determinants, altogether $(p!)^2$ terms. This shows that a very compact notation is required for handling expressions such as those that occur in the numerator and denominator of the formula for $E'$.

A convenient notation depends on the use of the set of numbers $\varepsilon_{\alpha\beta\gamma\cdots\pi}$ defined as follows: $\alpha, \beta, \gamma, \cdots, \pi$ are numbers, each of which may take any value from 1 to $p$, and

$$\begin{aligned} \varepsilon_{\alpha\beta\gamma\cdots\pi} &= 0 \text{ if any two of } \alpha, \beta, \gamma, \cdots, \pi \text{ are equal,} \\ &= +1 \text{ if } \alpha, \beta, \gamma, \cdots, \pi \text{ are all unequal and form an even permutation of } 1, 2, 3, \cdots, p, \\ &= -1 \text{ if } \alpha, \beta, \gamma, \cdots, \pi \text{ are all unequal and form an odd permutation of } 1, 2, 3, \cdots, p. \end{aligned}$$

It is convenient also to adopt the "summation convention," that a subscript symbol repeated in a single term or in a product implies summation over all values of that subscript from 1 to $p$.

In terms of this notation the determinant (1) can be written

$$\Phi = \varepsilon_{\alpha\beta\gamma\cdots\pi}\psi_\alpha(1)\psi_\beta(2)\psi_\gamma(3)\cdots\psi_\pi(p). \tag{2}$$

This can be seen as follows. In the sum of products on the right-hand side of (2), the repeated subscripts imply a summation over all values of *each* subscript $\alpha, \beta, \cdots$ separately. In this summation, any product in which any two of the functions $\psi_\alpha, \psi_\beta, \cdots$ are the same has coefficient zero, and so does not appear in the sum, whereas a product $\psi_\alpha(1)\psi_\beta(2)\cdots\psi_\pi(p)$ in which the functions $\psi_\alpha, \psi_\beta, \cdots, \psi_\pi$ are all different occurs with coefficient $+1$ or $-1$, according to the parity of the ordered set of numbers $(\alpha\beta\gamma\cdots\pi)$ regarded as a permutation of the numbers $(1, 2, 3, \cdots, p)$; and the sum (2) with the coefficients $\pm 1$ determined in this way is, by definition, the determinant (1).

The following properties of the set of coefficients $\varepsilon_{\alpha\beta\gamma\cdots\pi}$ are required:

$$\varepsilon_{\alpha\beta\gamma\cdots\pi}\varepsilon_{\alpha\beta\gamma\cdots\pi} = p!, \tag{3}$$

$$\varepsilon_{\alpha\beta\gamma\cdots\pi}\varepsilon_{\alpha'\beta\gamma\cdots\pi} = (p-1)!\delta_{\alpha\alpha'}, \tag{4}$$

$$\varepsilon_{\alpha\beta\gamma\cdots\pi}\varepsilon_{\alpha'\beta'\gamma\cdots\pi} = (p-2)!(\delta_{\alpha\alpha'}\delta_{\beta\beta'} - \delta_{\alpha\beta'}\delta_{\beta\alpha'}), \tag{5}$$

where $\delta_{\alpha\alpha'}$ is the set of numbers

$$\begin{aligned} \delta_{\alpha\alpha'} &= 1 \quad \text{when} \quad \alpha' = \alpha, \\ &= 0 \quad \text{when} \quad \alpha' \neq \alpha. \end{aligned} \tag{6}$$

Two properties of this set of numbers $\delta_{\alpha\alpha'}$ are required. First, if

$u_{\ldots\alpha\ldots}$ is any quantity depending on the value of $\alpha'$, then multiplication of $u_{\ldots\alpha'\ldots}$ by $\delta_{\alpha\alpha'}$ just replaces $\alpha'$ by $\alpha$. For in $\delta_{\alpha\alpha'}u_{\ldots\alpha'\ldots}$ the repeated subscript $\alpha'$ implies summation over all values of $\alpha'$ from 1 to $p$; but in this sum the coefficient $\delta_{\alpha\alpha'}$ is zero except for that term in the sum for which $\alpha'$ has the value $\alpha$, and then the coefficient $\delta_{\alpha\alpha'}$ is 1. Hence the sum reduces to the single term $u_{\ldots\alpha\ldots}$. The second property is

$$\delta_{\alpha\alpha} = p; \tag{7}$$

for, by the summation convention, $\delta_{\alpha\alpha}$ means, *not* the value of $\delta_{\alpha\alpha'}$ when $\alpha' = \alpha$, but the *sum* of such values for all relevant values of $\alpha$, and this is $p$.

The relations (3), (4), (5) can be proved separately, but, to illustrate the use of the notation, (5) will be proved first, and (4) and (3) derived from it.

If $\beta = \alpha$, then $\varepsilon_{\alpha\beta\gamma\cdots\pi} = 0$, irrespective of the values of $\gamma\cdots\pi$; similarly if $\beta' = \alpha'$; so

$$\varepsilon_{\alpha\beta\gamma\cdots\pi}\varepsilon_{\alpha'\beta'\gamma\cdots\pi} = 0 \quad \text{if} \quad \beta = \alpha \quad \text{or} \quad \beta' = \alpha'.$$

Suppose now $\alpha$ and $\beta$ specified, and $\beta \neq \alpha$. Then $\varepsilon_{\alpha\beta\gamma\cdots\pi} = 0$ unless the set of numbers $\gamma\cdots\pi$ is a permutation of the set of numbers $1\cdots p$ excluding $\alpha$ and $\beta$, and $\varepsilon_{\alpha'\beta'\gamma\cdots\pi}$ is zero unless $\alpha'$ and $\beta'$ are different from each other and from any of the numbers $\gamma\cdots\pi$. This can only occur if $\alpha' = \alpha$ and $\beta' = \beta$, or if $\alpha' = \beta, \beta' = \alpha$. Hence

$$\left.\begin{aligned} \varepsilon_{\alpha\beta\gamma\cdots\pi}\varepsilon_{\alpha'\beta'\gamma\cdots\pi} = 0 \quad \text{unless} \quad & \alpha' = \alpha, \quad \beta' = \beta \neq \alpha \\ \text{or} \quad & \beta' = \alpha, \quad \alpha' = \beta \neq \alpha. \end{aligned}\right\} \tag{8}$$

If $\alpha' = \alpha$ and $\beta' = \beta \neq \alpha$, then the ordered sets of numbers $\alpha\beta\gamma\cdots\pi$ and $\alpha'\beta'\gamma\cdots\pi$ are the same; and then $\varepsilon_{\alpha\beta\gamma\cdots\pi}\varepsilon_{\alpha'\beta'\gamma\cdots\pi}$ is the sum of contributions $+1$ for those sets of numbers $\gamma\cdots\pi$ which are permutations of the set of $(p-2)$ numbers from 1 to $p$ excluding $\alpha$ and $\beta$, and zero for other sets. There are $(n-2)!$ such permutations; hence

$$\varepsilon_{\alpha\beta\gamma\cdots\pi}\varepsilon_{\alpha'\beta'\gamma\cdots\pi} = (p-2)! \quad \text{if} \quad \alpha' = \alpha, \quad \beta' = \beta \neq \alpha;$$

Similarly

$$\varepsilon_{\alpha\beta\gamma\cdots\pi}\varepsilon_{\alpha'\beta'\gamma\cdots\pi} = -(p-2)! \quad \text{if} \quad \alpha' = \beta, \quad \beta' = \alpha \neq \beta. \tag{9}$$

Formulae (8) and (9) give the value of the left-hand side of (5) for any set of values of $\alpha$, $\beta$, $\alpha'$, and $\beta'$. Also $\delta_{\alpha\alpha'}$ and $\delta_{\beta\alpha'}$ are both zero unless $\alpha' = \alpha$ or $\beta$, and $\delta_{\alpha\beta'}$ and $\delta_{\beta\beta'}$ are both zero unless $\beta' = \alpha$ or $\beta$; so

$$\left.\begin{aligned} \delta_{\alpha\alpha'}\delta_{\beta\beta'} - \delta_{\alpha\beta'}\delta_{\beta\alpha'} = 0 \quad \text{unless} \quad & \alpha' = \alpha, \quad \beta' = \beta \\ \text{or} \quad & \beta' = \alpha, \quad \alpha' = \beta, \end{aligned}\right\} \tag{10}$$

and, if $\beta = \alpha$, then $\delta_{\beta\alpha'} = \delta_{\alpha\alpha'}$ and $\delta_{\beta\beta'} = \delta_{\alpha\beta'}$; so

$$\delta_{\alpha\alpha'}\delta_{\beta\beta'} - \delta_{\alpha\beta'}\delta_{\beta\alpha'} = 0 \quad \text{if} \quad \beta = \alpha; \quad (\text{or, if } \beta' = \alpha', \text{ similarly}), \tag{11}$$

whereas

$$\left.\begin{aligned} \delta_{\alpha\alpha'}\delta_{\beta\beta'} - \delta_{\alpha\beta'}\delta_{\beta\alpha'} &= 1\cdot 1 - 0\cdot 0 = +1 \quad \text{if} \quad \alpha' = \alpha, \quad \beta' = \beta, \beta \neq \alpha; \\ &= 0\cdot 0 - 1\cdot 1 = -1 \quad \text{if} \quad \alpha' = \beta, \quad \beta' = \alpha, \beta \neq \alpha. \end{aligned}\right\} \tag{12}$$

Comparison of the results (8), (9) with (10), (11), (12) establishes the relation (5) for any set of values of $\alpha$, $\beta$, $\alpha'$, $\beta'$.

Replacement of $\beta'$ by $\beta$ in formula (5) gives

$$\varepsilon_{\alpha\beta\gamma\cdots\pi}\varepsilon_{\alpha'\beta\gamma\cdots\pi} = (p-2)!(\delta_{\alpha\alpha'}\delta_{\beta\beta} - \delta_{\alpha\beta}\delta_{\beta\alpha'});$$

The repeated subscript $\beta$ implies summation over all values of $\beta$ from 1 to $p$ (in addition to the summations over $\gamma$ to $\pi$) on both sides. On the right-hand side, $\delta_{\beta\beta} = p$ [see (7)], and so the first term is $p\delta_{\alpha\alpha'}$, whereas in the second term the summation over $\beta$ gives just $\delta_{\alpha\alpha'}$. Hence

$$\varepsilon_{\alpha\beta\gamma\cdots\pi}\varepsilon_{\alpha'\beta\gamma\cdots\pi} = (p-2)!(p\delta_{\alpha\alpha'} - \delta_{\alpha\alpha'}),$$

which gives formula (4). Similarly, replacement of $\alpha'$ in formula (4) by $\alpha$ and further use of the result (7) gives formula (3).

In the determinant (1), it is no restriction to suppose that the one-electron wave functions $\psi$ form an orthonormal set, for, if $\psi_\beta$ were not orthogonal to $\psi_\alpha$, there is a linear combination $\psi_\beta + A\psi_\alpha$ of $\psi_\beta$ and $\psi_\alpha$ which is orthogonal to $\psi_\alpha$, and the determinant $\Phi$ is not affected by replacing $\psi_\beta$ by $\psi_\beta + A\psi_\alpha$. And, further, if any one of the functions $\psi$ is multiplied by a constant $C$, the whole determinant is multiplied by $C$, and this does not affect the value of $E'$; we can suppose such constants inserted so that the individual wave functions $\psi$ are normalized.

We shall suppose that the $\psi$'s do form such an orthonormal set; that is

$$\int \psi^*_\alpha(j)\psi_\beta(j)\, d\tau_j = \delta_{\alpha\beta}. \tag{13}$$

This simplifies considerably the algebra of obtaining the expression for $E'$ in terms of the radial wave functions $P$, and the expressions for the variation of $E'$ with variations $\Delta P$ in these radial wave functions. But they impose conditions on these variations $\Delta P$, and these must be remembered and taken into account in applying the variation principle to obtain the equations for the radial wave functions.

### 3.3. FIRST STAGE; DERIVATION OF THE EXPRESSION FOR E′

With the Hamiltonian operator for a many-electron system, neglecting spin-orbit interaction, namely,

$$H = -\Sigma_j(\tfrac{1}{2}\nabla_j^2 + N/r_j) + \Sigma'_{ij}(1/r_{ij}),$$

three kinds of integrals occur in the expression for $E'$: namely,

$$\int \Phi^* \Phi \, dr, \tag{1}$$

$$\int - \Phi^* \Sigma_j (\tfrac{1}{2} \nabla_j^2 + N/r_j) \Phi \, d\tau, \tag{2}$$

$$\int \Phi^* \Sigma'_{ij} (1/r_{ij}) \Phi \, d\tau. \tag{3}$$

The values of these integrals, over the whole coordinate space of the many-electron system, can be reduced to simpler integrals over the coordinates of single electrons or pairs of electrons only. These integrals are of three types:

$$I_\alpha = - \tfrac{1}{2} \int \psi^*_\alpha(j) (\nabla_j^2 + 2N/r_j) \psi_\alpha(j) \, d\tau_j, \tag{4}$$

$$J_{\alpha\beta} = \int |\psi_\alpha(i)|^2 (1/r_{ij}) |\psi_\beta(j)|^2 \, d\tau_i \, d\tau_j, \tag{5}$$

$$K_{\alpha\beta} = \int \psi^*_\alpha(i) \psi_\beta(i) (1/r_{ij}) \psi_\alpha(j) \psi^*_\beta(j) \, d\tau_i \, d\tau_j. \tag{6}$$

Here the integral $I_\alpha$ depends on $\alpha$, the label of the wave function occurring in the integral, *but not* on the value of $j$, which specifies the electron over whose coordinates the integral is taken; similarly the integrals $I_{\alpha\beta}$, $K_{\alpha\beta}$ depend only on the wave functions $\alpha$, $\beta$.

The function $\Phi^*\Phi$ is

$$[\varepsilon_{\alpha\beta\gamma \cdots \pi} \psi^*_\alpha(1) \psi^*_\beta(2) \psi^*_\gamma(3) \cdots \psi^*_\pi(p)] \times [\varepsilon_{\alpha'\beta'\gamma' \cdots \pi'} \psi_{\alpha'}(1) \psi_{\beta'}(2) \psi_{\gamma'}(3) \cdots \psi_{\pi'}(p)].$$

Here different symbols have been used for the subscripts over which the summations for $\Phi^*$ (first square bracket) and those for $\Phi$ (second square bracket) are taken; so the brackets can be removed and the terms rearranged without altering the summations indicated by the repeated subscripts. Hence

$$\Phi^*\Phi = \varepsilon_{\alpha\beta\gamma \cdots \pi} \varepsilon_{\alpha'\beta'\gamma' \cdots \pi'} [\psi^*_\alpha(1) \psi_{\alpha'}(2)][\psi^*_\beta(2) \psi_{\beta'}(2)] \cdots [\psi^*_\pi(p) \psi_{\pi'}(p)], \tag{7}$$

the sum being over all values of $\alpha, \beta, \gamma, \cdots, \pi$ *and* over all values of $\alpha', \beta', \gamma', \cdots, \pi'$, separately.

Consider first the integral $\int \Phi^*\Phi \, d\tau$, the denominator in the expression for $E'$. The integrations over $\tau_1, \tau_2, \cdots, \tau_p$ separate, and integration of (7) gives

$$\begin{aligned} \int \Phi^*\Phi \, d\tau &= \varepsilon_{\alpha\beta\gamma \cdots \pi} \varepsilon_{\alpha'\beta'\gamma' \cdots \pi'} [\textstyle\int \psi^*_\alpha(1) \psi_{\alpha'}(1) \, d\tau_1] \times [\textstyle\int \psi^*_\beta(2) \psi_{\beta'}(2) \, d\tau_2] \cdots [\textstyle\int \psi^*_\pi(p) \psi_{\pi'}(p) \, d\tau_p] \\ &= \varepsilon_{\alpha\beta\gamma \cdots \pi} \varepsilon_{\alpha'\beta'\gamma' \cdots \pi'} \delta_{\alpha\alpha'} \delta_{\beta\beta'} \delta_{\gamma\gamma'} \cdots \delta_{\pi\pi'} \quad [\text{from § 3.2(13)}] \\ &= \varepsilon_{\alpha\beta\gamma \cdots \pi} \varepsilon_{\alpha\beta\gamma \cdots \pi} \quad (\text{summing over } \alpha'\beta'\gamma' \cdots \pi') \\ &= p! \quad [\text{from § 3.2(3)}]. \end{aligned} \tag{8}$$

Now consider the contribution to the integral (2) from a single term in the sum, say from that with $j = 1$. Again the integrations over $\tau_1, \tau_2, \cdots, \tau_p$ separate. Those over $\tau_2, \tau_3, \cdots, \tau_p$ are the same as in $\int\Phi^*\Phi\, d\tau$; only that over $\tau_1$ is different. Hence

$$
\begin{aligned}
&-\tfrac{1}{2}\int\Phi^*(\nabla_1^2 + 2N/r_1)\Phi\, d\tau \\
&= -\tfrac{1}{2}\varepsilon_{\alpha\beta\gamma\cdots\pi}\varepsilon_{\alpha'\beta'\gamma'\cdots\pi'}[\int\psi^*_\alpha(1)(\nabla_1^2 + 2N/r_1)\psi_{\alpha'}(1)\, d\tau_1] \times \\
&\qquad\qquad\qquad\qquad\qquad\qquad \delta_{\beta\beta'}\delta_{\gamma\gamma'}\cdots\delta_{\pi\pi'} \\
&= -\tfrac{1}{2}\varepsilon_{\alpha\beta\gamma\cdots\pi}\varepsilon_{\alpha'\beta\gamma\cdots\pi}[\int\psi^*_\alpha(1)(\nabla_1^2 + 2N/r_1)\psi_{\alpha'}(1)\, d\tau_1 \\
&\qquad\qquad\qquad\qquad\qquad\qquad (\text{summing over } \beta', \gamma', \cdots, \pi') \\
&= -\tfrac{1}{2}(p-1)!\delta_{\alpha\alpha'}[\int\psi^*_\alpha(1)(\nabla_1^2 + 2N/r_1)\psi_{\alpha'}(1)\, d\tau_1 \quad [\text{from } \S\, 3.2(4)] \\
&= -\tfrac{1}{2}(p-1)!\int\psi^*_\alpha(1)(\nabla_1^2 + 2N/r_1)\psi_\alpha(1)\, d\tau_1. \quad (\text{summing over } \alpha'). \qquad (9)
\end{aligned}
$$

The integral here is the integral $I_\alpha$ defined by (4), and the repeated subscript $\alpha$ implies summation over values of $\alpha$ from 1 to $p$; hence the value of the integral (9) is $(p-1)!\Sigma_\alpha I_\alpha$. There are $p$ equal terms in the sum over $j$ in the integral (2); so the total contribution of the integral (2) to $\int\Phi^* H\Phi\, d\tau$ is

$$p!\Sigma_\alpha I_\alpha \qquad (10)$$

It should be noted that a sum over *all electrons* $j$ in the integral (2) has been transformed into a sum over all *one-electron wave functions* $\alpha$.

Now consider one of the terms in the sum $\int\Phi^*\Sigma'_{ij}(1/r_{ij})\Phi\, d\tau$, for example that with $i = 1, j = 2$. Then the integrations over $\tau_3, \cdots, \tau_p$ separate, and are the same as in $\int\Phi^*\Phi\, d\tau$; but those over $\tau_1, \tau_2$ do not separate. For short write:

$$\int\int\psi^*_\alpha(1)\psi_{\alpha'}(1)(1/r_{12})\psi^*_\beta(2)\psi_{\beta'}(2)\, d\tau_1\, d\tau_2 = u_{\alpha\alpha'\beta\beta'}$$

Then

$$
\begin{aligned}
\int\Phi^*(1/r_{12})\Phi\, d\tau &= \varepsilon_{\alpha\beta\gamma\cdots\pi}\varepsilon_{\alpha'\beta'\gamma'\cdots\pi'}u_{\alpha\alpha',\beta\beta'}\delta_{\gamma\gamma'}\cdots\delta_{\pi\pi'} \\
&= \varepsilon_{\alpha\beta\gamma\cdots\pi}\varepsilon_{\alpha'\beta'\gamma\cdots\pi}u_{\alpha\alpha',\beta\beta'} \qquad (\text{summing over } \gamma', \cdots \pi') \\
&= (p-2)!(\delta_{\alpha\alpha'}\delta_{\beta\beta'} - \delta_{\alpha\beta'}\delta_{\beta\alpha'})u_{\alpha\alpha',\beta\beta'} \; (\text{from } \S\, 3.2(5)) \\
&= (p-2)!(u_{\alpha\alpha,\beta\beta} - u_{\alpha\beta,\alpha\beta}) \qquad (\text{summing over } \alpha', \beta')
\end{aligned}
$$

Now $u_{\alpha\alpha,\beta\beta}$ is the sum, over all wave-function labels $\alpha$ and $\beta$, of integrals of the type defined by formula (5), and $u_{\alpha\beta,\alpha\beta}$ is a similar sum of integrals of the type defined by (6). Hence

$$\int\Phi^*(1/r_{12})\Phi\, d\tau = (p-2)!\Sigma_{\alpha\beta}(I_{\alpha\beta} - K_{\alpha\beta}). \qquad (11)$$

There are $\frac{1}{2}p(p-1)$ terms $(1/r_{ij})$ in the integrand of the integral (3), each of which gives a contribution of this amount; hence altogether

$$\int\Phi^*\Sigma'_{ij}(1/r_{ij})\Phi\, d\tau = \tfrac{1}{2}p!\Sigma_{\alpha\beta}(J_{\alpha\beta} - K_{\alpha\beta}).$$

The sum on the right here is a sum over *all* values of $\alpha$ and *all* values of $\beta$ separately; further, for $\beta = \alpha$, $K_{\alpha\beta} = J_{\alpha\beta}$, so that the term with $\beta = \alpha$ does not contribute to the sum and can be omitted. Hence, if $\Sigma'_{\alpha\beta}$ indicates a sum over all pairs $(\alpha\beta)$, each pair being included *once*, and with $\beta = \alpha$ omitted,

$$\int \Phi^* \Sigma'_{ij}(1/r_{ij}) \Phi \, d\tau = p! \Sigma'_{\alpha\beta}(J_{\alpha\beta} - K_{\alpha\beta}). \tag{12}$$

From formulae (10) and (12),

$$\int \Phi^* H \Phi \, d\tau = p![\Sigma_\alpha I_\alpha + \Sigma'_{\alpha\beta}(J_{\alpha\beta} - K_{\alpha\beta})],$$

and, from formula (8), $\int \Phi^* \Phi \, d\tau = p!$; hence for a single-determinant wave function, constructed from an orthonormal set of one-electron wave functions $\psi_\alpha$, $E'$ is given by

$$E' = \Sigma_\alpha I_\alpha + \Sigma'_{\alpha} J_{\alpha\beta} - \Sigma'_{\sigma\beta} K_{\alpha\beta}.$$

On account of the orthogonality of the spin wave functions, $K_{\alpha\beta}$ is zero unless $\psi_\alpha$ and $\psi_\beta$ are wave functions with the same spin; it is convenient to indicate by $\Sigma''_{\alpha\beta}$ the sum over all pairs of wave functions *with the same spin* ($\beta = \alpha$ omitted). Then

$$E' = \Sigma_\alpha I_\alpha + \Sigma'_{\alpha\beta} J_{\alpha\beta} - \Sigma''_{\alpha\beta} K_{\alpha\beta}. \tag{13}$$

This result was first given by Slater.[1]

### 3.4. USE OF CENTRAL-FIELD WAVE FUNCTIONS

The argument of the previous section applies not only to the electrons in an atom, but also to any system of electrons, or indeed to any system of particles to which Pauli's exclusion principle applies.

For an *atom*, considerable further simplification of the expression for $E'$ can be achieved if the one-electron wave functions $\psi_\alpha$ are taken to be of central-field type, with the same radial function $P(nl; r)$ for all wave functions of any one $(nl)$ group. Then the integrations over the spherical polar angles can be carried out formally, leaving integrals over radial coordinates only. It will be convenient, here and later, to write $U_k(r, s)$ for the function

$$\left.\begin{aligned} U_k(r, s) &= r^k/s^{k+1} \quad \text{for} \quad r < s \\ &= s^k/r^{k+1} \quad \text{for} \quad r > s. \end{aligned}\right\} \tag{1}$$

Then these integrals are of the following types:

$$I(nl) = -\frac{1}{2}\int_0^\infty P(nl; r)\left[\frac{d^2}{dr^2} + \frac{2N}{r} - \frac{l(l+1)}{r^2}\right] P(nl; r)\, dr, \tag{2}$$

[1] J. C. Slater, *Phys. Rev.*, **34**, 1293 (1929).

$$F_k(nl, n'l') = \int_0^\infty \int_0^\infty P^2(nl; r) P^2(n'l'; s) U_k(r, s)\, dr\, ds, \tag{3}$$

$$G_k(nl, n'l') = \int_0^\infty \int_0^\infty P(nl; r) P(n'l'; r) U_k(r, s) P(nl; s) P(n'l'; s)\, dr\, ds, \tag{4}$$

the wave functions being normalized:

$$\int_0^\infty P^2\, dr = 1. \tag{5}$$

In the integral $I_\alpha$[§ 3.3(4)], integration over the spherical polar angles gives just $I(n_\alpha l_\alpha)$, so that, if $q(nl)$ is the number of wave functions in the $(nl)$ group,

$$\Sigma_\alpha I_\alpha = \Sigma_{nl} q(nl)\, I(nl). \tag{6}$$

The simplification of the integrals $J_{\alpha\beta}$ and $K_{\alpha\beta}$ depends on the use of an expansion of $1/r_{ij}$ in terms of $r_i$, $r_j$, and $\mu = \cos\theta_{ij}$: namely,

$$1/r_{ij} = \Sigma_k U_k(r, s) P_k(\mu), \tag{7}$$

where $P_k(\mu)$ is the Legendre polynomial of order $k$. $P_k(\mu)$ can be expressed in terms of $\theta_i$, $\theta_j$ and $(\phi_j - \phi_i)$ and the integrations over $\theta_i$, $\theta_j$, $\phi_i$, $\phi_j$ can be carried out formally. The results depend on the $(l, m)$ values specifying the variation with direction of the central field wave functions $\psi_\alpha$, $\psi_\beta$.

The result is

$$J_{\alpha\beta} = \Sigma_k a_k(l_\alpha m_\alpha, l_\beta m_\beta) F_k(n_\alpha l_\alpha, n_\beta l_\beta), \tag{8}$$

$$K_{\alpha\beta} = \Sigma_k b_k(l_\alpha m_\alpha, l_\beta m_\beta) G_k(n_\alpha l_\alpha, n_\beta l_\beta). \tag{9}$$

The sums over $k$ result from the sum over $k$ in (7), and the factor $U_k(r, s)$ in the integrals (3) and (4) arise from the corresponding factor in each term of (7). However, although the series (7) is an infinite series in $k$, the sums over $k$ in (8) and (9) are finite sums, with $k$ not greater than $l_\alpha + l_\beta$, and having the same parity as $l_\alpha + l_\beta$; thus, in configurations involving wave functions with $l$ not greater than 2 ($d$ wave functions), as in the normal configurations of all atoms up to the rare earths, values of $k$ greater than 4 do not occur.

The values of the coefficients $a_k$, $b_k$ in the expressions (8) and (9) have been evaluated and tabulated;[2] a table of values up to $l_\alpha = 2$, $l_\beta = 2$ is given in Table 1. The contributions to $E'$ from complete $(nl)$ groups are found by summing over all pairs of wave functions in the groups.

[2] See E. U. Condon and G. H. Shortley, *Theory of Atomic Spectra*, § 9[6], Tables 1[6], 2[6], Cambridge (1935).

**Table 1. Slater coefficients**

| | | | $a_k(lm_l;\, l'm_{l'})$ | | | $b_k(lm_l,\, l'm_{l'})$ | | | | |
|---|---|---|---|---|---|---|---|---|---|---|
| $ll'$ | $m_l$ | $m_{l'}$ | $k=0$ | 2 | 4 | $k=0$ | 1 | 2 | 3 | 4 |
| *ss* | 0 | 0 | 1 | | | 1 | | | | |
| *sp* | 0 | $\pm 1$ | 1 | | | | 1/3 | | | |
| | 0 | 0 | 1 | | | | 1/3 | | | |
| *pp* | $\pm 1$ | $\pm 1$ | 1 | 1/25 | | 1 | | 1/25 | | |
| | $\pm 1$ | 0 | 1 | − 2/25 | | | | 3/25 | | |
| | $\pm 1$ | $\mp 1$ | 1 | 1/25 | | | | 6/25 | | |
| | 0 | 0 | 1 | 4/25 | | 1 | | 4/25 | | |
| *sd* | 0 | $\pm 2$ | 1 | | | | | 1/5 | | |
| | 0 | $\pm 1$ | 1 | | | | | 1/5 | | |
| | 0 | 0 | 1 | | | | | 1/5 | | |
| *pd* | $\pm 1$ | $\pm 2$ | 1 | 2/35 | | | 6/15 | | 3/245 | |
| | $\pm 1$ | $\pm 1$ | 1 | − 1/35 | | | 3/15 | | 9/245 | |
| | $\pm 1$ | 0 | 1 | − 2/35 | | | 1/15 | | 18/245 | |
| | $\pm 1$ | $\mp 1$ | 1 | − 1/35 | | | | | 30/245 | |
| | $\pm 1$ | $\mp 2$ | 1 | 2/35 | | | | | 45/245 | |
| | 0 | $\pm 2$ | 1 | − 4/35 | | | | | 15/245 | |
| | 0 | $\pm 1$ | 1 | 2/35 | | | 3/15 | | 24/245 | |
| | 0 | 0 | 1 | 4/35 | | | 4/15 | | 27/245 | |
| *dd* | $\pm 2$ | $\pm 2$ | 1 | 4/49 | 1/441 | 1 | | 4/49 | | 1/441 |
| | $\pm 2$ | $\pm 1$ | 1 | − 2/49 | − 4/441 | | | 6/49 | | 5/441 |
| | $\pm 2$ | 0 | 1 | − 4/49 | 6/441 | | | 4/49 | | 15/441 |
| | $\pm 2$ | $\mp 1$ | 1 | − 2/49 | − 4/441 | | | | | 35/441 |
| | $\pm 2$ | $\mp 2$ | 1 | 4/49 | 1/441 | | | | | 70/441 |
| | $\pm 1$ | $\pm 1$ | 1 | 1/49 | 16/441 | 1 | | 1/49 | | 16/441 |
| | $\pm 1$ | 0 | 1 | 2/49 | − 24/441 | | | 1/49 | | 30/441 |
| | $\pm 1$ | $\pm 1$ | 1 | 1/49 | 16/441 | | | 6/49 | | 40/441 |
| | 0 | 0 | 1 | 4/49 | 36/441 | 1 | | 4/49 | | 36/441 |

In columns 3 and 4, upper signs must be taken together or lower signs together.

Absence of an entry implies that the corresponding coefficient is zero.

Formula § 3.3(13) has been derived on the understanding that the one-electron wave functions $\psi_\alpha$ are orthogonal. Central-field wave functions involving different spherical-harmonic variations with $(\theta, \phi)$, or different spin functions, are orthogonal through the properties of the spherical harmonics and spin functions, and to ensure this orthonormal property generally it is only necessary to impose the condition

$$\int_0^\infty P(nl;r)P(n'l;r)\,dr = \delta_{nn'} \tag{10}$$

on the radial wave functions.

**Example. Contribution to E′ from pairs of wave functions within a single $(np)^6$ group.** Let the different wave functions of the $(np)^6$ group be distinguished by $(nlm+)$ and $(nlm-)$, $m$ being given its numerical value ($-1$ written as $\bar{1}$), and the two different spin states being indicated by the terminal $+$ or $-$. In Table 2 the first two columns give the $(nlm\pm)$ specifications of pairs of wave functions [$\beta = \alpha$ omitted as implied by the $\Sigma'_{\alpha\beta}$ in formula § 3.3(13)]; the next three columns give the corresponding values of $a_0$, $a_2$, and $b_2$, the coefficients of $F_0(np, np)$, $F_2(np, np)$, and $-G_2(np, np)$ in the contributions to $E'$ from the various pairs of wave functions; these values are obtained from Table 1.

**Table 2**

| $\alpha$ | $\beta$ | $a_0$ | $25a_2$ | $25b_2$ |
|---|---|---|---|---|
| $(np1+)$ | $(np0+)$ | 1 | $-2$ | $+3$ |
| | $\bar{1}+$ | 1 | $+1$ | $+6$ |
| | $1-$ | 1 | $+1$ | |
| | $0-$ | 1 | $-2$ | 0 |
| | $\bar{1}-$ | 1 | $+1$ | |
| $(np0+)$ | $(np\bar{1}+)$ | 1 | $-2$ | |
| | $1-$ | 1 | $-2$ | |
| | $0-$ | 1 | $+4$ | 0 |
| | $\bar{1}-$ | 1 | $-2$ | |
| $(np\bar{1}+)$ | $(np1-)$ | 1 | $+1$ | |
| | $0-$ | 1 | $-2$ | 0 |
| | $\bar{1}-$ | 1 | $+1$ | |
| $(np1-)$ | $(np0-)$ | 1 | $-2$ | $+3$ |
| | $\bar{1}-$ | 1 | $+1$ | $+6$ |
| $(np0-)$ | $(np\bar{1}-)$ | 1 | $-2$ | $+3$ |
| Total | | 15 | $-6$ | $+24$ |

Hence

Contribution to $E'$ from pairs of wave functions within a single $(np)$ group

$$= 15F_0(np, np) - \tfrac{6}{25}F_2(np, np) - \tfrac{24}{25}G_2(np, np).$$

But, for any $(nl)$, it follows from the definitions (3) and (4) that

$$G_k(nl, nl) = F_k(nl, nl).$$

Hence this contribution to $E'$ is

$$15F_0(np, np) - \tfrac{6}{5}F_2(np, np). \tag{11}$$

For any pair of wave functions $(\alpha\beta)$, the coefficient $a_0$ is 1; and within a single group of $q(nl)$ occupied wave functions there are $\frac{1}{2}q(nl)[q(nl) - 1]$ pairs. Hence the coefficient of each $F_0(nl, nl)$ is always $\frac{1}{2}q(nl)[q(nl) - 1]$. Similarly[3] for $(n'l') \neq (nl)$ the coefficient of each $F_0(nl, n'l')$ is $q(nl)q(n'l')$.

Further, the $a_k$ coefficients have the property that, for $k > 0$ and for a complete group,

$$\Sigma_{m_\beta} a_k(l_\alpha m_\alpha, l_\beta m_\beta) = 0 \tag{12}$$

for all $m_\alpha$, the sum being over all values of $m_\beta$ in a complete $(n_\beta l_\beta)$ group.[4] Consequently the only contributions to $E'$ involving $F_k$ integrals with $k > 0$ are from integrals $F_k(nl, nl)$.

Thus, for a configuration of complete groups, $E'$ is reduced to a sum of multiples of $I(nl)$, $F_0(nl, n'l')$, $F_k(nl, nl)$ and $G_k(nl, n'l')$ integrals, with coefficients which can be written down for the $I$ and $F_0$ integrals, and can be found as in the above example for the others:

$$\begin{aligned} E' = {} & \Sigma_{nl} q(nl)I(nl) + \Sigma_{nl} \tfrac{1}{2}q(nl)[q(nl) - 1]F_0(nl, nl) \\ & + \Sigma_{nl, n'l' \neq nl} q(nl)q(n'l')F_0(nl, n'l') - \Sigma_{nlk} A_{lk} F_k(nl, nl) \\ & - \Sigma_{nl, n'l', k} B_{ll'k} G_k(nl, n'l'); \end{aligned} \tag{13}$$

the last two contributions are written with negative signs so that the values of the coefficients $A_{lk}$ and $B_{ll'k}$ shall be positive; their values for configurations of complete groups are given in Table 3.

For example, for the normal configuration of a ten-electron system (such as Ne, $Na^+$, $Si^{+4}$), namely $(1s)^2(2s)^2(2p)^6$,

$$\begin{aligned} E' = {} & 2I(1s) + 2I(2s) + 6I(2p) + F_0(1s, 1s) + F_0(2s, 2s) + 15F_0(2p, 2p) \\ & - \tfrac{6}{5}F_2(2p, 2p) + 4F_0(1s, 2s) + 12F_0(1s, 2p) + 12F_0(2s, 2p) \\ & - 2G_0(1s, 2s) - 2[G_1(1s, 2p) + G_1(2s, 2p)]. \end{aligned} \tag{14}$$

[3] The notation $(n'l') = (nl)$ is used for short to indicate that $n' = n$ and $l' = l$; and the notation $(n'l') \neq (nl)$ to indicate that either $l' \neq l$ or, if $l' = l$, then $n' \neq n$.

[4] See E. U. Condon and G. H. Shortley, *Theory of Atomic Spectra*, § 9[6], formula (11), Cambridge (1935).

**Table 3**

Coefficient of $F_k(nl, nl) = -A_{lk}$ $(k > 0)$

Coefficient of $G_k(nl, n'l') = -B_{ll'k}$ $[(n'l') \neq (nl)]$

| Group | $A_{lk}$: $k = 2$ | 4 | 6 |
|---|---|---|---|
| $(ns)^2$ | | | |
| $(np)^6$ | 6/5 | | |
| $(nd)^{10}$ | 10/7 | 10/7 | |
| $(nf)^{14}$ | 28/15 | 14/11 | 700/429 |

| Groups | $B_{ll'k}$: $k = 0$ | 1 | 2 | 3 | 4 | 5 |
|---|---|---|---|---|---|---|
| $(ns)^2(n's)^2$ | 2 | | | | | |
| $(ns)^2(n'p)^6$ | | 2 | | | | |
| $(ns)^2(n'd)^{10}$ | | | 2 | | | |
| $(ns)^2(n'f)^{14}$ | | | | 2 | | |
| $(np)^6(n'p)^6$ | 6 | | 12/5 | | | |
| $(np)^6(n'd)^{10}$ | | 4 | | 18/7 | | |
| $(np)^6(n'f)^{14}$ | | | 18/5 | | 8/3 | |
| $(nd)^{10}(n'd)^{10}$ | 10 | | 20/7 | | 20/7 | |
| $(nd)^{10}(n'f)^{14}$ | | 6 | | 8/3 | | 100/33 |

### 3.5. THE $Y_k$ AND $Z_k$ FUNCTIONS

Both for the application of the variation principle and for the handling of the equations resulting from this application, it is convenient to introduce a set of functions of $r$ defined by

$$\begin{aligned} Y_k(nl, n'l'; r) &= r\int_0^\infty U_k(r, s)P(nl; s)P(n'l'; s)\,ds \\ &= \int_{s=0}^{r} \left(\frac{s}{r}\right)^k P(nl; s)P(n'l'; s)\,ds \\ &\quad + \int_{s=r}^{\infty} \left(\frac{r}{s}\right)^{k+1} P(nl; s)P(n'l'; s)\,ds. \end{aligned} \tag{1}$$

In terms of these functions, the integral $F_k(nl, n'l')$ [see § 3.4(3)] can be written in the alternative forms,

$$F_k(nl, n'l') = \int_0^\infty P^2(nl; r)\,\frac{1}{r}\,Y_k(n'l', n'l'; r)\,dr, \tag{2}$$

$$= \int_0^\infty P^2(n'l'; r)\,\frac{1}{r}\,Y_k(nl, nl; r)\,dr, \tag{3}$$

and the integral $G_k(nl, n'l')$ [see § 3.4(4)] is

$$G_k(nl, n'l') = \int_0^\infty P(nl; r)P(n'l'; r)\,\frac{1}{r}\,Y_k(nl, n'l'; r)\,dr. \tag{4}$$

It will also be convenient later to have a notation for the first of the two integrals on the right-hand side of formula (1) by itself. This also is a function of $r$ and will be written $Z_k(nl, n'l'; r)$:

$$Z_k(nl, n'l'; r) = \int_{s=0}^{r} \left(\frac{s}{r}\right)^k P(nl; s)P(n'l'; s)\, ds. \tag{5}$$

By multiplying both sides of formula (5) by $r^k$ and differentiating, it is easily verified that

$$\frac{d}{dr} Z_k(nl, n'l'; r) = P(nl; r)P(n'l'; r) - \frac{k}{r} Z_k(nl, n'l'; r). \tag{6}$$

Also, from formulae (1) and (5),

$$Y_k(nl, n'l'; r) = Z_k(nl, n'l'; r) + \int_{s=r}^{\infty} \left(\frac{r}{s}\right)^{k+1} P(nl; s)P(n'l'; s),$$

and, by multiplying by $r^{-(k+1)}$ and differentiating, and substituting for $dZ_k/dr$ from (6), it follows that

$$\frac{d}{dr} Y_k(nl, n'l'; r) = -\frac{1}{r} [(2k+1)Z_k(nl, n'l'; r) - (k+1)Y_k(nl, n'l'; r)]. \tag{7}$$

From the definitions (1) and (5) it follows that

$$\left.\begin{aligned} &Z_k(nl, n'l'; 0) = 0 \\ \text{and} \quad &Y_k(nl, n'l'; r) - Z_k(nl, n'l'; r) \to 0 \quad \text{as} \quad r \to \infty; \end{aligned}\right\} \tag{8}$$

the functions $Y_k$ and $Z_k$ can be regarded as the solutions of equations (6) and (7), respectively, with boundary conditions (8).

A second-order equation for $Y_k$ is obtained by differentiating equation (7), substituting for $dZ_k/dr$ from (6) and then for $Z_k$ in terms of $Y_k$ and $dY_k/dr$ from (7). The terms in $dY_k/dr$ go out, and there remains

$$\frac{d^2}{dr^2} Y_k(nl, n'l'; r) = \frac{k(k+1)}{r^2} Y_k(nl, n'l'; r) - \frac{2k+1}{r} P(nl; r)P(n'l'; r). \tag{9}$$

The functions $Z_0(nl, n'l'; r)$ and $Y_0(nl, n'l'; r)$ can be interpreted as follows. If we write $U(r)$ for the charge per unit *radius* of a spherically symmetrical charge distribution (charge density $\rho = U(r)/4\pi r^2$), then $Z_0(nl, n'l'; r)/r^2$ is the field at radius $r$ of a distribution with radial charge density $U(r) = P(nl; r)P(n'l'; r)$, and $Y_0(nl, n'l'; r)/r$ is the potential at radius $r$ of this field. The functions $Y_k$ and $Z_k$ are similarly related to the potential and radial field of a distribution whose space-charge density has a variation with direction given by the Legendre polynomial $P_k(\cos\theta)$.

### 3.6. APPLICATION OF THE VARIATION PRINCIPLE

To obtain the equations for the "best" radial wave functions $P(nl; r)$, in the sense of the variation principle, for an atomic system, we have to obtain an expression for $\Delta E'$, the variation of $E'$ for variations $\Delta P(nl; r)$ in the radial wave functions. Consider these variations individually, and let $P(nl; r)$ denote that wave function which *is* to be varied, and $P(n'l'; r)$ the others.

The contributions to $E'$ depending on $P(nl; r)$ consist of numerical multiples of integrals $I(nl)$, $F_k(nl, nl)$, $F_k(nl, n'l')$ with $(n'l') \neq (nl)$, and $G_k(nl, n'l')$. We shall consider first-order variation of a typical integral of each of these kinds for a variation of $P(nl; r)$, and then build up the expression for the variation of $E'$.

The variation of the integral $I(nl)$ is

$$\Delta I(nl) = -\frac{1}{2}\left\{\int_0^\infty \Delta P(nl; r)\left[\frac{d^2}{dr^2} + \frac{2N}{r} - \frac{l(l+1)}{r^2}\right] P(nl; r)\, dr \right.$$
$$\left. + \int_0^\infty P(nl; r)\left[\frac{d^2}{dr^2} + \frac{2N}{r} - \frac{l(l+1)}{r^2}\right] \Delta P(nl; r)\, dr\right\}. \quad (1)$$

But, from formula § 2.1(7),

$$\int_0^\infty P \frac{d^2}{dr^2} \Delta P\, dr = \int_0^\infty \Delta P \frac{d^2 P}{dr^2}\, dr;$$

so the two integrals in formula (1) have equal values, and

$$\Delta I(nl) = -\int_0^\infty \Delta P(nl; r)\left[\frac{d^2}{dr^2} + \frac{2N}{r} - \frac{l(l+1)}{r^2}\right] P(nl; r)\, dr. \quad (2)$$

In an integral $F_k(nl, n'l')$ with $(n'l') \neq (nl)$, the function $Y_k(n'l', n'l'; r)$ does not vary with a variation of $P(nl)$; hence, from formula § 3.5(2),

$$\Delta F_k(nl, n'l') = 2\int_0^\infty P(nl; r)\Delta P(nl; r)\frac{1}{r}\, Y_k(n'l', n'l'; r)\, dr. \quad (3)$$

But, for $(n'l') = (nl)$,

$$\Delta F_k(nl, nl) = \int_0^\infty \Delta[P^2(nl; r)]\frac{1}{r}\, Y_k(nl, nl; r)\, dr$$
$$+ \int_0^\infty P^2(nl; r)\frac{1}{r}\,\Delta Y_k(nl, nl; r)\, dr.$$

However, from formulae § 3.5(2) and (3), it follows that, for any $(n'l')$ [including $(n'l') = (nl)$],

$$\int_0^\infty \Delta[P^2(nl; r)]\frac{1}{r}\, Y_k(n'l', n'l'; r)\, dr = \int_0^\infty P^2(n'l'; r)\frac{1}{r}\,\Delta Y_k(nl, nl; r)\, dr.$$

Hence,

$$\Delta F_k(nl, nl) = 4\int_0^\infty P(nl; r)\Delta P(nl; r)\,\frac{1}{r}\,Y_k(nl, nl; r)\,dr. \tag{4}$$

Similarly,

$$\Delta G_k(nl, n'l') = 2\int_0^\infty P(n'l'; r)\Delta P(nl; r)\,\frac{1}{r}\,Y_k(nl, n'l'; r)\,dr. \tag{5}$$

Hence altogether, for a variation $\Delta P(nl; r)$ of one of the radial wave functions, the variation $\Delta E'$ of $E'$ is given by

$$\Delta E' = \int_0^\infty \Delta P(nl; r)Q(nl; r)\,dr, \tag{6}$$

where for a configuration of complete groups, for which $E'$ is given by § 3.4(13), $Q(nl; r)$ is made up of terms of the following kinds:

From $\Delta I(nl)$, $\quad -q(nl)\left[\frac{d^2}{dr^2} + \frac{2N}{r} - \frac{l(l+1)}{r^2}\right] P(nl; r)$ [see (2)],

From $\Delta F_0(nl, nl)$, $\quad +\frac{1}{2}\,q(nl)[q(nl) - 1]\,\frac{4}{r}\,Y_0(nl, nl; r)P(nl; r)$ [see (4)],

From each $\Delta F_0(nl, n'l')$ $(n'l') \neq (nl)$, $\quad q(nl)q(n'l')\,\frac{2}{r}\,Y_0(n'l', n'l'; r)P(nl; r)$ [see (3)],

From each $\Delta F_k(nl, nl)$ $k \neq 0$, $\quad -A_{lk}\,\frac{4}{r}\,Y_k(nl, nl; r)P(nl; r)$ [see (4)],

From each $\Delta G_k(nl, n'l')$, $\quad -B_{ll'k}\,\frac{2}{r}\,Y_k(nl, n'l'; r)P(n'l'; r)$ [see (5)].

The total variation of $E'$ for variations of all the radial wave functions is a sum of such contributions from the various values of $(nl)$.

In the derivation of the formula for $E'$, it has been supposed that the radial wave functions $P$ are normalized and that those for the same $l$ are orthogonal. Hence the variations $\Delta P(nl; r)$ are subject to the conditions § 3.4(10) of orthonormality of the radial wave functions with the same value of $l$. These conditions can be incorporated by introducing Lagrange multipliers $\lambda_{nl,n'l}$ and requiring that the quantity

$$E'' = E' + \Sigma_{nn'l}\lambda_{nl,n'l}\int_0^\infty P(nl; r)P(n'l; r)\,dr \tag{7}$$

shall be stationary for all variations $\Delta P$ without restrictions (save those of differentiability and consistency with the boundary conditions).

For variation of any one radial wave function $P(nl; r)$, the variation of $E'$ is given by (6), and

$$\Delta E'' = \int_0^\infty \Delta P(nl; r)[Q(r) + 2\Sigma_{n'}\lambda_{nl,n'l}P(n'l; r)]\, dr$$

(the sum including $n' = n$); so the condition for $E''$ to be stationary is

$$Q(r) + 2\Sigma_{n'}\lambda_{nl,n'l}P(n'l; r) = 0. \qquad (8)$$

Multiplication by $-1/q(nl)$, to make the coefficient of $d^2P(nl; r)/dr^2$ unity, gives an equation of the general form

$$\left[\frac{d^2}{dr^2} + \frac{2}{r}\,Y(nl; r) - \varepsilon_{nl,nl} - \frac{l(l+1)}{r^2}\right] P(nl; r) = X(nl; r) + \Sigma_{n' \neq n}\varepsilon_{nl,n'l}\, P(n'l; r). \qquad (9)$$

The functions $Y(nl; r)$ and $X(nl; r)$ occurring in this equation are as follows. For short, let $Y(r)$ be written for the function

$$Y(r) = N - \Sigma_{nl}\, q(nl)\, Y_0(nl, nl; r). \qquad (10)$$

Then

$$Y(nl; r) = Y(r) + \Sigma_k \alpha_{lk}\, Y_k(nl, nl; r), \qquad (11)$$

where

$$\alpha_{l0} = 1 \quad \text{and} \quad \alpha_{lk} = 2A_{lk}/q(nl) \quad \text{for} \quad k \neq 0; \qquad (12)$$

and

$$X(nl; r) = -(2/r)\Sigma'_{n'l'k}\beta_{ll'k}\, Y_k(nl, n'l'; r)\, P(n'l'; r), \qquad (13)$$

where

$$\beta_{ll'k} = B_{ll'k}/q(nl), \qquad (14)$$

and the sum $\Sigma'$ is over all $(n'l')$ excluding $(n'l') = (nl)$; $B_{ll'k}$ is symmetrical in $l$ and $l'$, but, since $q(nl)$ depends on $l$, $\beta_{ll'k}$ is not symmetrical in $l$ and $l'$. The values of $\alpha_{lk}$ and $\beta_{ll'k}$ for configurations of complete groups are given in Table 4.

**Table 4**

| $l$ | $\alpha_{l0}$ | $\alpha_{l2}$ | $\alpha_{l4}$ | $l$ | $l'$ | $\beta_{ll'0}$ | $\beta_{ll'1}$ | $\beta_{ll'2}$ | $\beta_{ll'3}$ | $\beta_{ll'4}$ |
|---|---|---|---|---|---|---|---|---|---|---|
| 0 | 1 | | | 0 | 0 | 1 | | | | |
| 1 | 1 | 2/5 | | 0 | 1 | | 1 | | | |
| 2 | 1 | 2/7 | 2/7 | 0 | 2 | | | 1 | | |
| | | | | 1 | 0 | | 1/3 | | | |
| | | | | 1 | 1 | 1 | | 2/5 | | |
| | | | | 1 | 2 | | 2/3 | | 3/7 | |
| | | | | 2 | 0 | | | 1/5 | | |
| | | | | 2 | 1 | | 2/5 | | 9/35 | |
| | | | | 2 | 2 | 1 | | 2/7 | | 2/7 |

It should be noted that

$$\beta_{llk} = \alpha_{lk}; \tag{15}$$

this is not accidental, but is a consequence of the property that the determinantal wave function $\Phi$ is unaltered by an orthogonal transformation of the one-electron wave functions $\psi_\alpha$, and so the form of equations (9) must be unaltered by an orthogonal transformation of the radial wave functions $P(nl; r)$ for any one value of $l$.

Equations (9) are known as Fock's equations.[5] The functions $Y(nl; r)$ and $X(nl; r)$ occurring in them involve the functions $Y_k(nl, n'l'; r)$, which are integrals depending on the radial wave functions $P(nl; r)$ over the whole range of $r$; consequently these equations are integrodifferential equations for these wave functions. This aspect of the equations will be discussed more fully in § 3.7. Alternatively, since the $Y_k$ functions are solutions of differential equations § 3.5(9), or § 3.5(5) and (7), the set of differential equations (9) for the radial wave functions and § 3.5(9) for the $Y_k$ functions can be regarded as a set of simultaneous ordinary differential equations for the functions $P(nl; r)$ and $Y_k(nl, n'l'; r)$.

These equations form a *set* of simultaneous equations for a *set* of functions. However, the equation containing the term $d^2P(nl; r)/dr^2$ will be referred to as "the equation for" that one radial wave function $P(nl; r)$, since the practical integration procedure each $P(nl; r)$ is in fact evaluated by twofold integration of the corresponding second derivative.

### 3.6.1. EQUATIONS FOR THE NORMAL CONFIGURATION OF A TEN-ELECTRON SYSTEM

To illustrate the derivation of Fock's equations, consider the example of a ten-electron system, for which the expression for $E'$ has already been given in formula § 3.4(14). Consider first the equation for $P(2p; r)$. The terms in $E'$ which depend on this radial wave function, and whose values are therefore affected by a variation in this function, are

$$6I(2p) + 15F_0(2p, 2p) - \tfrac{6}{5}F_2(2p, 2p) + 12F_0(1s, 2p) + 12F_0(2s, 2p) \\ - 2\,[G_1(1s, 2p) + G_1(2s, 2p)].$$

The contributions to the function $Q(r)$ in the integrand of the integral § 3.6(6) are:

From $\Delta I(2p)$, $\quad -6\left[\dfrac{d^2}{dr^2} + \dfrac{2N}{r} - \dfrac{2}{r}\right] P(2p; r)$,

From $\Delta F_0(2p, 2p)$, $\quad 60[Y_0(2p, 2p; r)/r]P(2p; r)$,

From $\Delta F_0(1s, 2p)$, $\quad 24[Y_0(1s, 1s; r)/r]P(2p; r)$,

[5] V. Fock, *Z. Physik*, **61**, 126 (1930); **62**, 795 (1930). For other derivations and discussion, see P. A. M. Dirac, *Proc. Cambridge Phil. Soc.*, **27**, 240 (1931); J. E. Lennard-Jones, *Proc. Cambridge Phil. Soc.*, **27**, 469 (1931). The first solution was evaluated by V. Fock and M. J. Petrashen, *Physik Z. Sowjetunion*, **6**, 368 (1934).

From $\Delta F_0(2s, 2p)$, $\qquad 24[Y_0(2s, 2s; r)/r]P(2p; r)$,
From $\Delta F_2(2p, 2p)$ $\qquad -(24/5)[Y_2(2p, 2p; r)/r]P(2p; r)$,
From $\Delta G_1(1s, 2p)$, $\qquad -4[Y_1(1s, 2p; r)/r]P(1s; r)$,
From $\Delta G_1(2s, 2p)$, $\qquad -4[Y_1(2s, 2p; r)/r]P(2s; r)$;

The sum of the first four terms (that is, of the contributions from $\Delta I(2p)$ and the $\Delta F_0(n'l', 2p)$ integrals) is

$$-6\left\{\frac{d^2}{dr^2} + \frac{2}{r}[N - 2Y_0(1s, 1s; r) - 2Y_0(2s, 2s; r) - 5Y_0(2p, 2p; r)] - \frac{2}{r^2}\right\} P(2p; r).$$

The quantity in the square brackets here is $Y(r) + Y_0(2p, 2p; r)$, where $Y(r)$ is defined by formula § 3.6(10), which in this case becomes

$$Y(r) = N - 2Y_0(1s, 1s; r) - 2Y_0(2s, 2s; r) - 6Y_0(2p, 2p; r). \qquad (1)$$

Hence altogether the function $Q(r)$ of formula § 3.6(6) is

$$Q(r) = -6\left\{\frac{d^2}{dr^2} + \frac{2}{r}\left[Y(r) + Y_0(2p, 2p; r) + \frac{2}{5}Y_2(2p, 2p; r)\right] - \frac{2}{r^2}\right\} P(2p; r) - \frac{4}{r}[Y_1(1s, 2p; r)P(1s; r) + Y_1(2s, 2p; r)P(2s; r)].$$

Since there is no other $p$ group in the configuration, the only condition on $\Delta P(2p; r)$ is that $P(2p; r) + \Delta P(2p; r)$ should be normalized; hence the only term in the sum in the formula § 3.6(8) is that for $n' = n = 2$. Hence this equation, multiplied by $-\frac{1}{6}$, is

$$\left\{\frac{d^2}{dr^2} + \frac{2}{r}\left[Y(r) + Y_0(2p, 2p; r) + \frac{2}{5}Y_2(2p, 2p; r)\right] - \varepsilon_{2p,2p} - \frac{2}{r^2}\right\} P(2p; r) = -\frac{2}{3r}[Y_1(1s, 2p; r)P(1s; r) + Y_1(2s, 2p; r)P(2s; r)]. \quad (2)$$

For the $(1s)$ and $(2s)$ functions, the variations $\Delta P(1s; r)$ and $\Delta P(2s; r)$ are subject to a condition of orthogonality as well as to the conditions of normalization. The corresponding argument in this case leads to the equations

$$\left\{\frac{d^2}{dr^2} + \frac{2}{r}[Y(r) + Y_0(1s, 1s; r)] - \varepsilon_{1s,1s}\right\} P(1s; r) = -\frac{2}{r}[Y_0(1s, 2s; r)\, P(2s; r) + Y_1(1s, 2p; r)\, P(2p; r)] + \varepsilon_{1s,2s}\, P(2s; r); \qquad (3)$$

$$\left\{\frac{d^2}{dr^2} + \frac{2}{r}[Y(r) + Y_0(2s, 2s; r)] - \varepsilon_{2s,2s}\right\} P(2s; r) = -\frac{2}{r}[Y_0(1s, 2s; r)\, P(1s; r) + Y_1(2s, 2p; r)\, P(2p; r)] + \varepsilon_{1s,2s}\, P(1s; r). \qquad (4)$$

The coefficients $\varepsilon_{1s,2s}$ in equations (3) and (4) are the same, since they arise from the same Lagrange multiplier $\lambda_{1s,2s}$ in equations §3.6(8), divided by $q(1s)$ and $q(2s)$, respectively, and $q(1s)$ and $q(2s)$ are equal since the $(1s)$ and $(2s)$ groups are both complete.

From the point of view of the calculation of atomic structures, there would be no purpose in carrying out the details of the algebra of § 3.3—3.6 if the equations to which it led were such that it was still impracticable to obtain a solution of them. However, solution of a set of equations such as (2), (3), and (4) is quite practicable. Some of the general methods available for the work are considered in Chapter 4, and their application to these equations in Chapter 5.

### 3.7. FOCK'S EQUATIONS AS INTEGRODIFFERENTIAL EQUATIONS

The integrodifferential character of equations § 3.6(9) can be exhibited as follows. As in § 3.4, let $U_k(r, s)$ be the function

$$\begin{aligned} U_k(r, s) &= r^k/s^{k+1} \quad \text{if} \quad r < s, \\ &= s^k/r^{k+1} \quad \text{if} \quad r > s; \end{aligned} \tag{1}$$

also let $\kappa_k(n'l'; r, s)$ be the function

$$\kappa_k(n'l'; r, s) = P(n'l'; r)\, U_k(r, s)\, P(n'l'; s). \tag{2}$$

Then

$$\frac{1}{r} Y_k(nl, n'l'; r)\, P(n'l'; r) = \int_0^\infty \kappa_k(n'l'; r, s)\, P(nl; s)\, ds,$$

and equation (9) can be written

$$\left[\frac{d^2}{dr^2} + \frac{2Y(nl; r)}{r} - \varepsilon_{nl,nl} - \frac{l(l+1)}{r^2}\right] P(nl; r)$$

$$= -2\int_0^\infty K_0(nl; r, s)\, P(nl; s)\, ds + \Sigma_{n' \neq n} \varepsilon_{nl,n'l} P(n'l; r), \tag{3}$$

where the kernel $K_0(nl; r, s)$ in the equation for $P(nl; r)$ is

$$K_0(nl; r, s) = \Sigma'_{n'l'k} \kappa_k(n'l'; r, s), \tag{4}$$

the sum $\Sigma'$ excluding $(n'l') = (nl)$.

Another form will be convenient for use later. If we use the relation § 3.6(11) and take onto the right-hand side the terms arising from the difference $Y(r) - Y(nl; r)$, we obtain an equation similar in form to (3); namely,

$$\left[\frac{d^2}{dr^2} + \frac{2Y(r)}{r} - \varepsilon_{nl,nl} - \frac{l(l+1)}{r^2}\right] P(nl; r)$$

$$= -2\int_0^\infty K(nl; r, s)\, P(nl; s)\, ds + \Sigma_{n' \neq n} \varepsilon_{nl,n'l}\, P(n'l; r), \tag{5}$$

in which the kernel $K$ is now

$$K(nl; r, s) = K_0(nl; r, s) + \Sigma_k \alpha_{kl} \kappa_k(nl; r, s). \tag{6}$$

### 3.8. THE NONDIAGONAL $\varepsilon$ PARAMETERS

The property of equations § 3.61(3) and (4), that the nondiagonal $\varepsilon$ parameters in these equations are equal, is clearly a case of a more general property, for a similar reason. For any configuration of closed groups, the parameters $\varepsilon_{nl,n'l}$ $(n' \neq n)$ occurring in the equation for $P(nl)$ and in that for $P(n'l)$ are equal, since they arise from the same Lagrange multiplier $\lambda_{nl,n'l}$ in equation § 3.6(8), divided by $q(nl)$ and $q(n'l)$ respectively, and these are equal since the $(nl)$ and $(n'l)$ groups are complete groups with the same $l$.

From this it follows that, for a configuration of complete groups, the conditions of orthogonality are satisfied by any solution of equations § 3.6(9). This can best be seen from the integrodifferential form § 3.7(5) of this set of equations. The equations for two radial wave functions $P(n_1l; r)$ and $P(n_2l; r)$ with the same $l$ are

$$\left[\frac{d^2}{dr^2} + \frac{2}{r}\,Y(r) - \varepsilon_{n_1l,n_1l} - \frac{l(l+1)}{r^2}\right] P(n_1l; r)$$

$$= -2\int_0^\infty K(n_1l; r, s)\, P(n_1l; s)\, ds + \Sigma_{n'\neq n_1}\varepsilon_{n_1l,n'l}\, P(n'l; r), \quad (1)$$

$$\left[\frac{d^2}{dr^2} + \frac{2}{r}\,Y(r) - \varepsilon_{n_2l,n_2l} - \frac{l(l+1)}{r^2}\right] P(n_2l; r)$$

$$= -2\int_0^\infty K(n_2l; r, s)\, P(n_2l; s)\, ds + \Sigma_{n'\neq n_2}\varepsilon_{n_2l,n'l} P(n'l; r). \quad (2)$$

Multiply the first equation by $-P(n_2l; r)$ and the second by $P(n_1l; r)$, add, and integrate from $r = 0$ to $\infty$. All terms on the left-hand side vanish except those involving the $\varepsilon_{nl,nl}$ coefficients; and on the right the kernels $K$ are both symmetrical in $r$ and $s$, so the variables $r$ and $s$ in the double integrals can be interchanged. Hence

$$(\varepsilon_{n_1l,n_1l} - \varepsilon_{n_2l,n_2l})\int_0^\infty P(n_1l; r)\, P(n_2l; r)\, dr$$

$$= 2\int_0^\infty [K(n_1l; r, s) - K(n_2l; r, s)] P(n_1l; r)\, P(n_2l; s)\, dr\, ds$$

$$- \varepsilon_{n_1l,n_2l}\int_0^\infty [P^2(n_1l; r) - P^2(n_2l; r)]\, dr$$

$$- \Sigma_{n'\neq n_1,n_2}\left[\varepsilon_{n_1l,n'l}\int_0^\infty P(n_1l; r)\, P(n'l; r)\, dr\right.$$

$$\left. - \varepsilon_{n_2l,n'l}\int_0^\infty P(n_2l; r)\, P(n'l; r)\, dr\right]. \quad (3)$$

In the first of these integrals, the kernels $K(n_1l; r, s)$ and $K(n_2l; r, s)$ include sums of terms given by § 3.7(4); in the difference $K_0(n_1l; r, s) - K_0(n_2l; r, s)$, the only terms in these sums that do not cancel are those for which $l' = l$, $n' = n_2$ in $K(n_1l; r, s)$, and $l' = l$, $n' = n_1$ in $K(n_2l; r, s)$. Hence

$$K_0(n_1l; r, s) - K_0(n_2l; r, s) = \Sigma_k[\kappa_k(n_2l; r, s) - \kappa_k(n_1l; r, s)],$$

and, from § 3.7(6),

$$K(n_1l; r, s) - K(n_2l; r, s) = \Sigma_k\{\beta_{llk}[\kappa_k(n_2l; r, s) - \kappa_k(n_1l; r, s)] + \alpha_{llk}[\kappa_k(n_1l; r, s) - \kappa_k(n_2l; r, s)]\}.$$

But $\beta_{llk} = \alpha_{llk}$ [see § 3.6(15)]. Hence the integrand of the first integral in the expression (3) vanishes. The second integral also vanishes since the radial wave functions are normalized. Hence, in *any* solution of equations § 3.6(9) in which $P(n_1l; r)$ and $P(n_2l; r)$ are normalized and $\varepsilon_{n_1l,n'l} = \varepsilon_{n_2l,n'l} = 0$ for $n' \neq n_1$ or $n_2$, $P(n_1l; r)$ and $P(n_2l; r)$ are orthogonal, irrespective of the value given to $\varepsilon_{n_1l,n_2l}$.

Thus for a configuration of complete groups it is no restriction to impose on the solution to be evaluated the condition $\varepsilon_{nl,n'l} = 0$ for $n' \neq n$. However, the derivation of this result has depended not only on the radial wave functions $P(nl; r)$ satisfying equations § 3.6(9), but also on the $Y_k$ functions occurring in these equations being related to these radial wave functions by the relations of § 3.5. In the process of successive approximation used in the solution of these equations, the $Y_k$ functions used in solving equation § 3.6(9) will not be exactly those that would be derived from the solutions of these equations, and it may be necessary to include nondiagonal $\varepsilon$ parameters in order to ensure that the conditions of orthogonality are satisfied.

It should be noted that the result has only been established for a configuration of complete groups.

### 3.9. EQUATIONS WITHOUT EXCHANGE

The integral terms in equation § 3.7(3) derive from the $K_{\alpha\beta}$ integrals in formula § 3.3(13) for $E'$, and the same applies to the greater part of the contribution to $Y(nl; r)$ from the $Y_k(nl, nl; r)$ functions with $k \neq 0$. These terms in the expression for $E'$ result from the use of a determinantal wave function, and can be described as resulting from "exchange" of electrons between the different one-electron wave functions.

If these terms are omitted, and the nondiagonal $\varepsilon$ parameters are made zero, there results a much simpler system of equations; namely,

$$\left\{\frac{d^2}{dr^2} + \frac{2}{r}[Y(r) + Y_0(nl, nl, r)] - \varepsilon_{nl,nl} - \frac{l(l+1)}{r^2}\right\} P(nl; r) = 0, \quad (1)$$

each of which has the same form as the equation for the radial wave function for a particle in a central field, the potential of the field for calculating the $(nl)$ wave function being

$$\frac{1}{r}[Y(r) + Y_0(nl, nl; r)],$$

the potential of the field of the nucleus and of the spherically averaged charge distribution of the electrons in the other wave functions.

These are the equations that would be written down from the descriptive "self-consistent field" approach mentioned in § 1.9, without appeal to the variation principle. They are known as the equations of the "self-consistent field without exchange," the self-consistency arising from the fact that, for a solution of these equations, the radial wave functions $P(nl; r)$ from which the $Y_0$ functions are derived must be consistent with the functions $P(nl; r)$ obtained from the solution of these equations. A similar relation is required in the solution of Fock's equations, which are therefore also called the equations of the "self-consistent field with exchange."

A set of equations very similar to (1) is obtained if the variation principle is applied to an approximate wave function $\Phi$ which is a *single product*, § 1.9(1), of one-electron wave functions $\psi_\alpha, \psi_\beta, \cdots$, which are taken to be of central-field form.

### 3.9.1. SLATER'S SIMPLIFIED FORM OF THE EQUATIONS WITH EXCHANGE

For a configuration of complete groups, the "exchange terms" in Fock's equations, represented by the integral on the right-hand side of equation § 3.7(3), have qualitatively the same general effect on the radial wave function $P(nl; r)$ as an additional contribution to the potential energy in equation § 3.9(1), this contribution corresponding to an attractive force.

Slater[6] has given an argument which leads to a definite expression for a contribution $V_x(r)$ to the potential such that $V_x(r)\,P(nl; r)$ can be used as an approximate replacement for the integral term in equation § 3.7(3). The function $V_x(r)$ can be described as an "averaged exchange potential." Further, when this replacement is made, the radial wave functions are given by the equation

$$\left[\frac{d^2}{dr^2} + \frac{2}{r}\,Y^*(r) - \varepsilon_{nl,nl} - \frac{l(l+1)}{r^2}\right] P(nl; r) = 0, \tag{1}$$

in which $Y^*(r)$ is the same function of $r$ for all $(nl)$, so that the functions

[6] J. C. Slater, *Phys. Rev.*, **81**, 385 (1951).

$P(nl; r)$ for the same $l$ and different $n$ are orthogonal, as they are for the solutions of Fock's equations.

The process of evaluating numerical solutions is considerably simpler for the set of equations (1) than for Fock's equations, and corresponds more nearly to the process of solution of the equations of the self-consistent field without exchange. In particular, in the solution of Fock's equations the number of $Y_k$ functions increases approximately as the square of the number of electron groups, and, except for the lightest atoms, evaluation of these functions accounts for the greater part of the time and labor of evaluating a solution of these equations, whereas these $Y_k$ functions individually play no part in Slater's equation (1).

However, the solutions of equation (1) do not seem to give a good approximation to the solution of Fock's equations. Such a solution has been evaluated by Pratt[7] for the $Cu^+$ ion, for which a solution of Fock's equations[8] and of the equations of the self-consistent field without exchange[9] are also available. If one regards the difference between the solution of Fock's equations and the solution of the equations of the self-consistent field without exchange as the "effect of exchange" for this ion, then it seems that the replacement of the equations § 3.9(1) for the self-consistent field without exchange by Slater's equations (1) with an "averaged exchange potential" has overestimated considerably, by a factor of 1.5 to 2, the effect of exchange. As an approximation to the solution of Fock's equations, the solution of equation (1) is not greatly better than that of the equation of the self-consistent field without exchange. It might be possible to correct for this overestimate by including an empirical factor in the contribution to $Y^*(r)$ in equation (1) from the "averaged exchange potential."

However, the methods of Chapter 7 for obtaining initial approximations for a solution of Fock's equations, and the facilities provided by large automatic digital machines, make it seem not too optimistic to think that it will be practicable to evaluate solutions of Fock's equations up to the 46-electron (9 group) structure of $Ag^+$ at least. If this is practicable, then it would seem best to carry out such calculations without the introduction of further approximations.

Slater[10] has also suggested another approach to the problem of evaluating atomic structures. For a given position of any one electron, say electron 1, the electrostatic potential energy of this electron in the field of all the other electrons is $\Sigma_j(1/r_{1j})$, and the average of this, weighted

[7] G. W. Pratt, *Phys. Rev.*, **88**, 1217 (1952).
[8] D. R. and W. Hartree, *Proc. Roy. Soc.*, **157**, 490 (1936).
[9] D. R. Hartree, *Proc. Roy. Soc.*, **141**, 282 (1933).
[10] J. C. Slater, *Phys. Rev.*, **91**, 528 (1953).

according to the probability of the other electrons occupying the various regions of coordinate space, is

$$V_e(\mathbf{r}_1) = \int |\Psi^2|[\Sigma_j(1/r_{1j})]d\tau_2 \cdots d\tau_p / \int |\Psi|^2 \, d\tau_2 \cdots d\tau_p$$

This, added to the potential energy $-N/r_1$ of this electron in the field of the nucleus, gives the average potential energy of electron 1 when it is at $\mathbf{r}_1$. Because of the antisymmetry of $\Psi$ in all pairs of electrons, this potential is the same function of the electron coordinates for any electron. We can now introduce an approximation, not necessarily a determinant of one-electron wave function, for $\Psi$ and carry out the integration over $\tau_2 \cdots \tau_p$. As far as the writer is aware, no calculations of atomic structures based on this approach have yet been carried out.

# 4. NUMERICAL PROCEDURES

## 4.1. FINITE DIFFERENCES

In the solution of the equations for the radial wave functions $P(r)$, either with or without exchange, the main operations for which numerical procedures are required are quadrature (integration of a *given* function of the independent variable) and integration of differential equations. For both these purposes it is convenient to use a set of equal intervals in $r$ (though not necessarily the same intervals over the whole range of $r$) and to express the integration formulae in terms of a set of numbers called the *finite differences* of the integrand.

If $r_j = r_0 + j\,\delta r$ ($j$ integral) are a set of values of $r$ at equal intervals $\delta r$, and $f_j = f(r_j)$, the quantities

$$\delta f_{j+\frac{1}{2}} = f_{j+1} - f_j$$

are called the *first differences* of the function $f(r)$, at interval $\delta r$. The quantities

$$\delta^2 f_j = \delta f_{j+\frac{1}{2}} - \delta f_{j-\frac{1}{2}} = f_{j+1} - 2f_j + f_{j-1}$$

are called the *second differences* of $f(r)$; and in general the quantities

$$\delta^{2n+2} f_j = \delta^{2n} f_{j+1} - 2\delta^{2n} f_j + \delta^{2n} f_{j-1},$$
$$\delta^{2n+1} f_{j+\frac{1}{2}} = \delta^{2n} f_{j+1} - \delta^{2n} f_j$$

are called the $(2n+2)$th and $(2n+1)$th differences, respectively, of $f(r)$. (This notation for finite differences is called the "central difference" notation; other notations are sometimes used, but this is much the most convenient in practical work, and will here be used throughout.)

**Example.** $f(r) = \sin 2\pi r$, $\delta r = 1/36$ ($2\pi\,\delta r = \pi/18$ radian $= 10°$).

| $36r$ | $f(r)$ | $\delta f$ | $\delta^2 f$ | $\delta^3 f$ | $\delta^4 f$ |
|---|---|---|---|---|---|
| 0 | 0 | | 0 | | 0 |
| | | 17365 | | − 528 | |
| 1 | 0.17365 | | − 0528 | | 17 |
| | | 16837 | | − 511 | |
| 2 | 0.34202 | | − 1039 | | 30 |
| | | 15798 | | − 481 | |
| 3 | 0.50000 | | − 1520 | | 49 |
| | | 14278 | | − 432 | |
| 4 | 0.64278 | | − 1952 | | 57 |
| | | 12326 | | − 375 | |
| 5 | 0.76604 | | − 2327 | | |
| | | 09999 | | | |
| 6 | 0.86603 | | | | |

*Notes*

(i) Differences are normally written in terms of the last significant figure of the tabulated function as unit.

(ii) Since in this case $f(r)$ is an odd function of $r$, the values at $r = 0$ of all differences of even order are zero.

For a function $f(r)$ differentiable at least $n$ times, the ratios $\delta^m f/(\delta r)^m$ $(m \leq n)$ are closely related to the derivatives $d^m f/dr^m$; however, in numerical work the differences $\delta^m f$ themselves are more useful than the difference ratios $\delta^m f/(\delta r)^m$.

## 4.2. THE MAIN FORMULAE IN FINITE DIFFERENCES

In the calculation of atomic structures there are six formulae in finite differences which we shall require. These will be quoted without proof.[1]

*(i) Halfway Interpolation.* There are formulae in terms of finite differences for interpolation at any fraction of the tabular interval. However, in the present context the only interpolation likely to be required is interpolation for a value of the independent variable halfway between the values for which $f(r)$ is tabulated.[2] The formula for this is

$$f_{j+\frac{1}{2}} = f_j + \tfrac{1}{2}\delta f_{j+\frac{1}{2}} - \tfrac{1}{16}(\delta^2 f_j + \delta^2 f_{j+1}) + \tfrac{3}{256}(\delta^4 f_j + \delta^4 f_{j+1}) + O(\delta r)^6. \quad (1)$$

*(ii) Relation between $\delta^2 f$ and $f''$ and Its Differences.*

$$\delta^2 f_j = (\delta r)^2[f''_j + \tfrac{1}{12}\delta^2 f''_j - \tfrac{1}{240}\delta^4 f''_j] + O(\delta r)^8. \quad (2)$$

*(iii) Four Integration Formulae.*

$$f_{j+1} - f_j = \tfrac{1}{2}(\delta r)[f'_j + f'_{j+1} - \tfrac{1}{12}(\delta^2 f'_j + \delta^2 f'_{j+1}) + \tfrac{11}{720}(\delta^4 f'_j + \delta^4 f'_{j+1})] + O(\delta r)^7 \quad (3)$$

$$= \tfrac{1}{2}(\delta r)\{f'_j + f'_{j+1} - \tfrac{1}{6}(\delta r)[(f''_{j+1} - f''_j) - \tfrac{1}{60}(\delta^2 f''_{j+1} - \delta^2 f''_j)]\} + O(\delta r)^7 \quad (4)$$

$$= \tfrac{1}{2}(\delta r)(f'_j + f'_{j+1}) - \tfrac{1}{12}(\delta^2 f_{j+1} - \delta^2 f_j) + \tfrac{1}{90}(\delta^4 f_{j+1} - \delta^4 f_j) + O(\delta r)^7. \quad (5)$$

[1] For proofs of these, or closely related formulae from which they can be derived, see texts on finite differences or on numerical analysis [for example, L. M. Milne-Thomson, *Calculus of Finite Differences*, Macmillan (1933); C. Jordon, *Calculus of Finite Differences*, Budapest (1939); E. T. Whittaker and G. Robinson, *Calculus of Observations*, Blackie, London (1934); J. B. Scarborough, *Numerical Mathematical Analysis*, Johns Hopkins Press, Baltimore (1930); D. R. Hartree, *Numerical Analysis*, Oxford (1955); F. B. Hildebrand, *Introduction to Numerical Analysis*, McGraw Hill (1956)].

[2] For more general interpolation formulae, see one of the texts on finite differences or numerical analysis cited.

These are integration formulae since they relate the change of $f = \int f'\,dr$ in an interval $\delta r$ to the integrand $f'$. The first term alone

$$f_{j+1} - f_j = \tfrac{1}{2}(\delta r)(f'_j + f'_{j+1})$$

gives what is termed the "trapezium rule" or "trapezoidal formula"; the other terms in formulae (3), (4), (5) are alternative forms of the correction to the trapezoidal formula. When values of the *derivative* of the integrand are available as well as values of the integrand itself, formula (4) is useful on account of the small coefficient in the error term. Formula (5) gives the correction in terms of higher differences of the integral itself, rather than in terms of higher differences of the integrand; we will see later (§ 4.7) a context in which this is useful.

A useful formula for integration through two adjacent intervals is

$$f_{j+2} - f_j = 2(\delta r)[f'_{j+1} + \tfrac{1}{6}\delta^2 f'_{j+1} - \tfrac{1}{180}\delta^4 f'_{j+1}] + O(\delta r)^7. \qquad (6)$$

The first two terms in the square brackets here, expressed in terms of the successive values of $f'$, give the integration formula usually known as "Simpson's rule." For hand calculations the form (6) is often the more convenient.

These formulae are given to different orders of accuracy in the interval $(\delta r)$. This is done so that the results obtained from them in applications shall be of the same order of accuracy. In the application of formulae (3) to (6), for example, we require to integrate not over a single interval but over a *given range* of $r$. The number of intervals in a given range of $r$ will be proportional to $1/(\delta r)$; so, if the error in each interval is $O(\delta r)^7$, the aggregate error in $f$ over a given *range* of $r$ is $O(\delta r)^6$. Similarly in the use of formula (2) the aggregate error in $\delta f$ over a given range of $r$ is $O(\delta r)^7$, and the aggregate error in $f$ itself is $O(\delta r)^6$.

### 4.3. QUADRATURE

In the integration of a given function of $r$, two kinds of results may be wanted, a definite integral $\int_a^b F(r)\,dr$ for fixed values of $a$ and $b$, or an integral $\int_a^r F(s)\,ds$ as a function of the upper limit $r$.

*(i) Definite Integral.* To evaluate $\int_a^b F(r)\,dr$ for fixed values of $a$ and $b$, take an even number of intervals in the range $r = a$ to $b$, and let $r_0 = a$, $r_{2J} = b$, $[J = (b - a)/2(\delta r)]$. Then, using formula § 4.2(6) with $f' = F$

$$\begin{aligned} f_{2J} - f_0 &= (f_2 - f_0) + (f_4 - f_2) + \cdots + (f_{2J} - f_{2J-2}) \\ &= 2(\delta r)(\Sigma_i F_{2i+1} + \tfrac{1}{6}\Sigma_i \delta^2 F_{2i+1} - \tfrac{1}{180}\Sigma_i \delta^4 F_{2i+1}) + O(\delta r)^6. \qquad (1) \end{aligned}$$

**Example 4.1. Quadrature (definite integral).** (From calculation of $\int_0^\infty P^2\,dr$ for $(3d)$ radial wave function of $Mn^+$.)

| $r$ | $P(r)$ | $P^2(r)$ | | $\delta^2(P^2)$ |
|---|---|---|---|---|
| 0.25 | 0.330 | 0.109 | | |
| | | | 79 | |
| 0.30 | 0.431 | 0.186 | | 11 |
| | | | 90 | |
| 0.35 | 0.525 | $\boxed{0.276}$ | | $\boxed{4}$ |
| | | | 94 | |
| 0·40 | 0.608 | 0.370 | | −3 |
| | | | 91 | |
| 0.45 | 0.679 | $\boxed{0.461}$ | | $\boxed{-7}$ |
| | | | 84 | |
| 0.50 | 0.738 | 0.545 | | −14 |
| | | | 70 | |
| 0.55 | 0.784 | $\boxed{0.615}$ | | $\boxed{-14}$ |
| | | | 56 | |
| 0.60 | 0.819 | 0.671 | | −16 |
| | | | 40 | |
| 0.65 | 0.843 | $\boxed{0.711}$ | | $\boxed{-13}$ |
| | | | 27 | |
| 0.70 | 0.859 | 0.738 | | −12 |
| | | | 14 | |
| 0.75 | 0.867 | $\boxed{0.752}$ | | $\boxed{-11}$ |
| | | | 3 | |
| 0.80 | 0.869 | 0.755 | | |

$r = 0.3$ to $0.8$

$\Sigma\delta^2(P^2) = -41$

$\Sigma P^2 = 2.815$

$+\frac{1}{6}\Sigma\delta^2(P^2) \quad -7$

$2.808$

$2(\delta r) = 0.1$

Contribution to $\int P^2\,dr = 0.281$

| $r$ | $P(r)$ | $P^2(r)$ | | $\delta^2(P^2)$ |
|---|---|---|---|---|
| 0.7 | 0.859 | 0.738 | | |
| | | | 17 | |
| 0.8 | 0.869 | 0.755 | | −36 |
| | | | −19 | |
| 0.9 | 0.858 | $\boxed{0.736}$ | | $\boxed{-23}$ |
| | | | −42 | |
| 1.0 | 0.833 | 0.694 | | −15 |
| | | | −57 | |
| 1.1 | 0.798 | $\boxed{0.637}$ | | $\boxed{-4}$ |
| | | | −61 | |
| 1.2 | 0.759 | 0.576 | | −1 |
| | | | −62 | |
| 1.3 | 0.717 | $\boxed{0.514}$ | | $\boxed{4}$ |
| | | | −58 | |
| 1.4 | 0.675 | 0.456 | | 4 |
| | | | −54 | |
| 1.5 | 0.634 | $\boxed{0.402}$ | | $\boxed{5}$ |
| | | | −49 | |
| 1.6 | 0.594 | 0.353 | | |

$r = 0.8$ to $1.6$

$\Sigma\delta^2(P^2) = -18$

$\Sigma P^2 = 2.289$

$+\frac{1}{6}\Sigma\delta^2(P^2) \quad -3$

$2.286$

$2(\delta r) = 0.2$

Contribution to $\int P^2\,dr = 0.457$

Contributions from $\delta^4(P^2)$ are negligible.

The values included in the sums are those enclosed in "boxes" $\square$.

The sums here are over *alternate* values of the integrand and of its differences of even order. It is convenient to pick out these values by enclosing each in a "box," as illustrated in Example 4.1. This example is taken from the evaluation of a normalization integral $\int_0^\infty P^2\,dr$, and shows the calculation of two contributions to this integral, from two ranges of $r$ with different values of $\delta r$. The contributions from the fourth differences of the integrand are negligible.

(*ii*) *Integral as Function of the Upper Limit of Integration*; $\int_a^r F(s)\,ds$ *as a Function of* $r$. Values of the integral will usually be required at the same intervals (in $r$) as those at which the values of the integrand are given. Then § 4.2(3) [or (4) if applicable] is the appropriate integration formula.

The result of taking second differences of both sides of formula § 4.2(3) is

$$\delta^2(\delta f_{j+\frac{1}{2}}) = \tfrac{1}{2}(\delta r)[\delta^2 F_0 + \delta^2 F_1 - \tfrac{1}{12}(\delta^4 F_0 + \delta^4 F_1)], \tag{2}$$

and this can be used to check the values of the contributions $\delta f_{j+\frac{1}{2}}$ to the integral. The second differences of these contributions are taken and compared with the values of the right-hand side of (2) evaluated from the differences of the integrand. Exact agreement is not to be expected on account of the effect of rounding errors in the $\delta f$ values on the second differences of these values; but if discrepancies of more than 1 in the last figure occur in successive entries, they should usually be in opposite directions. The $\delta^4 F$ term may give an appreciable contribution in formula (2) although it is negligible in the integration formula § 4.2(3) itself.

A specimen of such an integration is given in Example 4.2, which shows part of an evaluation of a function $Z_0(3d, 3d; r) = \int_0^r P^2(3d; s)\,ds$. In this integration, three decimals were required in the values of $Z_0$; the fourth was kept as a guarding figure, and is written as a subscript.

An overlap should *always* be taken between two ranges of $r$ in which different values of the interval of integration $(\delta r)$ is used; a change of interval is a place at which the systematic procedure of the integration is broken, and such breaks are points at which mistakes are liable to occur and to be overlooked if they do occur. An overlap is illustrated in example 4.2; the integration at intervals $(\delta r) = 0.1$ ends at $r = 1.6$, and the range $r = 1.4$ to $1.6$ is also covered at interval $(\delta r) = 0.2$. As in the use of the check based on formula (2), exact agreement is not to be expected; but discrepancies of more than 1 in the last figure are to be suspected.

**Example 4.2. Quadrature integral (as function of upper limit).** (From calculation of $Z_0(3d, 3d; r)$ for $Mn^+$.) $Z'_0(r) = P^2(r)$

| $r$ | $Z'_0(r)$ | | $\delta^2 Z'_0$ | (a) (b) | $Z_0(r)$ | $\delta Z_0$ | $\delta^2 Z_0$ | $\delta^3 Z_0$ |
|---|---|---|---|---|---|---|---|---|
| 0.7 | 0.738 | | | | | | | |
| | | 17 | | | | | | |
| 0.8 | 0.755 | | − 36 | | $0.294_0$ (c) | | | |
| | | − 19 | | 1.491 + 5 = 1.496 | | $74_8$ | | |
| 0.9 | 0.736 | | − 23 | | $0.368_8$ | | $-3_2$ | |
| | | − 42 | | 1.430 + 3 = 1.433 | | $71_6$ | | $-1_8$ |
| 1.0 | 0.694 | | − 15 | | $0.440_4$ | | $-5_0$ | |
| | | − 57 | | 1.331 + 2 = 1.333 | | $66_6$ | | $-0_9$ |
| 0.1 | 0.637 | | − 4 | | $0.507_0$ | | $-5_9$ | |
| | | − 61 | | 1.213 + 0 = 1.213 | | $60_7$ | | $-0_3$ |
| 0.2 | 0.576 | | − 1 | | $0.567_7$ | | $-6_2$ | |
| | | − 62 | | 1.090 + 0 = 1.090 | | $54_5$ | | $0_1$ |
| 0.3 | 0.514 | | 4 | | $0.622_2$ | | $-6_1$ | |
| | | − 58 | | 0.970 − 1 = 0.969 | | $48_4$ | | $0_5$ |
| 0.4 | 0.456 | | 4 | | $0.670_6$ | | $-5_6$ | |
| | | − 54 | | 0.858 − 1 = 0.857 | | $42_8$ | | $0_5$ |
| 0.5 | 0.402 | | 5 | | $0.713_4$ | | $-5_1$ | |
| | | − 49 | | 0.755 − 1 = 0.754 | | $37_7$ | | |
| 0.6 | 0.353 | | | | $0.751_1$ | | | |
| 1.4 | 0.456 | | 17 | | $0.670_6$ | | | |
| | | − 103 | | [0.809 − 3 = 0.806] | | $80_5$ | | |
| 1.6 | 0.353 | | 17 | | $0.751_1$ | | $-18_8$ | |
| | | − 86 | | 0.620 − 3 = 0.617 | | $61_7$ | | $3_6$ |
| 1.8 | 0.267 | | 20 | | $0.812_8$ | | $-15_2$ | |
| | | − 66 | | 0.468 − 3 = 0.465 | | $46_5$ | | $3_5$ |
| 2.0 | 0.201 | | 14 | | $0.859_3$ | | $-11_7$ | |
| | | − 52 | | 0.350 − 2 = 0.348 | | $34_8$ | | |
| 2.2 | 0.149 | | | | $0.894_1$ | | | |

(a) $Z'_0(r_{j+1}) + Z'_0(r_j)$. (b) $-\frac{1}{12}[\delta^2 Z'_0(r_{j+1}) + \delta^2 Z'_0(r_j)]$

(c) This value of $Z_0(0.8)$ obtained from integration up to $r = 0.8$ with smaller intervals.

## 4.4. SECOND-ORDER DIFFERENTIAL EQUATION WITH THE FIRST DERIVATIVE ABSENT

This is the simplest kind of differential equation for integration by numerical process. The equations for the radial wave functions $P(nl; r)$ are fortunately of this kind; that they are linear is a further advantage, though less important.

Let the equation be

$$d^2y/dr^2 = f(r, y). \tag{1}$$

The integration is carried out by use of formula § 4.2(2). The working can be set out as shown in the following scheme.

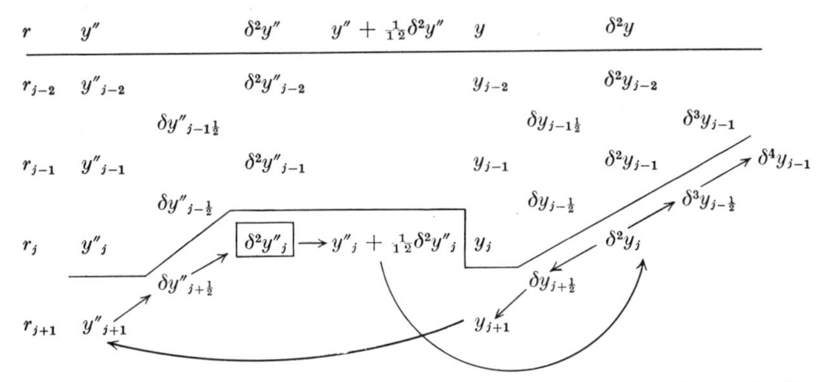


If the integration has been carried to $r = r_j$, quantities above the line are known. The integration for the interval $\delta r$ from $r_j$ to $r_{j+1}$ starts from an estimate of $\delta^2 y''_j$ (shown in a "box"), and the sequence in which the other quantities are derived from it is shown by arrows. If the final value of $\delta^2 y''_j$, obtained from the differences derived from $y''_{j+1}$, differs from the estimate by an amount enough to affect $\delta y_{j+\frac{1}{2}}$ to the accuracy to which the calculations are carried out, the correction should be made; and, if this affects $y''_{j+1}$, this correction should also be made. It should seldom be necessary to repeat the whole calculation for the interval.

When the value of $\delta^2 y_j$ has been finalized (and not before), it should be checked as follows. The result of taking differences of both sides of formula § 4.2(2), and lowering the subscript values by 1, is

$$\delta^4 f_{j-1} = (\delta r)^2(\delta^2 f''_{j-1} + \tfrac{1}{12}\delta^4 f''_{j-1}) + O(\delta r)^8. \tag{2}$$

The quantity $\delta^4 f_{j-1}$ can be derived from the value of $\delta^2 y_j$ just calculated (as indicated by the upward-sloping arrows on the right), and $(\delta r)^2(\delta^2 f''_{j-1} + \frac{1}{12}\delta^4 f''_{j-1})$ can be calculated from the differences of $f''$; the values required are available at this stage of the calculation. The comment in § 4.3 on the use of formula (2) to check the $\delta f$ values there also applies here. The comments on taking an overlap between two ranges of integration with different values of $(\delta r)$ also apply.[3]

A portion of an integration of the radial wave equation with exchange is shown in Example 4.3. The equation is written

$$d^2P/dr^2 = -[S(r)\, P/r] + X(r),$$

where $S(r)$ and $X(r)$ are functions of $r$ whose exact forms are not important for this example, and which, in the integration for the function $P$, are to be treated as *given* functions of $r$; their general character can be seen from the equations for a ten-electron system derived in § 3.4.

[3] For further notes on practical procedure, see D. R. Hartree, *Numerical Analysis*, § 7.2, Oxford (1955).

**Example 4.3. Integration of second-order equation**

$$d^2P/dr^2 = -(SP/r) + X(r) \quad \text{for} \quad (3d) \text{ of } \mathrm{Mn}^+$$

$$S = \{2Y(r) + 2Y_0(3d, 3d; r) + \tfrac{10}{21}[Y_2(3d, 3d; r) + Y_4(3d, 3d; r)]\} - \varepsilon_{3d,3d}r - 6/r$$

$$X(r) = \text{"exchange terms."}$$

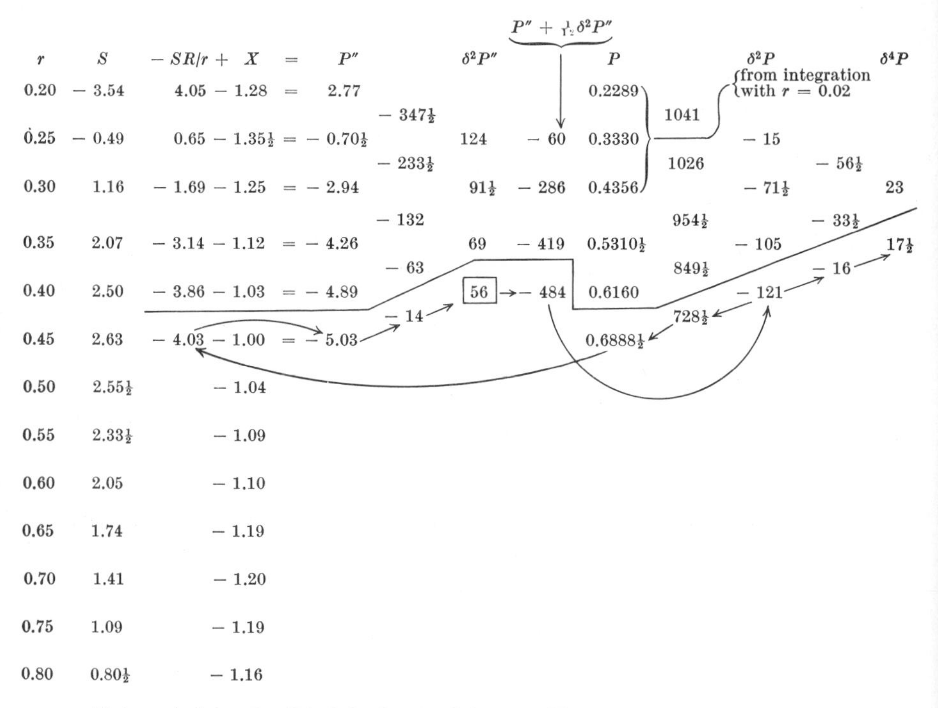

| $r$ | $S$ | $-SR/r + X$ | = | $P''$ | | $\delta^2P''$ | $P'' + \frac{1}{12}\delta^2P''$ | $P$ | | $\delta^2P$ | | $\delta^4P$ |
|---|---|---|---|---|---|---|---|---|---|---|---|---|
| 0.20 | − 3.54 | 4.05 − 1.28 | = | 2.77 | | | | 0.2289 | | {from integration with $r$ = 0.02 | | |
| | | | | | − 347½ | | | | 1041 | | | |
| 0.25 | − 0.49 | 0.65 − 1.35½ | = | − 0.70½ | | 124 | − 60 | 0.3330 | | − 15 | | |
| | | | | | − 233½ | | | | 1026 | | − 56½ | |
| 0.30 | 1.16 | − 1.69 − 1.25 | = | − 2.94 | | 91½ | − 286 | 0.4356 | | − 71½ | | 23 |
| | | | | | − 132 | | | | 954½ | | − 33½ | |
| 0.35 | 2.07 | − 3.14 − 1.12 | = | − 4.26 | | 69 | − 419 | 0.5310½ | | − 105 | | 17½ |
| | | | | | − 63 | | | | 849½ | | − 16 | |
| 0.40 | 2.50 | − 3.86 − 1.03 | = | − 4.89 | | 56 | − 484 | 0.6160 | | − 121 | | |
| | | | | | − 14 | | | | 728½ | | | |
| 0.45 | 2.63 | − 4.03 − 1.00 | = | − 5.03 | | | | 0.6888½ | | | | |
| 0.50 | 2.55½ | − 1.04 | | | | | | | | | | |
| 0.55 | 2.33½ | − 1.09 | | | | | | | | | | |
| 0.60 | 2.05 | − 1.10 | | | | | | | | | | |
| 0.65 | 1.74 | − 1.19 | | | | | | | | | | |
| 0.70 | 1.41 | − 1.20 | | | | | | | | | | |
| 0.75 | 1.09 | − 1.19 | | | | | | | | | | |
| 0.80 | 0.80½ | − 1.16 | | | | | | | | | | |

*Note.* A 5 in the third decimal of $S(r)$ or $X(r)$, or in the fifth decimal of $\delta^2P$, is written ½.

In this example, the procedure once the integration has got under way is illustrated by the numbers below the full line; it follows the general procedure illustrated above. It is supposed that the integration has been carried to $r = 0.4$. From the run of previous values of $\delta^2P''$, an estimate of 56 is made for the value of $\delta^2P''$ at $r = 0.4$; from this, the consequent values of $\delta^2P$, $P$, $P''$ follow in the sequence indicated by the arrows. The value $P''(0.45) = -5.03$, with the previous values of $P''$, gives $\delta^2P''(0.4) = 49$; but the replacement of the estimate 56 by 49 does not change the value of $P(0.45)$ to the accuracy to which it is kept; so this interval of the integration can be regarded as completed. The values of $\delta^3P$ and $\delta^4P$, derived from $\delta^2P(0.4)$ and previous values, are then entered and the check based on formula (2) is applied. In the example, the input data [the functions $S(r)$ and $X(r)$] are given as far as $r = 0.8$, so that the reader can, if he wishes, get some slight experience of the integration process by continuing the integration.

In this example, the numbers above the broken line were obtained from the results of an integration with intervals $\delta r = 0.02$, the value of $P(0.25)$ being obtained by "halfway" interpolation between $r = 0.24$ and $r = 0.26$ by use of the formula § 4.2(1). In such a change of interval, it is good practice to interpolate the value of $P''$ similarly, and to check that the value so interpolated agrees with the value derived from the interpolated value of $P(r)$ and the differential equation. From these values of $P''$ at interval $\delta r = 0.05$, the value of $P'' + \frac{1}{12}\delta^2 P''$ at $r = 0.25$ is evaluated, and from it the value of $\delta^2 P$ at $r = 0.25$. Agreement of this value of $\delta^2 P$ with the value obtained by interpolation checks this interpolation. It is important to have a check here, as the whole of the subsequent integration is going to be based on the value of $P(0.3) - P(0.25)$ derived from the interpolation, and, if the value of $P(0.25)$ is wrong, all the subsequent integration is vitiated.

## 4.5. NUMEROV'S PROCESS FOR A LINEAR SECOND-ORDER EQUATION

The process explained in the previous section does not depend on the equation to be integrated being linear. For a linear equation there is an alternative process, generally ascribed to Numerov,[4] which avoids the estimation of $\delta^2 P''$ and revision of this estimate if necessary.

Let the equation be

$$y'' = F(r)y + G(r). \tag{1}$$

Then, from formula § 4.2(2) with the $\delta^4 f''$ term omitted, and the differential equation (1)

$$\delta^2 y_1 = (\delta r)^2\{F_j y_j + G_j + \tfrac{1}{12}[\delta^2(Fy + G)]_j\}, \tag{2}$$

or, more fully,

$$\begin{aligned} y_{j+1} &- 2y_j + y_{j-1} \\ &= (\delta r)^2\{F_j y_j + G_j + \tfrac{1}{12}[F_{j+1}y_{j+1} - 2F_j y_j + F_{j-1}y_{j-1}] + \tfrac{1}{12}\delta^2 G_j\}, \end{aligned}$$

whence

$$\begin{aligned} [1 - \tfrac{1}{12}(\delta r)^2 F_{j+1}]y_{j+1} - 2[1 - \tfrac{1}{12}(\delta r)^2 F_j]y_j + [1 - \tfrac{1}{12}(\delta r)^2 F_{j-1}]y_{j-1} \\ = (\delta r)^2(F_j y_j + G_j + \tfrac{1}{12}\delta^2 G_j) \end{aligned} \tag{3}$$

This can be written more shortly as follows. Let

$$[1 - \tfrac{1}{12}(\delta r)^2 F]y = Y; \tag{4}$$

then

$$\delta^2 Y_j = (\delta r)^2 \left[\frac{F_j}{1 - \tfrac{1}{12}(\delta r)^2 F_j} Y + G_j + \tfrac{1}{12}\delta^2 G_j\right]. \tag{5}$$

If this form is used, it must be remembered that the function $Y$ depends on the interval length $\delta r$ as well as on the solution $y$, so that, at a point

[4] B. Numerov, *Publs. observatoire central astrophys. Russ.*, **2**, 188 (1933).

at which the integration interval is changed, the values of $Y$ must be modified in accordance with formula (4).

The calculation of atomic structure by the solution of Fock's equations is based on an approximation to the wave function of a many-electron atom which may be only a rather rough one. In view of this, no high degree of numerical precision is called for in the numerical solution of these equations, and my own experience suggests that for hand calculations in this context the procedure of § 4.4, involving the estimation of $\delta^2 P''$, is so simple and straightforward to carry out to the accuracy required that there is no advantage in the Numerov process. On the other hand, the latter may be the more appropriate for use on an automatic digital machine, for which a strictly specified process is preferable to one that involves making estimates and adjusting them if necessary, as this depends to a certain extent on an individual's "hunch" and experience of previous calculations, which it is difficult to build into a program for an automatic machine.

Olver has given a process[5] for correcting for the truncation error of formula (2). But in the present context, with the integration intervals which are likely to be used, this correction will seldom be required.

## 4.6. FIRST-ORDER EQUATION

For a first-order equation

$$y' = \phi(x, y), \tag{1}$$

not necessarily linear, the following is one procedure. From formula § 4.2(3), neglecting the term in $\delta^4 f'$,

$$y_{j+1} - y_j = \tfrac{1}{2}(\delta r)[y'_j + y'_{j+1} - \tfrac{1}{12}(\delta^2 y'_j + \delta^2 y'_{j+1})]. \tag{2}$$

If the integration has been carried out to $r = r_j$, $y_j$ and $y'_j$ are known, but $y'_{j+1}$ is unknown, and the latest second difference of $y'$ known is $\delta^2 y'_{j-1}$. Estimate $\delta^2 y_j$, either from the run of previous values or from the approximate relation

$$\delta^2 y_j = \tfrac{1}{2}(\delta r)[\delta y'_{j-\frac{1}{2}} + \delta y'_{j+\frac{1}{2}}], \tag{3}$$

the second term in the square bracket in (3) being estimated. Build up $y_{j+1}$ from this estimated $\delta^2 y_j$, evaluate $y'_{j+1}$ from the differential equation, and use it to obtain $\delta^2 y'_j$; estimate $\delta^2 y'_{j+1}$, and evaluate $y_{j+1} - y_j$ from (2). If the value of $y_{j+1}$ obtained results in any appreciable change of $y'_{j+1}$, make this change, and repeat the integration for the interval if necessary.

[5] See D. R. Hartree, *Numerical Analysis*, § 7.52.

Alternatively, $y_{j+1}$ can be estimated from

$$y_{j+1} - y_{j-1} = 2(\delta r)(y'_j + \tfrac{1}{6}\delta^2 y'_j),$$

[see § 4.2(6)] using an estimate of $\delta^2 y'_j$.

This process is illustrated in Example 4.4, which is taken from the integration for a $Z_2(nl, nl; r)$ function [see equation § 3.6(2)]. In this calculation, three decimals in $Z_2$ were required; the fourth was kept as a guarding figure. If the integration has been carried to $r = 0.45$, the quantities above the heavy line are known. The calculation for the interval $r = 0.45$ to $r = 0.5$ starts with an estimate of $\delta^2 Z_2$ at $r = 0.45$, which is enclosed in a "box", and proceeds as indicated by the arrows. The final value of $\delta Z_2$ (0.475) is obtained from formula (2).

**Example 4.4. Integration of a first-order equation.** [From calculation of $Z_2(3d, 3d; r)$ for $Mn^{+2}$]

$$\frac{dZ_2}{dr} = P^2(3d) - \frac{2}{r} Z_2$$

| $r$ | $P^2 - \frac{2}{r} Z_2 = Z'_2$ | | $\delta^2 Z'_2$ | $Z_2$ | $\delta Z_2$ | $\delta^2 Z_2$ |
|---|---|---|---|---|---|---|
| 0.25 | 0.109 − 0.033 = 0.076 | | | $0.004_2$ | | |
| | | 48 | | | | |
| 0.30 | 0.186 − 0.062 = 0.124 | | 9 | $0.009_3$ | | |
| | | 57 | | | $7_6$ | |
| 0.35 | 0.276 − 0.095 = 0.181 | | − 5 | $0.016_9$ | | $2_8$ |
| | | 52 | | | $10_4$ | |
| 0.40 | 0.370 − 0.137 = 0.233 | | − 3 | $0.027_3$ | | $2_5$ |
| | | 49 | | | $12_9$ | |
| 0.45 | 0.461 − 0.179 = 0.282 | | − 8 | $0.040_2$ | | $\boxed{2_3}$ |
| | | 41 | | | $15_2$ | |
| 0.50 | 0.545 − 0.222 = 0.323 | | | $0.055_4$ | | |
| 0.55 | 0.615 | | | | | |
| 0.60 | 0.671 | | | | | |

## 4.7. FOX–GOODWIN PROCESS FOR LINEAR FIRST-ORDER EQUATIONS

For a *linear* first-order equation, Fox and Goodwin[6] have given a method that avoids any estimation of $y_{j+1}$. Let the equation be

$$y' = F(r)y + G(r). \tag{1}$$

Then

$$y_{j+1} - y_j = \tfrac{1}{2}(\delta r)(F_{j+1}y_{j+1} + G_{j+1} + F_j y_j + G_j) + C_{j+\frac{1}{2}}, \tag{2}$$

[6] L. Fox and E. T. Goodwin, *Proc. Cambridge Phil. Soc.*, **45**, 373 (1949).

where $C_{j+\frac{1}{2}}$, the correction to the "trapezoidal formula," expressed in terms of values of $y$, is [see § 4.2(5)]

$$C_{j+\frac{1}{2}} = [-\tfrac{1}{12}(\delta^2 y_{j+1} - \delta^2 y_j) + \tfrac{1}{90}(\delta^4 y_{j+1} - \delta^4 y_j) - \cdots]. \tag{3}$$

Equation (2) can be written as an equation for $y_{j+1}$, in terms of the known functions $F$ and $G$ and the value of $y_j$:

$$[1 - \tfrac{1}{2}(\delta r)F_{j+1}]y_{j+1} = [1 + \tfrac{1}{2}(\delta r)F_j]y_j + \tfrac{1}{2}(\delta r)(G_{j+1} + G_j) + C_{j+\frac{1}{2}}, \tag{4}$$

or as an equation for $(y_{j+1} - y_j)$:

$$[1 - \tfrac{1}{2}(\delta r)F_{j+1}](y_{j+1} - y_j) = \tfrac{1}{2}(\delta r)[(F_j + F_{j+1})y_j + (G_{j+1} + G_j)] + C_{j+\frac{1}{2}}. \tag{5}$$

For hand calculation (5) is more convenient than (4); for calculation with an automatic digital machine there does not seem much to choose.

The following is one procedure for correcting for the leading terms in the truncation error of the trapezoidal formula. Consider the result of integrating from $r_j$ to $r_{j+2}$, using the trapezoidal formula obtained by omitting the $C_{j+\frac{1}{2}}$ term in formula (2), and using, first, two intervals of length $\delta r = h$, and second, one interval of length $\delta r = 2h$. Let $z_j$ be an approximation to $y_j$, and $z_{j+1}$, $z_{j+2}$ the approximations to $y_{j+1}$, $y_{j+2}$ evaluated from the relations

$$\left.\begin{aligned} z_{j+1} - z_j &= \tfrac{1}{2}h(F_{j+1}z_{j+1} + G_{j+1} + F_j z_j + G_j), \\ z_{j+2} - z_{j+1} &= \tfrac{1}{2}h(F_{j+2}z_{j+2} + G_{j+2} + F_{j+1}z_{j+1} + G_{j+1}), \end{aligned}\right\} \tag{6}$$

of which the first is obtained by omitting the correction term $C_{j+\frac{1}{2}}$ from formula (2), and the second by replacing $j$ by $j+1$ in the first. Also let $z^*_j$ satisfy the corresponding relation with $\delta r = 2h$; namely,

$$z^*_{j+2} - z^*_j = h(F_{j+2}z^*_{j+2} + G_{j+2} + F_j z_j^* + G_j).$$

Write

$$w_j = y_j - z_j; \qquad w^*_j = y_j - z^*_j, \tag{7}$$

and suppose that, at $r_j$,

$$z_j = z^*_j = y_j + O(h^5), \quad \text{so that} \quad w_j = w^*_j = O(h^5). \tag{8}$$

Then

$$w_{j+1} - w_j = \tfrac{1}{2}h(F_{j+1}w_{j+1} + F_j w_j) + C_{j+\frac{1}{2}},$$

and, from formula (3),

$$C_{j+\frac{1}{2}} = -\tfrac{1}{12}h^3 y'''_{j+\frac{1}{2}} + O(h^5);$$

so

$$(1 - \tfrac{1}{2}hF_{j+1})w_{j+1} = -\tfrac{1}{12}h^3 y'''_{j+\frac{1}{2}} + O(h^5), \tag{9}$$

and

$$(1 - \tfrac{1}{2}hF_{j+2})w_{j+2} = (1 + \tfrac{1}{2}hF_{j+1})w_{j+1} - \tfrac{1}{12}h^3 y'''_{j+1\frac{1}{2}}.$$

Elimination of $w_{j+1}$ gives

$$(1 - \tfrac{1}{2}hF_{j+1})(1 - \tfrac{1}{2}hF_{j+2})w_{j+2} = -\tfrac{1}{12}h^3[(1 + \tfrac{1}{2}hF_{j+1})y'''_{j+\frac{1}{2}} + (1 - \tfrac{1}{2}hF_{j+1})y'''_{j+1\frac{1}{2}}] + O(h^5)$$
$$= -\tfrac{1}{6}h^3y'''_{j+1} + O(h^5).$$

Also $F_{j+2} - F_{j+1} = O(h)$; so

$$(1 - hF_{j+2})w_{j+2} = -\tfrac{1}{6}h^3y'''_{j+1} + O(h^5). \tag{10}$$

For the one large interval of length $\delta r = 2h$, centered on $r_{j+1}$, the formula corresponding to (9) is

$$[1 - \tfrac{1}{2}(2h)F_{j+2}]w^*_{j+2} = -\tfrac{1}{12}(2h)^3y'''_{j+1} + O(h^5);$$

that is,

$$[1 - hF_{j+2}]w^*_{j+2} = -\tfrac{2}{3}h^3y'''_{j+1} + O(h^5); \tag{11}$$

and it follows from formulae (10) and (11) that

$$4w_{j+2} - w^*_{j+2} = O(h^5),$$

and hence from formula (7) that

$$y_{j+2} = \tfrac{1}{3}(4z_{j+2} - z^*_{j+2}) + O(h^5). \tag{12}$$

Thus the quantity $\frac{1}{3}(4z_{j+2} - z^*_{j+2})$ gives an approximation to $y_{j+2}$ with an error of the same order as that supposed already to exist in $z_j$. The construction of this quantity from the results $z_{j+2}$ and $z^*_{j+2}$ of two separate calculations using two different sizes of integration intervals is a special case of the process called by L. F. Richardson[7] "$h^2$ extrapolation." A convenient form of this formula (12) for practical work is [neglecting the $O(h^5)$ error term]

$$y_{j+2} = z_{j+2} + \tfrac{1}{3}(z_{j+2} - z^*_{j+2}); \tag{13}$$

that is, extrapolate outside $z_{j+2}$ (the result for two small intervals) by one third of the difference between the results for two small and for one large interval. In the present context, this process of $h^2$ extrapolation can be applied after each pair of small intervals, the integration being continued from the value given by formula (13).

The value of $z_{j+1}$ can also be corrected for the leading term in the truncation error of formulae (6) as follows. From formulae (11) and (12),

$$(1 - hF_{j+2})(w_{j+2} - w^*_{j+2}) = \tfrac{1}{2}h^3y'''_{j+1} + O(h^5),$$

and so, from formula (9),

$$w_{j+1} = -\tfrac{1}{6}(w_{j+2} - w^*_{j+2}) + O(h^4),$$

[7] L. F. Richardson, *Phil. Trans. Roy. Soc.*, **226**, 300 (1927).

and hence

$$y_{j+1} = z_{j+1} + \tfrac{1}{6}(z_{j+2} - z^*_{j+2}) + O(h^4). \tag{14}$$

Thus the intermediate value $z_{j+1}$ at the end of the first of the two small intervals can be corrected for the leading term in the truncation error, though the residual error in $y_{j+1}$ is $O(h^4)$ whereas that in $y_{j+2}$ is $O(h^5)$. However, the errors $O(h^5)$ in formula (12) accumulate as the integration is carried through successive pairs of intervals, and for a given *range* of integration they give an aggregate error of order $h^4$, whereas the errors in the intermediate values, given by (14), do not accumulate, and can be accepted as being of the same order as the aggregate error arising from the use of formula (13).

An alternative procedure, of an iterative character, for correcting for the truncation error of the trapezium rule (6) has been suggested by Fox and Goodwin. It has the advantage that it can be applied to take into account higher-order terms in the truncation error as well as the leading terms. However, for work on an automatic digital calculating machine use of formulae (13) and (14) makes considerably smaller demands on storage capacity than the iterative process does, and in the present context, with the integration intervals likely to be used in practice, the accuracy of formulae (13) and (14) should be adequate.

# 5. APPLICATION OF THE NUMERICAL PROCEDURES

## 5.1. EQUATIONS WITHOUT EXCHANGE

We shall consider first the process for obtaining solutions of the equations for the radial wave functions in the approximation expressed by the term "without exchange" (see § 3.9), as this is somewhat simpler and considerably shorter than the procedure for obtaining solutions in the better approximation "with exchange."

The general character of the equations to be solved is illustrated by equation § 3.9(1). Let $q(nl)$ be the number of occupied wave functions in the $(nl)$ group, and

$$Y(r) = N - \Sigma_{n'l'} q(n'l') Y_0(n'l', n'l'; r), \tag{1}$$

$$Y(nl; r) = Y(r) + Y_0(nl, nl; r); \tag{2}$$

$Y(r)/r$ is the potential of the field of the nucleus and of the average charge distribution of the electrons; $Y(nl; r)$ is the potential of the field which, in this approximation, is to be used in evaluating the radial wave function of an electron in the $(nl)$ group. The equation for this radial wave function is

$$\left[\frac{d^2}{dr^2} + \frac{2}{r} Y(nl; r) - \varepsilon_{nl} - \frac{l(l+1)}{r^2}\right] P(nl; r) = 0. \tag{3}$$

It is convenient also to write $Z(r)$ for the function

$$Z(r) = N - \Sigma_{n'l'} q(n'l') Z_0(n'l', n'l'; r); \tag{4}$$

$Z(r)/r^2$ is the field at radius $r$ due to the charge $N$ on the nucleus and the average charge distribution of the electrons. For an $i$-times ionized atom, $Z(r) \to i$ as $r \to \infty$. The function

$$q(n'l')[1 - Z_0(n'l', n'l'; r)] = q(n'l') \int_r^\infty P^2(n'l'; s)\, ds \tag{5}$$

is the contribution to $Z(r)$ from the average charge distribution of the electrons in the $(n'l')$ group and $q(n'l')$ positive charges on the nucleus; it tends to zero as $r \to \infty$, and for this reason it has been found a somewhat more convenient function with which to work than $Z_0(n'l', n'l'; r)$.

The functions $Z(r)$ and $Y(r)$ can be regarded as giving the "effective nuclear charge for field" and "effective nuclear charge for potential" at radius $r$, respectively. They are related by the equation

$$\frac{dY(r)}{dr} = \frac{1}{r}[Y(r) - Z(r)], \tag{6}$$

and the contributions to them from each $(nl)$ group are related in a similar way [see equation § 3.6(1), with $k = 0$]. For a Coulomb field, these functions are constant and equal; equation (6) shows that these properties are related. But for a non-Coulomb field, they may not be even roughly equal. For example, for $Z(r) = (1 + kr)e^{-kr}$, which may represent roughly the behavior of $Z(r)$ in the outer regions of a neutral atom,

$$Y(r) = e^{-kr} = Z(r)/(1 + kr),$$

which for $kr = 4$ gives $Y(r) = \frac{1}{5}Z(r)$.

The different radial wave functions $P(nl; r)$ are coupled through the dependence of the function $Y(r)$ on the solutions of all the equations (3) for the different electron groups. The process of solution that has been most used is one of successive approximation, and this will be considered first; an alternative process is mentioned later in § 5.4. A successive approximation process is the following:

(i) Estimate contributions (5) to $Z(r)$ from the $(nl)$ groups; these will be called the "input" contributions to $Z(r)$.
(ii) Calculate $Y(r)$ and the functions $Y(nl; r)$ for the various $(nl)$ groups.
(iii) With these function $Y(nl; r)$, calculate solutions $P(nl; r)$ of equation (3) for the radial wave functions.
(iv) Evaluate contributions (5) to $Z(r)$ from these solutions of equation (3); these will be called the "output" contributions to $Z(r)$ from this stage of the successive approximation.
(v) Revise the estimates if necessary, and repeat the procedure until satisfactory agreement is obtained between "input" and "output" contributions to $Z(r)$.

The first step, that of making the initial estimate, is an important one, as the total amount of work involved in the whole calculation can be greatly reduced by the use of good initial estimates. As is often the case in a calculation carried out by a method of successive approximation, refining an initially good approximation to the solution is much less trouble than reaching a moderately good approximation from a poor one, or from a blind guess. A process of making initial estimates will be considered in Chapter 7.

### 5.1.1. CALCULATION OF $Y(r)$ AND CONTRIBUTIONS TO IT

The calculation of $Y(r)$ is carried out by integration of equation § 5.1(6). The integration is carried inwards, from the initial condition $Y(R) = Z(R)$ for a value of $R$ so large that the departure of $Z(r)$ from a constant is negligible, to the accuracy of the numerical work, for $r > R$. This inward integration of equation § 5.1(6) is stable. Either of the methods given in §§ 4.6, 4.7 can be used.

The solution of equation § 5.1(6) can be reduced to a quadrature:

$$\frac{d}{dr}\left[\frac{Y(r)}{r}\right] = -\frac{Z(r)}{r^2}; \tag{1}$$

however, in integrating equation § 5.1(6) we only integrate the *departures* from a Coulomb field, which remain finite as $r \to \infty$, whereas in using (1) we would be integrating the *whole* field. In equation (1) the singularities at $r = 0$ in the integrand and in the integral would be troublesome in numerical work, though they could be removed by writing this equation as

$$\frac{d}{dr}\left[\frac{N - Y(r)}{r}\right] = -\frac{N - Z(r)}{r^2}; \tag{2}$$

the right-hand side of equation (2) is finite at the origin, and indeed it is $O(r)$ for small $r$ since from § 5.1(4)

$$N - Z(r) = \Sigma_{n'l'}\, q(n'l')Z_0(nl', n'l'; r)$$

and

$$Z_0(n'l', n'l'; r) = \int_0^r P^2(n'l'; s)\, ds = O(r^{2l'+3}). \tag{3}$$

We shall require later a result which follows from this, namely that for $r$ small

$$Y(r) = N + v_0 r + O(r^3) \tag{4}$$

with no term in $r^2$. Here $v_0$ is a constant, which is negative and is the potential, at the origin, of the field of the Schrödinger charge distribution of the electrons.

If $Y(r)$ is obtained by integration of equation § 5.1(6), the very last interval of the integration needs special treatment, since $Y(r)$ and $Z(r)$ both tend to $N$ as $r \to 0$, so that the right-hand side of this equation becomes indeterminate at $r = 0$. However, since $Y(r) \to N$ as $r \to 0$

$$Y'(0) = -\lim_{r \to 0}\left[\frac{N - Y(r)}{r}\right];$$

so, from equation (2),

$$\frac{N - Y(\delta r)}{\delta r} + Y'(0) = -\int_0^{\delta r} \frac{N - Z(r)}{r^2}\, dr,$$

and hence

$$-Y'(0) = \frac{N - Y(\delta r)}{\delta r} + \int_0^{\delta r} \frac{N - Z(r)}{r^2}\, dr. \tag{5}$$

The evaluation of the contributions to $Y(r)$ follows the same lines as that of $Y(r)$ itself. To avoid accumulation of the rounding errors in the different contributions to $Y(r)$, it is best to evaluate by integration both $Y(r)$ itself and the functions $Y_0(nl, nl)$, and then to construct by means of formula § 5.1(2) the function $Y(nl; r)$ to be used in solving each equation § 5.1(3).

## 5.2. SOLUTION OF THE RADIAL WAVE EQUATION

The solution of the radial wave equation § 5.1(5) required, for each $(nl)$, is that which satisfies the boundary conditions

$$P(0) = 0, \qquad P(r) \to 0 \quad \text{as} \quad r \to \infty, \tag{1}$$

together with the normalization condition

$$\int_0^\infty P^2\, dr = 1. \tag{2}$$

Since the equation is homogeneous, the determination of such a solution can be carried out in two stages, the first concerned with the evaluation of a solution satisfying conditions (1) without regard to condition (2), and the second with normalizing that solution.

Each equation contains a parameter $\varepsilon_{nl,nl}$ which has to be determined so that the solution satisfies conditions (1). Such a solution can be obtained by integrating outwards from the condition $P(0) = 0$ and inwards from the condition (1), and adjusting $\varepsilon_{nl,nl}$ until the solutions match at some intermediate radius or radii. Since the equation is homogeneous, both the solution obtained by outward integration, which will be written $P_{\text{out}}$, and that obtained by inward integration, which will be written $P_{\text{in}}$, are arbitrary to the extent of a multiplying constant. If the outward and inward solutions are matched at a single radius $r_0$, the matching condition is

$$P'_{\text{out}}(r_0)/P_{\text{out}}(r_0) = P'_{\text{in}}(r_0)/P_{\text{in}}(r_0); \tag{3}$$

then, if the multiplying constants in the outward and inward solutions are chosen so that the ordinates $P_{\text{out}}(r_0)$ and $P_{\text{in}}(r_0)$ of the graphs of the solutions at $r = r_0$ are equal, the slopes of these curves are also equal.

The outward and inward solutions can also be matched by comparing their values only at two radii, say $r = r_0$ and $r_1$. Then the matching condition is

$$P_{\text{out}}(r_1)/P_{\text{out}}(r_0) = P_{\text{in}}(r_1)/P_{\text{in}}(r_0). \tag{4}$$

Condition (3) can be regarded as the limit of condition (4) as $r_1 \to r_0$.

The procedure for starting the outward and inward integrations is considered in the next two sections. The process of integration, once it has been started, is explained in § 4.3 and illustrated in Example 4.3 (the function $X(r)$ in Example 4.3 is zero in calculations "without exchange").

### 5.2.1. STARTING THE OUTWARD INTEGRATIONS

The outward integrations can be started by means of an expansion in power series. We have [see § 5.1.1.(4)]

$$Y(r) = N + v_0 r + O(r^3),$$

and similarly

$$Y(nl; r) = N + v_0(nl) r + O(r^3),$$

so that for small $r$ equation § 5.1.(3) becomes

$$\left\{\frac{d^2}{dr^2} + \frac{2N}{r} + [2v_0(nl) - \varepsilon] - \frac{l(l+1)}{r^2} + O(r^2)\right\} P(nl; r) = 0, \tag{1}$$

with no term in $r$ in the coefficient of $P(nl; r)$. Then solution in series gives

$$P = Ar^{l+1}\left\{1 - \frac{N}{l+1} r + \alpha r^2 - \beta r^3 + O(r^4)\right\} \tag{2}$$

where

$$\alpha = \{2N^2 - (l+1)[2v_0(nl) - \varepsilon]\}/2(2l+3)(l+1),$$
$$\beta = N\{2N^2 - (3l+4)[2v_0(nl) - \varepsilon]\}/6(l+1)(l+2)(2l+3).$$

Further terms in the expansion (2) for the radial wave function depend on the $O(r^2)$ terms in the coefficient of $P(nl; r)$ in equation (1).

In most atomic-structure calculations the only values of $l$ that occur are 0, 1, 2, and 3, and for these the general result (2) gives

$l = 0$ $$P(r) = Ar\{1 - Nr + \tfrac{1}{6}[2N^2 - (2v_0(nl) - \varepsilon)]r^2 - \tfrac{1}{18}N[N^2 - 2(2v_0(nl) - \varepsilon)]r^3 + O(r^4)\}$$

and $P''(0) = -2AN$;

$l = 1$ $$P(r) = Ar^2\{1 - \tfrac{1}{2}Nr + \tfrac{1}{10}[N^2 - (2v_0(nl) - \varepsilon)]r^2 - \tfrac{1}{180}N[2N^2 - 7(2v_0(nl) - \varepsilon)]r^3 + O(r^4)\}$$

and $P''(0) = +2A$;

$l = 2 \qquad P(r) = Ar^3\{1 - \frac{1}{3}Nr + \frac{1}{42}[2N^2 - 3(2v_0(nl) - \varepsilon)]r^2$
$\qquad\qquad - \frac{1}{252}N[N^2 - 5(2v_0(nl) - \varepsilon)]r^3 + O(r^4)\};$

$l = 3 \qquad P(r) = Ar^4\{1 - \frac{1}{4}Nr + \frac{1}{36}[N^2 - 2(2v_0(nl) - \varepsilon)]r^2$
$\qquad\qquad - \frac{1}{1080}N[2N^2 - 13(2v_0(nl) - \varepsilon)]r^3 + O(r^4)\};$

for $l = 2$ and 3, $P''(0) = 0$.

In using these series expansions, it is advisable to evaluate *at least two* values of the function $P(r)$ (as well as the value at $r = 0$), to derive the corresponding values of $P''$ from the differential equation, and to verify that the second difference of the values of $P$ conforms with the values of $P''$ and their differences. This verifies the starting values of the function $P(r)$ on which all the rest of the solution is going to be based. The values of $P''(0)$ are required in this check, and are given for this purpose. It may be necessary to use rather small intervals $\delta r$ at the start of the integration in order that the available terms of the series shall be enough to give $P$ at $r = 2\delta r$ to the accuracy required; smaller intervals may be necessary for $l = 0$ and perhaps $l = 1$ than for larger values of $l$. For $l = 3$ and higher, and perhaps for $l = 2$, it may be practicable to start the integration by evaluating $P$ at three values of $r$ *not* including $r = 0$, and applying the check indicated above.

The value of $A$ is arbitrary. A convenient choice is a value such that the greatest value of $|P|$ is about 1; a suitable value to use in any particular calculation can be judged by inspection of results of calculations for other atoms.

### 5.2.2. STARTING THE INWARD INTEGRATIONS

An inward integration can be started as follows. Suppose it to be started from $r = R$, and let the equation be written for short

$$P'' = F(r)P, \tag{1}$$

where $F(r)$ is certainly positive in the neighborhood of $r = R$. If $F(r)$ is not too rapidly varying, an approximate solution of equation (1) is

$$P \sim F^{-1/4}[A \exp( + \textstyle\int F^{1/2}\, dr) + B \exp( - \textstyle\int F^{1/2}\, dr)], \tag{2}$$

and we require the solution that increases, roughly exponentially, as $r$ decreases. Its values at three points equally spaced in $r$ will be approximately in geometrical progression, and the more nearly so the smaller the interval in $r$. Let us for the present suppose that they are exactly in geometrical progression, and examine later the consequences of the error we make in so doing; that is, let its values at $r = (R + \delta r)$, $R$, and $(R - \delta r)$ be $P(r) = A/(1 + x)$, $A$ and $A(1 + x)$, respectively. Then

$$\delta^2 P(R) = A(1 + x) - 2A + A/(1 + x) = Ax^2/(1 + x). \quad (3)$$

Also $P''(R) = F(R)\,P(R) = AF(R)$; so

$$\delta^2 P(r) = A(\delta r)^2\,F(R) + O(\delta r)^4. \quad (4)$$

Comparison of (3) and (4), omitting the $O(\delta r)^4$ term in (4), gives

$$x^2/(1 + x) = (\delta r)^2\,F(R) \quad (5)$$

or

$$x = [(1 + x)(\delta r)^2\,F(R)]^{1/2}. \quad (6)$$

Equation (5) is a quadratic for $F(R)$ and could, of course, be solved by use of the elementary formal solution; but, as so often happens in numerical work, this use of a formal solution is not the most convenient method, and in this case an iterative process based on formula (6) is more convenient.

**Example.** (From calculation of $P(3d; r)$ for $Mn^+$.) Values of $F(r)$ for $r = 6.2, 6.0, 5.8$ are given in the second column.

| $r$ | $F(r)$ | $P''$ | $P$ | $\delta^2 P$ |
|---|---|---|---|---|
| 6.2 | 0.70 | | $A/(1 + x)$ | |
| 6.0 | 0.70 | $0.70A$ | $A$ | $Ax^2/(1 + x)$ |
| 5.8 | 0.69 | | $A(1 + x)$ | |

Here $\delta r = 0.2$; so $\delta^2 P = (\delta r)^2 P''$ [neglecting $(\delta r)^4$],

$$\delta^2 P(6.0) = 0.70A(\delta r)^2 = 0.028A,$$

$$x^2 = 0.028(1 + x).$$

First approximation, $x = (0.028)^{1/2} = 0.167$

Second approximation, $x = (0.028 \cdot 1.17)^{1/2} = 0.181.$

Third approximation, $x = (0.028 \cdot 1.181)^{1/2} = 0.182.$

Hence, with $A = 0.01$, the inward integration can be started as follows:

| $r$ | $F(r)$ | $P''$ | $P$ | | |
|---|---|---|---|---|---|
| 6.2 | 0.70 | | 0.00846 | | |
| | | | | 154 | |
| 6.0 | 0.70 | 0.070 | 0.01000 | | 28 |
| | | | | 182 | |
| 5.8 | 0.69 | | 0.01182 | | |

If an error is made in the starting value of $P(R - \delta r)/P(R)$, the result will be to include a small multiple of the unwanted solution which increases with $r$ [represented by the first term in the approximate form (2) for the general solution]. This solution decreases inwards at the same rate (very nearly) as the wanted solution increases. If $R$ is taken large enough, this contribution from the unwanted solution will be negligible at the values of $r$ at which values of the solution are going to be used in the subsequent work.

### 5.3. VARIATION EQUATIONS

In obtaining the value of $\varepsilon_{nl,nl}$ required to match the inward and outward integrations, it will usually be necessary to obtain solutions of equation § 5.1(3) for several value of $\varepsilon_{nl,nl}$.

It is often convenient to obtain these, not directly by separate solutions of equation § 5.1(3), but by evaluating one solution of this equation and then considering the *variation* of the solution with a *variation* $\Delta\varepsilon$ of $\varepsilon$. As before, $\Delta P(r)$ will be used for a difference between the values of two functions *at the same value of r*.

As only one $\varepsilon$ parameter and one $(nl)$ are involved here, let us for short write just $\varepsilon$ for the $\varepsilon_{nl,nl}$ of equation § 5.1(3) and $P$ for $P(nl; r)$. Then this equation is

$$\left[\frac{d^2}{dr^2} + \frac{2Y(r)}{r} - \varepsilon - \frac{l(l+1)}{r^2}\right] P = 0. \tag{1}$$

Let $P + \Delta P$ be a solution when $\varepsilon$ is replaced by $\varepsilon + \Delta\varepsilon$, so that

$$\left[\frac{d^2}{dr^2} + \frac{2Y(r)}{r} - (\varepsilon + \Delta\varepsilon) - \frac{l(l+1)}{r^2}\right] (P + \Delta P) = 0. \tag{2}$$

Then

$$\left[\frac{d^2}{dr^2} + \frac{2Y(r)}{r} - (\varepsilon + \Delta\varepsilon) - \frac{l(l+1)}{r^2}\right] \Delta P = P\,\Delta\varepsilon. \tag{3}$$

This equation, with the varied value of $\varepsilon$ in the square brackets, is exact, not first-order in $\Delta\varepsilon$. If the second-order term $\Delta\varepsilon\,\Delta P$ is omitted, it gives

$$\left[\frac{d^2}{dr^2} + \frac{2Y(r)}{r} - \varepsilon - \frac{l(l+1)}{r^2}\right] \Delta P = P\,\Delta\varepsilon. \tag{4}$$

Equation (3) is linear inhomogeneous in $\Delta P$. The most convenient particular integral to evaluate is that for which $(\Delta P/r^{l+1})_0 = 0$. It follows from § 5.2.1(2) that for this solution $\Delta P = O(r^{l+3})$, so that, for small $r$, $|\Delta P| \ll |P|$, and integration of equation (3) is much lighter than integration of equation (2); it is usually practicable to take longer intervals of integration and work to a smaller number of significant figures over a considerable part of the range. Furthermore, if results are required for several different values of $\varepsilon$, it will not usually be necessary to start every integration of equation (3) from $r = 0$; inspection of the integration will show when the term $\Delta P \, \Delta\varepsilon$ first begins to make a contribution to $\Delta P''$ big enough to affect $\Delta P$ to the accuracy to which $\Delta P$ is required. For smaller values of $r$, $\Delta P$ is proportional to $\Delta\varepsilon$ to this accuracy, and this can be used to obtain starting values for an integration for another $\Delta\varepsilon$, this being started from a value of $r$ a few intervals before the product term $\Delta P \, \Delta\varepsilon$ becomes appreciable.

These considerations are more appropriate to a hand calculation than to one done by means of an automatic machine. For the machine, a calculation to four significant figures is no lighter than one to seven figures; furthermore, the use of larger intervals in a variation calculation would require an interpolation procedure to give results at the intervals used in the integration of the original equation, and this would require a longer program. It would probably be best then to carry out a set of solutions of equation (1) with different values of $\varepsilon$ rather than to use the variation equation. However, then the variation equation has another application, which will now be considered.

### 5.3.1. MATCHING THE INWARD AND OUTWARD INTEGRATIONS

The integrations for the first trial value of $\varepsilon$ are unlikely to match exactly at $r = r_0$ [see § 5.2(3)]. The following argument, due to A. S. Douglas and Mrs. E. C. Ridley,[1] enables an estimate of the variation $\Delta\varepsilon$ of $\varepsilon$, required to produce a match, to be estimated from the degree of the mismatch, as measured by the difference between the values of $(P'/P)_{\text{out}}$ and $(P'/P)_{\text{in}}$ at $r = r_0$.

Multiply equations § 5.3(4) and (1) by $P$ and $-\Delta P$, respectively, and add. This gives

$$P \frac{d^2}{dr^2} \Delta P - \Delta P \frac{d^2 P}{dr^2} = P^2 \, \Delta\varepsilon. \tag{1}$$

The left-hand side is $\dfrac{d}{dr}\left(P \dfrac{d}{dr} \Delta P - \Delta P \dfrac{dP}{dr}\right)$; and, since $\Delta P$ is the difference between the values of two solutions *at the same value of* $r$, $\dfrac{d}{dr} \Delta P = \Delta\left(\dfrac{dP}{dr}\right) = \Delta P'$. Hence integration of (1) gives

$$\Big| P \, \Delta P' - P' \, \Delta P \Big|_a^b = \Delta\varepsilon \int_a^b P^2 \, dr. \tag{2}$$

Now for the outward integration, $P = \Delta P = 0$ at $r = 0$, so that at $r = r_0$

$$(P \, \Delta P' - P' \, \Delta P)_{\text{out}} = \Delta\varepsilon \int_0^{r_0} (P_{\text{out}})^2 \, dr;$$

[1] E. C. Ridley, *Proc. Cambridge Phil. Soc.*, **51**, 702 (1955).

and, for the inward integration, $P = \Delta P = 0$ at $r = \infty$ and $\int P^2\,dr$ converges at $r = \infty$, so that at $r = r_0$

$$-(P\,\Delta P' - P'\,\Delta P)_{\text{in}} = \Delta\varepsilon \int_{r_0}^{\infty} (P_{\text{in}})^2\,dr.$$

Also $\Delta(P'/P) = (P\,\Delta P' - P'\,\Delta P)/P^2$, so that at $r = r_0$

$$\left.\begin{aligned} \Delta\left(\frac{P'}{P}\right)_{\text{out}} &= \Delta\varepsilon \left[\int_0^{r_0} (P_{\text{out}})^2\,dr\right] \Big/ (P_{\text{out}}(r_0))^2, \\ \Delta\left(\frac{P'}{P}\right)_{\text{in}} &= -\,\Delta\varepsilon \left[\int_{r_0}^{\infty} (P_{\text{in}})^2\,dr\right] \Big/ (P_{\text{in}}(r_0))^2. \end{aligned}\right\} \tag{3}$$

Now suppose that inward and outward integrations have been carried out for some trial value of $\varepsilon$, and give values of $(P'/P)_{\text{out}}$ and $(P'/P)_{\text{in}}$ that do not match. We want to make such a change $\Delta\varepsilon$ of $\varepsilon$ that

$$(P'/P)_{\text{out}} + \Delta(P'/P)_{\text{out}} = (P'/P)_{\text{in}} + \Delta(P'/P)_{\text{in}};$$

from formulae (3) the required change of $\varepsilon$ is given by

$$\left[\frac{\int_0^{r_0} (P_{\text{out}})^2\,dr}{(P_{\text{out}}(r_0))^2} + \frac{\int_{r_0}^{\infty} (P_{\text{in}})^2\,dr}{(P_{\text{in}}(r_0))^2}\right] \Delta\varepsilon = -\,[(P'/P)_{\text{out}} - (P'/P)_{\text{in}}]_{r=r_0}. \tag{4}$$

This can be expressed in a simpler form as follows. Let $P_N(r)$ be the function

$$\left.\begin{aligned} P_N(r) &= A P_{\text{out}}(r)/P_{\text{out}}(r_0) \quad \text{for} \quad r \leq r_0 \\ &= A P_{\text{in}}(r)/P_{\text{in}}(r_0) \quad \text{for} \quad r \geq r_0 \end{aligned}\right\} \tag{5}$$

with $A$ determined by the normalization condition $\int_0^{\infty} [P_N(r)]^2\,dr = 1$. This function is continuous at $r = r_0$, where it has the value $P(r_0) = A$; its gradient is of course discontinuous there. Then the coefficient of $\Delta\varepsilon$ in (4) is $1/A^2 = 1/[P_N(r_0)]^2$; so

$$\Delta\varepsilon = -\,[P_N(r_0)]^2[(P'/P)_{\text{out}} - (P'/P)_{\text{in}}]_{r=r_0}. \tag{6}$$

Since the formula (4) for $\Delta\varepsilon$ is derived from equation § 5.3(4), which is only first-order in $\Delta\varepsilon$, it is not exact, and further analysis shows that it also is first-order in $\Delta\varepsilon$. However, it forms a valuable guide to the value of $\Delta\varepsilon$ to be taken to improve the match between the outward and inward integrations. In calculations with an automatic computer, the integrals $\int_0 (P_{\text{out}})^2\,dr$ and $\int^{\infty} (P_{\text{in}})^2\,dr$ can be accumulated concurrently with the evaluation of the solutions $P_{out}$ and $P_{in}$, so that the value of the coefficient of $\Delta\varepsilon$ in formula (4) can be calculated as soon as both inward and outward integrations have reached $r_0$. Then the value of $\Delta\varepsilon$ can be calculated and a new integration started with a new value of $\varepsilon$ obtained by adding $\Delta\varepsilon$ to the old value of $\varepsilon$. In this way the determination of $\varepsilon$ and the corresponding solution $P(nl; r)$ can be made quite automatic.

### 5.3.2. NORMALIZATION

Once a solution $P(nl; r)$ of the radial wave equation § 5.1(3), satisfying the boundary conditions § 5.2(1), has been found, it can be normalized by evaluating $\int_0^\infty P^2\,dr$ and dividing $P(r)$ by $\left[\int_0^\infty P^2\,dr\right]^{1/2}$

However, it is not necessary to carry out this quadrature separately from the calculation of the "output" contributions to $Z(r)$. In terms of the unnormalized solutions of the radial wave equations § 5.1(3), these output contributions to $Z(r)$ are

$$q(nl)[1 - Z_0(nl, nl; r)] = q(nl)\int_r^\infty P^2(nl; s)\,ds \Big/ \int_0^\infty P^2(nl; s)\,ds. \quad (1)$$

The value of $\int_0^\infty P^2(nl; s)\,ds$ is the end result of the evaluation of $\int_r^\infty P^2(nl; s)\,ds$ as a function of $r$.

### 5.3.3. REVISION OF THE ESTIMATES OF CONTRIBUTIONS TO $Z(r)$

The sensitiveness of the radial wave functions $P(nl; r)$, and of the "output" contributions to $Z(r)$, to the "input" contributions to $Z(r)$ is considerably different for the different electron groups. The inner groups are relatively insensitive to the estimates, and for them it is usually a good approximation to use a straight iterative process: that is, to take the output contributions to $Z(r)$ of one stage of the successive approximation process, without modification, as the input contributions for the next stage.

The outer electron groups are much more sensitive to the estimates, and such a straight iterative procedure may converge only slowly, or even diverge. The outermost electron group of a negative ion [for example, the $(3p)^6$ group in $Cl^-$], the $(3d)$ group in the neutral or slightly ionized atoms of the first long period [and probably the $(4d)$ group in similar atoms of the second long period and the $(4f)$ group in the rare earths] are particularly sensitive.

The following process has often been found satisfactory in improving the estimates in such cases. Let I and II refer to stages of the successive approximation using different estimates for a single $(nl)$ group only. Then, if

$$(\text{Input})_{\text{I}} + \beta[(\text{Input})_{\text{II}} - (\text{Input})_{\text{I}}] \tag{1}$$

were used as input, with a constant value of $\beta$, the output would be (approximately)

$$(\text{Output})_{\text{I}} + \beta[(\text{Output})_{\text{II}} - (\text{Output})_{\text{I}}]. \tag{2}$$

It may be possible to find a value of $\beta$ so as to give agreement between the quantities (2) and (1) considerably closer, over most of the range of $r$, than the agreement between the output and input for either stage I or stage II. The values of expression (2) for this value of $\beta$ are then taken as the input for the next stage. An example of this process, applied to the estimation of radial wave functions $P(nl; r)$ in calculations with exchange, is given in § 5.8.

This process requires the results of calculations with two different inputs. At an earlier stage, results from only one input are available, and then some such rule as

$$(\text{Input})_{\text{II}} = (\text{Input})_{\text{I}} + \gamma[(\text{Output})_{\text{I}} - (\text{Input})_{\text{I}}], \tag{3}$$

with a constant value of $\gamma$, may be satisfactory; $\gamma = 1$ corresponds to taking $(\text{Input})_{\text{II}} = (\text{Output})_{\text{I}}$, which is satisfactory for inner groups. For outer groups, smaller values of $\gamma$ such as $\frac{1}{2}$, or even $\frac{1}{3}$, may be required.

Because of the sensitiveness of the outer groups, and relative insensitiveness of the inner groups, it is usually best *not* to calculate *all* the radial wave functions $P(nl; r)$ at each stage of the successive approximations. It is better first to do calculations for the outermost group or outer groups only and get this group or groups self-consistent in the field of the nucleus and estimated contributions to $Z(r)$ from the inner groups, then to do calculations for the inner groups, then to return to the outer groups with revised estimates for the inner groups. The best procedure to follow in any particular case will depend on how good the estimates for the different $(nl)$ groups are believed to be, how good they are found to be as the calculation proceeds, and how sensitive to the estimates the outputs for the different groups are first expected, and later found, to be.

## 5.4. TORRANCE'S METHOD

The procedure explained in the previous sections has involved the estimation and revision of the estimates of a set of *functions*, the contributions to $Z(r)$ [in calculations with exchange, the radial wave functions $P(nl; r)$]. Torrance[2] has proposed an alternative procedure which

[2] C. C. Torrance, *Phys. Rev.*, **46**, 388 (1934).

avoids this estimation of functions and replaces it by an estimation of a set of parameters.

The functions $Y_0(nl, nl; r)$ satisfy the equation

$$\frac{d^2}{dr^2} Y_0(nl, nl; r) = -\frac{1}{r} P^2(nl; r) \tag{1}$$

[see equation § 3.5(9) with $k = 0$], and in Torrance's method these equations for the $Y_0$'s are integrated outwards simultaneously with the integrations of the radial wave equations [§ 5.1(3)]

$$\left[\frac{d^2}{dr^2} + \frac{2Y(nl; r)}{r} - \varepsilon_{nl,nl} - \frac{l(l+1)}{r^2}\right] P(nl; r) = 0 \tag{2}$$

for all the electron groups, the function $Y(nl; r)$ being built up from the solutions of equation (1) step-by-step as the integration proceeds. The complementary function of equation (1) is $A + Br$; furthermore, $Y_0(0) = 0$ so that $A = 0$, and the sum of the contributions $Br$ can be incorporated in $\varepsilon_{nl,nl}$ in equation (2); so the solutions of equation (1) can be started from $Y_0(0) = Y'_0(0) = 0$ [though the solutions of equation (1) will then differ from the functions $Y_0$ defined in § 3.5 by terms linear in $r$].

The radial wave functions $P(nl; r)$ to be used in equations (1) must be normalized, so that the normalization of the solutions of equation (2) cannot now be postponed until after solutions of these equations satisfying the conditions at $r = 0$ and $\infty$ have been satisfied; values of the multiplying constants in these solutions must be determined such that, when the solutions satisfying the boundary conditions have been found, they are normalized. Thus both of the parameters to be determined for each $(nl)$, namely $[P(nl; r)/r^{l+1}]_0$ and $\varepsilon_{nl,nl}$, have to be estimated in advance, and adjusted such that the functions $P(nl; r)$ obtained from the set of equations (1) and (2), evaluated as a set of simultaneous equations, satisfy the boundary and normalization conditions.

Torrance successfully applied this method to the neutral carbon atom, but for atoms with more $(nl)$ groups the process of simultaneous solution of a set of equations (2) with two-point boundary conditions seems involved, and Yost[3] has reported that, as a result of trying both Torrance's method and a method depending on the estimation and revision of estimates of wave functions, in calculations for $Mg^{+2}$, he regards the second as the more practicable.

However, it may be practicable to apply Torrance's process not to the whole set of $(nl)$ functions, but to a limited number at a time, for example in a 36-electron structure isoelectronic with Kr to apply Torrance's

[3] W. J. Yost, *Phys. Rev.*, **58**, 557 (1940).

process to the $(4s)^2(4p)^6$ groups only, in the estimated field of the other groups. With the facilities provided by automatic computing machines, the possibilities of such a method might be worth exploring.

### 5.5. EQUATIONS WITH EXCHANGE

The equations "with exchange" differ from those without exchange in three main features, all of which affect their numerical treatment.

(i) The equations are inhomogeneous, so that we can no longer find a solution satisfying the boundary conditions

$$P(0) = 0, \qquad P(r) \to 0 \quad \text{as} \quad r \to \infty \tag{1}$$

and the normalization condition

$$\int_0^\infty P^2\, dr = 1 \tag{2}$$

by finding first some solution satisfying conditions (1) only and then, as a separate and subsequent step, multiplying it by a constant factor to normalize it.

(ii) The equations involve $Y_k(nl, n'l'; r)$ functions with $k \neq 0$ and with $(n'l') \neq (nl)$.

(iii) The equations also include nondiagonal parameters $\varepsilon_{nl,n'l}$ which have to be determined so that the orthogonality relations

$$\int_0^\infty P(nl; r)\, P(n'l; r)\, dr = 0 \qquad (n' \neq n) \tag{3}$$

between the radial wave functions are satisfied. Although for a configuration of closed groups, conditions (3) are necessarily satisfied, irrespective of the values of $\varepsilon_{nl,n'l}$, by the final solution of the equations (see § 3.8) they may not be satisfied exactly in the intermediate stages of the calculation unless parameters $\varepsilon_{nl,n'l}$ are introduced to ensure that they are satisfied.

As for the equations without exchange, the process of solution that has been most used is one of successive approximation. For the equations without exchange, the only functions $Y_k(nl, n'l'; r)$ occurring are those with $k = 0$ and $(n'l') = (nl)$; then the number of functions to be estimated is the same whether the functions estimated are $Y_k$'s, $Z_k$'s, or $P$'s. But in calculations with exchange the number of $Y_k$ functions is considerably greater than the number of electron groups, because of the occurrence of $Y_k$ functions with $(n'l') \neq (nl)$ and with $k \neq 0$; for example in the equations for the normal state of a 36-electron atom with exchange, with configuration $(1s)^2(2s)^2(2p)^6(3s)^2(3p)^6(3d)^{10}(4s)^2(4p)^6$ there are eight groups, and so eight radial wave functions, whereas there are 47 $Y_k$ functions. For this reason it is best now to start from estimates of the radial wave functions themselves.

The general form of the equation for the radial wave functions is

$$\left[\frac{d^2}{dr^2}+\frac{2Y(nl;r)}{r}-\varepsilon_{nl,nl}-\frac{l(l+1)}{r^2}\right]P(nl;r)$$
$$=X(nl;r)+\Sigma_{n'}\varepsilon_{nl,n'l}P(n'l;r), \quad (4)$$

in which the term $X(nl;r)$ is a sum of terms of the form

$$r^{-1}Y_k(nl,n'l';r)P(n'l';r)$$

with $(n'l')\neq(nl)$, with numerical coefficients depending on the configuration. The functions $Y(nl;r)$ and $X(nl;r)$ for configurations of complete groups can be written down from formulae § 3.6(9)–(14) and the values of coefficients listed in Table 4.

One possible procedure is to evaluate the relevant $Y_k(nl,n'l';r)$ functions simultaneously with the solution of equation (1) for $P(nl;r)$. However, the $Y_k$ functions satisfy equations with two-point boundary conditions, as does $P(nl;r)$ itself, and it is not easy to find the values of the parameters required to obtain a solution satisfying all these two-point boundary conditions simultaneously.

Another procedure, which so far has been found more practicable, is to evaluate the whole of the function $X(r)$ from the estimates, including those of $P(nl;r)$ itself, which is also used in evaluating the $Y_k(nl,nl;r)$ functions which occur in the function $Y(nl;r)$. Then in the solution of equation (1), $X(r)$ is a *given* function of $r$ and this equation is an inhomogeneous equation for $P(nl;r)$.

If this procedure is adopted, then, starting from estimates of the radial wave functions, the first step is to calculate the relevant $Y_k$ functions, and the second to solve the radial wave equation. These two steps are considered in § 5.6 and § 5.7, respectively.

## 5.6. CALCULATION OF THE $Y_k$ FUNCTIONS

From the estimates of the radial wave functions, the $Y_k$ functions can calculated by integration of equations § 3.5(6) and (7). An example of part of an integration for a $Z_k$ function is given in example 4.4. The integration for a $Y_k$ function is similar but is carried inwards. For $k=0$ the evaluation of $Z_k(nl,n'l';r)$ is a quadrature; example 4.2 illustrates part of such a calculation.

For $k\neq 0$, the beginning of the outward integration for $Z_k$ may be assisted by the following result. For small $r$, it follows from the definition of $Z_k(nl, n'l'; r)$ that

$$Z_k(nl, n'l'; r) = r^{-k}\int_0^r s^{l+l'+k+2}A[1 + O(s)]\, ds,$$

where

$$A = [P(nl; r)/r^{l+1}]_0 [P(n'l'; r)/r^{l'+1}]_0$$

Hence

$$\begin{aligned} Z_k(nl, n'l'; r) &= [A/(l + l' + k + 3)]r^{l+l'+3}[1 + O(r)] \\ &= [1/(l + l' + k + 3)]rP(nl; r)P(n'l'; r)[1 + O(r)]. \quad (1) \end{aligned}$$

In the inward integration for $Y_k$, $Z_k$ may be negligible for the last few intervals, and then the relation § 5.7.1(1) below may be useful for completing the solution.

The following is an alternative method, due to L. C. Green, for calculating the $Z_k$ and $Y_k$ functions. By definition

$$Z_k(nl, n'l'; r) = r^{-k}\int_0^r s^k P(nl; s)P(n'l'; s)\, ds, \quad (2)$$

and

$$Z_k(nl, n'l'; r + \delta r) = (r + \delta r)^{-k}\int_0^{r+\delta r} s^k P(nl; s)P(n'l'; s)\, ds;$$

so

$$Z_k(nl, n'l'; r + \delta r) = \left(\frac{r}{r + \delta r}\right)^k Z_k(nl, n'l'; r) + \int_r^{r+\delta r}\left(\frac{s}{r + \delta r}\right)^k P(nl; s)P(n'l'; s)\, ds. \quad (3)$$

For small $r$, direct evaluation of $Z_k$ from the defining formula (2) may be awkward for $k \neq 0$, on account of the range of numerical magnitude of the integral and of the factor $r^k$ by which it is divided; this is the reason for adopting an alternative method involving integration of a differential equation. With an automatic digital machine this large range of numerical values may give rise to scaling difficulties (unless floating-point operation, which is unnecessary in the rest of the calculation, is used). These are avoided by the use of formula (3), in which the factors $[r/(r + \delta r)]^k$ in the first term and $[s/(r + \delta r)]^k$ in the integrand are both of numerical order of magnitude 1. The value of $Z_k$ at the end of the first interval from the origin can be taken as given by formula (1).

A similar treatment can be applied to the evaluation, by inward integration, of the function

$$Y_k(nl, n'l'; r) - Z_k(nl, n'l'; r) = \int_r^\infty \left(\frac{r}{s}\right)^{k+1} P(nl; s)P(n'l'; s)\, ds.$$

### 5.7. RADIAL WAVE EQUATION

Consider first the treatment of the equation for a radial wave function $P(nl;r)$ when there is only one group for that value of $l$, so that the question of orthogonality between different radial wave functions for the same $l$ does not arise; an example is the equation for the $(2p)$ function of the $(1s)^2(2s)^2(2p)^6$ configuration of a ten-electron system, equation §3.6.1(2). Its general form is that of equation § 5.5(4) without the $\varepsilon_{nl,n'l}$ terms, namely,

$$\left[\frac{d^2}{dr^2} + \frac{2Y(nl;r)}{r} - \varepsilon_{nl,nl} - \frac{l(l+1)}{r^2}\right] P(nl;r) = X(nl;r), \tag{1}$$

and the solution is required to satisfy the conditions

$$P(0) = 0, \quad P(r) \to 0 \quad \text{as} \quad r \to \infty, \quad \int_0^\infty P^2\,dr = 1. \tag{2}$$

The boundary condition $P(0) = 0$ implies that $(P/r^{l+1})$ remains finite at $r = 0$; thus there are two parameters, $(P/r^{l+1})_0$ and $\varepsilon_{nl,nl}$, to be determined so that the solution satisfies the conditions $P(r) \to \infty$ as $r \to \infty$ and $\int_0^\infty P^2\,dr = 1$. There are two ways of proceeding to the determination of these parameters and the corresponding solution. One is first to select a trial value of $(P/r^{l+1})_0$ and, keeping it fixed, determine the value of $\varepsilon_{nl,nl}$ to satisfy the condition at $r = \infty$; then evaluate $\int_0^\infty P^2\,dr$ for the solution so obtained and, if the value of this integral is not 1, carry out the same procedure with another trial value of $(P/r^{l+1})_0$. This follows the procedure used for the equations without exchange, and was used for much of the prewar work on solution of Fock's equations.

An alternative procedure, which has been found satisfactory in all cases in which it has been tried up to the time of writing, is the following.[4] For any trial value of $\varepsilon_{nl,nl}$, equation (1) has a particular integral (p.i.) and a complementary function (c.f.) satisfying the conditions on $P(r)$ at $r = 0$, and a p.i. and a c.f. satisfying the conditions at $r = \infty$. Let the former be $P_{\text{out}}$ (p.i.) and $R_{\text{out}}$ (c.f.), and the latter $P_{\text{in}}$ (p.i.) and $R_{\text{in}}$ (c.f.); the complementary functions $R$ satisfy the equation

$$\left[\frac{d^2}{dr^2} + \frac{2Y(nl;r)}{r} - \varepsilon_{nl,nl} - \frac{l(l+1)}{r^2}\right] R = 0, \tag{3}$$

which is the same equation that occurs in the calculation without exchange.

[4] See D. R. Hartree, *J. Opt. Soc. Amer.*, **46**, 350 (1956); C. Froese, *Proc. Cambridge Phil. Soc.* (in press).

Then, for any constant $\alpha$, the function $P_{\text{out}} + \alpha R_{\text{out}}$ is a solution of equation (1) satisfying the boundary condition at $r = 0$, and, for any constant $\beta$, $P_{\text{in}} + \beta R_{\text{in}}$ is a solution satisfying the condition at $r = \infty$. As in calculations without exchange, there are two forms of the conditions required to match the results of the outward and inward integrations. One form requires that the graphs of the two solutions should have the same ordinate and the same slope at some intermediate radius $r_0$; that is, that

$$P_{\text{out}}(r_0) + \alpha R_{\text{out}}(r_0) = P_{\text{in}}(r_0) + \beta R_{\text{in}}(r_0) \tag{4}$$

and

$$P'_{\text{out}}(r_0) + \alpha R'_{\text{out}}(r_0) = P'_{\text{in}}(r_0) + \beta R'_{\text{in}}(r_0). \tag{5}$$

The other form requires that at each of two values of $r$, say $r = r_0$ and $r = r_1 > r_0$, the two functions should have the same value; that is, that the relation (4) should hold at $r_0$, and a similar relation

$$P_{\text{out}}(r_1) + \alpha R_{\text{out}}(r_1) = P_{\text{in}}(r_1) + \beta R_{\text{in}}(r_1) \tag{6}$$

at $r = r_1$. Unless the first derivatives are evaluated in the course of the integrations, equations (4) and (6) form the most convenient matching conditions. If these equations are used, $r_0$ and $r_1$ should not be taken too close together, otherwise $\alpha$ and $\beta$ will not be well determined; a ratio $r_1/r_0 = 3/2$ or thereabouts has been found satisfactory.

For any trial value of $\varepsilon_{nl,nl}$, equations (4) and (5) have a unique solution for $\alpha$ and $\beta$ unless

$$[R'(r_0)/R(r_0)]_{\text{out}} = [R'(r_0)/R(r_0)]_{\text{in}}.$$

This is the condition that $\varepsilon_{nl,nl}$ should be a characteristic value of the homogeneous equation for $R$, and normally (and probably always) the characteristic value of the inhomogeneous equation with the relevant boundary and normalization conditions will differ from that of the homogeneous equation. However, this indicates that there may be trouble if as a trial value $\varepsilon_{nl,nl}$ is taken too close to a characteristic value of the homogeneous equation.

If equations (4) and (6) are used as matching conditions, the most convenient way of using them is expressed by

$$\frac{P_{\text{out}}(r_1) - P_{\text{in}}(r_1) + \alpha R_{\text{out}}(r_1)}{P_{\text{out}}(r_0) - P_{\text{in}}(r_0) + \alpha R_{\text{out}}(r_0)} = \frac{R_{\text{in}}(r_1)}{R_{\text{in}}(r_0)}. \tag{7}$$

The value of $\alpha$ is determined from this relation; then for $r < r_1$ the solution of equation (1) satisfying the conditions at $r = 0$ and $\infty$ is

$$P(r) = P_{\text{out}}(r) + \alpha R_{\text{out}}(r), \tag{8}$$

and for $r > r_0$ this solution is

$$P(r) = [P(r_0) - P_{\text{in}}(r_0)][R_{\text{in}}(r)/R_{\text{in}}(r_0)] + P_{\text{in}}(r). \tag{9}$$

The agreement, over the range $r_0 < r < r_1$, of the values of $P(r)$ evaluated from formulae (8) and (9) confirms that the matching has been done correctly.

Except for the discrete set of values of $\varepsilon_{nl,nl}$ which are characteristic values of the homogeneous equation (2), this procedure gives a solution of equation (1) for any trial value of $\varepsilon_{nl,nl}$. Such a solution is unique, but it will not generally satisfy the normalization condition $\int_0^\infty P^2\,dr = 1$. Other trial values of $\varepsilon_{nl,nl}$ must then be taken, until the solution which satisfies the boundary conditions is also normalized, or until such a solution can be interpolated to adequate accuracy. A solution $P(r)$ which is not normalized can be normalized by dividing throughout by $\left[\int_0^\infty P^2\,dr\right]^{1/2}$, but the solution will no longer be a solution of equation (1) with the function $X(r)$ adopted in solving it. However, this may provide an adequate approximation when the determination of $\varepsilon_{nl,nl}$ has reached such a stage that $\int_0^\infty P^2\,dr$ differs from unity by only a few per cent.

Formally, $P_{\text{out}}$ may be *any* particular integral of equation (1) whatever. But for practical work it may be advisable to evaluate the particular integral with the best available approximation to the value of $(P/r^{l+1})_0$ for the solution which satisfies the conditions at $r = 0, \infty$. Otherwise the solution $P(r)$ given by (8) may come to be evaluated as the relatively small difference of two large numbers, a situation to be avoided if possible in numerical work. If the particular integral $P_{\text{out}}(r)$ evaluated is already a good approximation to the solution $P(nl; r)$ required, the coefficient $\alpha$ in formula (8) is small and this situation does not arise.

### 5.7.1. STARTING THE INTEGRATIONS

The equation for the complementary function is the same as the radial wave equation in calculations without exchange, and the integrations can be started in the same way (see § 5.2.2).

The inward integration for the particular integral can be started by taking $P_{\text{in}} = 0$ until the exchange term $X(r)$ in equation § 5.7(1) begins to become appreciable.

For the particular integral for the outward integration, the exchange term $X(nl; r)$ will usually be negligible for the first few intervals. This term $X(nl; r)$ in the equation for $P(nl; r)$ is the sum of terms of the form $-(2/r)Y_k(nl, n'l'; r)P(n'l'; r)$. For small $r$, $P(nl; r) = O(r^{l+1})$ and

$k \leq l + l'$; so the second integral in the expression defining $Y_k(nl, n'l'; r)$ [see formula § 3.5(1)] converges at $s = 0$, and this expression can be written

$$Y_k(nl, n'l'; r) = r^{-k}\int_0^r s^k P(nl; s)P(n'l'; s)\,ds$$
$$- r^{k+1}\int_0^r s^{-(k+1)} P(nl; s)P(n'l'; s)\,ds + r^{k+1}\int_0^\infty s^{-(k+1)} P(nl; s)P(n'l'; s)\,ds.$$

The first two terms are both $O(r^{l+l'+3})$, the third is $O(r^{k+1})$ which is of smaller order since $k \leq l + l'$. Hence

$$Y_k(nl, n'l'; r) = O(r^{k+1}) \tag{1}$$

for small $r$, and $X(nl; r)$ is $O(r^m)$ where $m$ is the smallest value of $k + l' + 1$.

For a configuration of complete groups, the smallest values of $k$ for each $l, l'$ are as follows

$$\left.\begin{array}{llll} l = 0, & l' = 0, & k = 0 & k + l' + 1 = 1 \\ l = 1, & l' = 0, & k = 1 & \multirow{2}{*}{} k + l' + 1 = 2 \\ & l' = 1, & k = 0 & \\ l = 2, & l' = 0, & k = 2 & \\ & l' = 1, & k = 1 & k + l' + 1 = 3 \\ & l' = 2, & k = 0 & \end{array}\right\} \min(k + l' + 1) = l + 1.$$

Hence $X(r)$ is $O(r^{l+1})$, and its contribution to $P(nl; r)$ is $O(r^{l+3})$, whereas $P(nl; r)$ itself is $O(r^{l+1})$.

If appreciable, this contribution to $P(nl; r)$ can be evaluated by carrying out a few intervals of integration of a solution with $P(nl; r) = 0$ at $r = 0$ and at $r = \delta r$; this is then added to a multiple of the complementary function determined so as to give the required value of $(P/r^{l+1})_0$.

## 5.8. REVISION OF ESTIMATES OF THE RADIAL WAVE FUNCTIONS

The comments of § 5.33 on the sensitiveness of the "output" contributions to $Z(r)$ to the estimates, and the procedure for revising the estimates apply, with the appropriate changes, to the "output" radial wave functions in calculations with exchange and to the revision of the estimates of the wave functions.

An example of the procedure using formulae § 5.3.3(1) and (2) is given in Table 5; the numbers in this table are taken from the first two stages of the calculation[5] for $Mn^{+2}$, which were concerned entirely with the $(3d)$ wave function. In this case (Input II) was taken as $\frac{1}{2}$[(Input I) + (Output I)], and only two decimals were kept in the inputs as it was not

[5] D. R. Hartree, *Proc. Cambridge Phil. Soc.*, **51**, 126 (1955).

thought that a third would be significant; in the use of formula § 5.3.3(1) a nominal third decimal has been kept and is written as a suffix. The choice of $\beta = 1.6$ in formulae § 5.3.3(1) and (2) has reduced the greatest difference between Input and Output values of $P(3d; r)$ from 0.14 for I and 0.05 for II to $0.01_1$. This is now certainly good enough to be used as input in the calculation of the $(3s)$ and $(3p)$ wave functions.

**Table 5. Revision of estimate of wave functions**

(Extract from calculation for $Mn^{+2}$ with exchange.)

Input and Output $P(3d)$ functions for first two stages of successive approximation procedure, and derivation of a better estimate.

| | Input I | Output I | Input II | Output II | (*a*) | (*b*) |
|---|---|---|---|---|---|---|
| 0 | 0 | 0 | 0 | 0 | 0 | 0 |
| 0.1 | 0.05 | 0.061 | $0.05_5$ | 0.060 | $0.05_8$ | 0.059 |
| 0.2 | 0.22 | 0.258 | 0.24 | 0.252 | $0.25_2$ | 0.249 |
| 0.3 | $0.40_5$ | 0.490 | 0.45 | 0.480 | $0.47_7$ | 0.476 |
| 0.4 | 0.57 | 0.693 | 0.63 | 0.677 | $0.66_6$ | 0.667 |
| 0.5 | 0.70 | 0.838 | 0.77 | 0.819 | $0.81_2$ | 0.808 |
| 0.6 | 0.79 | 0.920 | $0.85_5$ | 0.904 | $0.89_4$ | 0.894 |
| 0.7 | 0.84 | 0.955 | 0.90 | 0.943 | $0.93_6$ | 0.936 |
| 0.8 | 0.86 | 0.955 | 0.91 | 0.946 | $0.94_0$ | 0.941 |
| 0.9 | 0.86 | 0.927 | $0.89_5$ | 0.923 | $0.91_6$ | 0.921 |
| 1.0 | $0.84_5$ | 0.885 | 0.87 | 0.884 | $0.88_5$ | 0.883 |
| 1.2 | 0.78 | 0.776 | 0.78 | 0.782 | $0.78_0$ | 0.786 |
| 1.4 | 0.70 | 0.660 | $0.68_5$ | 0.668 | $0.67_6$ | 0.673 |
| 1.6 | 0.62 | 0.548 | $0.58_5$ | 0.561 | $0.56_4$ | 0.569 |
| 1.8 | 0.54 | 0.448 | 0.50 | 0.462 | $0.47_6$ | 0.470 |
| 2.0 | 0.47 | 0.367 | 0.42 | 0.377 | $0.39_0$ | 0.383 |
| 2.4 | 0.34 | $0.23_4$ | $0.28_5$ | 0.245 | $0.25_2$ | 0.252 |
| 2.8 | 0.25 | 0.145 | 0.20 | 0.154 | $0.17_0$ | 0.159 |
| 3.2 | 0.18 | 0.090 | 0.13 | 0.095 | $0.10_0$ | 0.098 |
| 3.6 | 0.12 | 0.052 | 0.08 | 0.057 | $0.05_6$ | 0.060 |
| 4.0 | 0.08 | 0.028 | 0.05 | 0.033 | $0.03_2$ | 0.036 |

(*a*) Initial II + 0.6(Initial II − Initial I).
(*b*) Final II + 0.6(Final II − Final I).

## 5.9. OTHER FORMS OF RADIAL WAVE EQUATION

Experience has shown that for hand calculations, either with or without exchange, the second-order form, § 5.7(1), of the radial wave equation is the most convenient for numerical work. However, there are other forms, and it may be that, with the development of the use of automatic digital calculating machines for this work, one or more of these alternative forms may come to be found more convenient.

On some machines a standard process is used for integrating differential equations, which involves reducing a higher-order equation to a set of first-order equations; an example is Gill's form of the Runge–Kutta method.[6] Use of such a method for the radial wave equation takes no advantage of two features of this equation, its linearity and the absence of a first-derivative term, but may nevertheless be regarded as preferable to programming a procedure which did take advantage of them. The obvious way to reduce equation § 5.7(1) to two first-order equations is to take $Q = dP/dr$ as an auxiliary variable; but there are two other ways which are probably more convenient. For short, let this equation be written

$$P'' + [2v - \varepsilon - l(l+1)/r^2]P = X, \tag{1}$$

and write

$$Q = P' + \beta P/r,$$

where $\beta$ is some constant. Then

$$\begin{aligned} Q' &= P'' + \beta P'/r - \beta P/r^2 \\ &= -[2v - \varepsilon - l(l+1)/r^2]P + X + \beta[Q - \beta P/r] - \beta P/r^2 \\ &= -\{2v - \varepsilon - [l(l+1) - \beta(\beta+1)]/r^2\}P + \beta Q/r + X. \end{aligned}$$

Hence, for the values $\beta = l$, $\beta = -(l+1)$, and for no others, the term in $1/r^2$ is eliminated, which is convenient for numerical work (particularly on an automatic digital machine, when the range of numerical magnitude of this term may give scaling difficulties). The values $\beta = l$, $\beta = -(l+1)$ give two choices for the auxiliary function $Q$, and the two alternative pairs of first-order equations:

$$\beta = l$$

$$\left.\begin{aligned} P' &= Q_1 - lP/r, \\ Q_1' &= -(2v - \varepsilon)P + lQ_1/r + X, \end{aligned}\right\} \tag{2}$$

$$\beta = -(l+1)$$

$$\left.\begin{aligned} P' &= Q_2 + (l+1)P/r, \\ Q_2' &= -(2v - \varepsilon)P - (l+1)Q_2/r + X. \end{aligned}\right\} \tag{3}$$

The second pair would probably be the more convenient, since the first of equations (3) gives

$$Q_2 = r^{l+1}\frac{d}{dr}(r^{-(l+1)}P),$$

[6] S. Gill, *Proc. Cambridge Phil. Soc.*, **47**, 96 (1951).

and, since $P \sim Ar^{l+1}$ for small $r$, it follows that $Q_2$ is of the same order, $r^{l+1}$, as $P$; whereas $Q_1$ is of order $r^l$.

It will appear later (Chapter 9) that equations (2) and (3) are very closely related to those occurring in a relativistic extension of this treatment of a many-electron atom.

The changes of integration interval $\delta r$ made in the course of a calculation with $r$ as independent variable are usually such as to keep $\delta r/r$ approximately constant. This indicates that such changes could be made much fewer, and perhaps eliminated altogether, by use of $\rho = \log r$ as independent variable. In terms of this variable, equation (1) becomes

$$\left\{\frac{d^2}{d\rho^2} - \frac{d}{d\rho} + [2r^2v - r^2\varepsilon - l(l+1)]\right\} P = r^2X. \tag{4}$$

This equation contains a first derivative, but, if the integration is carried out by a process that involves reducing a second-order equation to two first-order equations, this is no disadvantage. Alternatively, the substitution $\rho = \log r$ can be made in equations (2) or (3). Equation (4) (except for the use of $\log_{10} r$ rather than $\log_e r$ as independent variable) has been used by Altmann[7] in calculations without exchange.

The first-derivative term in (4) can be removed by the use of $r^{-1/2}P$ as dependent variable:

$$\left\{\frac{d^2}{d\rho^2} + [2r^2v - \varepsilon r^2 - (l + \tfrac{1}{2})^2]\right\} (r^{-1/2}P) = r^{3/2}X. \tag{5}$$

However, the experience of W. Hartree, who did a large amount of work on calculations of atomic structure before the outbreak of war in 1939, was that for hand calculations the disadvantages of equation (5) outweighed the advantages of the reduction of the number of changes of integration intervals; after using $\rho$ as independent variable in calculations for Hg,[8] he returned to the use of $r$ as independent variable in calculations for $Au^+$.[9]

In calculations without exchange, the Riccati form of equation (1) (with $X = 0$) may be useful. Let

$$\eta = -\frac{P'}{P} = -\frac{d}{dr}(\log P) \tag{6}$$

[7] S. Altmann, *Proc. Phys. Soc., A*, **68**, 987 (1955).

[8] D. R. and W. Hartree, *Proc. Roy. Soc.*, **149**, 210 (1935).

[9] See A. S. Douglas, D. R. Hartree, and W. A. Runciman, *Proc. Cambridge Phil. Soc.*, **51**, 486 (1955).

(the minus sign is inserted so that $\eta$ is positive for large $r$, on the exponential "tail" of the wave function). Then

$$\begin{aligned}\eta' &= -P''/P + \eta^2 \\ &= \eta^2 + [2v - \varepsilon - l(l+1)/r^2]. \end{aligned} \tag{7}$$

This equation can be integrated inwards from a starting value of $\eta$ determined by iteration from equation (7) expressed in the form

$$\eta = [\varepsilon - 2v + l(l+1)/r^2 + \eta']^{1/2}.$$

Equation (6) is not convenient for small $r$, but, if we write

$$\xi = -\frac{d}{dr}\log\frac{P}{r^{l+1}}, \tag{8}$$

then

$$\xi = \eta + (l+1)/r,$$

and

$$\begin{aligned}\xi' &= \xi^2 - 2(l+1)\xi/r + 2v - \varepsilon \\ &= \xi^2 + 2[Y - (l+1)\xi]/r - \varepsilon \end{aligned} \tag{9}$$

[here $Y$ is short for $Y(nl; r)$ in equation § 5.1(3)]. This equation can be integrated outwards from the initial value $\xi(0) = N/(l+1)$; the ascending power series for $\xi$ can be derived from that for $(P/r^{l+1})$, see § 5.2.1.

Equations (7) and (9) were used to a considerable extent in the earlier work on calculations of atomic structure, but from the experience of later work it has seemed that integration of the radial wave equation in the form § 5.1(3) is a more satisfactory procedure, at least for $l = 0$, 1, and 2. Values of $l$ above 4 or 5 do not occur in calculations of atomic structure but may occur in calculations concerning scattering, and for such values of $l$ there may be an advantage in using equation (9) for the outward integration as far as the first maximum of $P$.

The substitutions (6), (8) give no advantage in the integration of the equations with exchange.

# 6. CONFIGURATIONS COMPRISING INCOMPLETE GROUPS

## 6.1. RUSSELL-SAUNDERS COUPLING

For the lighter atoms, spin-orbit interaction is small. If it is neglected, the total orbital moment of momentum **L** and total spin moment of momentum **S** are individually conserved, and they can be quantized separately; their vector sum **J** is also quantized. The quantum values of $\mathbf{L}^2$, $\mathbf{S}^2$, and $\mathbf{J}^2$ are (in atomic units) $L(L+1)$, $S(S+1)$, and $J(J+1)$; $L$, $2S$, and $2J$ are integral, and $2S$ and $2J$ have the same parity as the total number of electrons.

This leads to a classification of energy states by *terms* and *levels*; a *level* comprises all those states which in the absence of an external magnetic field have the same energy, depending on $L$, $S$, and $J$; the variation of energy of a level with $J$ depends on spin-orbit interaction, and, if this is neglected, we get a set of levels of the same energy which can be grouped into a single *term* whose energy depends on $L$, $S$ only. Such a term is represented by the symbol ${}^{2S+1}L$, the numerical value of $L$ being indicated conventionally by capital letters, corresponding to the small letters used for representing values of $l$ (see § 1.6):

$$L = 0 \quad 1 \quad 2 \quad 3 \quad 4$$

represented by

$$S \quad P \quad D \quad F \quad G.$$

Thus a *term* is a set of states of the same energy in the absence of an external magnetic field and of spin-orbit interaction; a term is split into *levels* by spin-orbit interaction, and the energies of these *levels* are the quantities determined by analysis of spectra (apart from studies of the Zeeman effect); and a *level* is further split into *states* by an external magnetic field. The individual states are nondegenerate. For example, the single $(3p)$ *term* of neutral Na comprises two *levels* into which it is split by spin-orbit interaction, and these together are split into six *states* by an external magnetic field.

A wave function represents a single *state*; so a *term* is represented not by a single wave function but (except the case of a ${}^1S$ term, for which $L = 0$, $S = 0$ and which is nondegenerate) by a group of wave functions. For example, the six functions

$$\frac{1}{r} P(3p; r) \begin{Bmatrix} (x \pm iy)/r \\ z/r \end{Bmatrix} \begin{Bmatrix} \chi_1(s) \\ \chi_2(s) \end{Bmatrix} \tag{1}$$

are collectively the wave functions of the states of a $(3p)$ term of an electron in a central field.

A configuration comprising more than one $(nl)$ wave function in addition to complete groups gives a number of terms, each of which can be specified by the values of $(LS)$. For example, the normal configuration of neutral Si, $(1s)^2(2s)^2(2p)^6(3s)^2(3p)^2$, gives a $^3P$ term, a $^1D$ term and a $^1S$ term (this

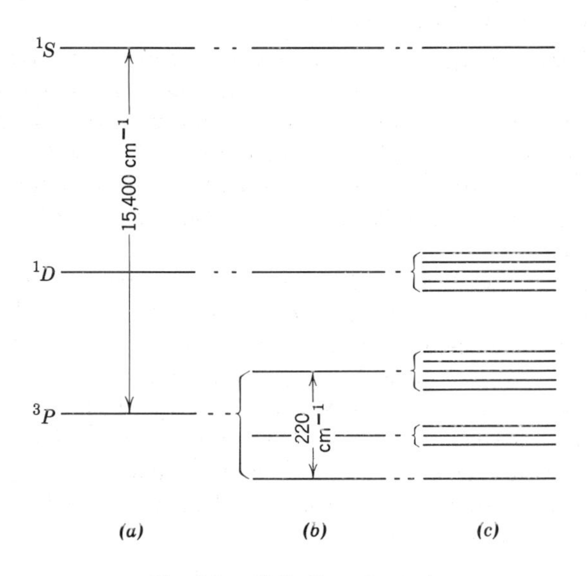


Fig. 6.1. Si $(3p)^2$ configuration.

(*a*) No spin-orbit interaction, no external magnetic field; three *terms*.
(*b*) With spin-orbit interaction, no external magnetic field; five *levels*.
(*c*) With spin-orbit interaction and small external magnetic field; 15 *states*.

Spin separations greatly exaggerated compared with term separations, and splitting due to external magnetic field exaggerated relative to spin separations.

result is derived in § 6.2); the $^3P$ term has three levels, of which the upper two split into five and three states in an external magnetic field; the $^1D$ and $^1S$ terms each have one level only, the $^1D$ level splits into five states in a magnetic field (see Fig. 6.1). The separation of the extreme levels of the $^3P$ term, which is a spin effect, is 220 cm$^{-1}$, whereas the separations of the terms are of the order of 10,000 cm$^{-1}$; this illustrates how small are the effects of spin-orbit interaction in the lighter elements.

In the calculation of atomic structures for configurations comprising incomplete groups, we will in this chapter suppose spin-orbit interaction neglected, as we have already done for configurations of complete groups. The results will suffice for the calculation of the effects of spin-orbit interaction on the energy as a first-order perturbation.

We shall still take the one-electron wave functions $\psi_\alpha(r_j)$, of which the approximate wave function $\Phi$ is to be constructed, to be of central-field type and, except in § 6.7, to have the same radial variation for all the wave functions $\psi_\alpha(r_j)$ in a single $(nl)$ group. Delbrück's argument (see § 1.9) for the adoption of central-field wave functions no longer applies, but the approximation is probably less serious than that of using a finite sum of separable wave functions at all.

### 6.2. *(LS)* TERMS FROM A GIVEN CONFIGURATION

For a configuration that includes an incomplete group, a single determinant of one-electron wave functions is not in general a suitable approximation; it is necessary to take a linear combination of such determinants containing different members of the set of wave functions of the incomplete group or groups.

Consider, for example, the normal configuration $(3p)^2$ (in addition to complete groups) of the normal state of neutral Si. The purpose of taking a determinant such as § 3.2(1) as an approximate wave function is to satisfy the condition of antisymmetry in all pairs of electrons, and, in order that the determinant should have this property, the same one-electron wave functions $\psi$ must occur in all columns of any one row of the determinant. Hence any one determinant can contain only two of the six possible $(3p)$ wave functions expressed by § 6.1(1). Out of these six $(3p)$ wave functions, two can be selected in $\frac{1}{2} \cdot 6 \cdot 5 = 15$ different ways. Hence there are 15 different determinants which contain just two $(3p)$ wave functions each, and the wave functions for different states of the $(3p)^2$ configuration may be either single members of this set of determinants or linear combinations of members of this set.

There are now two questions: the first concerned with the determination of the $(LS)$ values of the terms arising from a given configuration, and the second with the determination of the formula for $E'$ for the different terms. Once the formula for $E'$ has been obtained, the procedure for deriving and solving Fock's equations is the same as for a configuration of complete groups.

Answers to these questions were given by Slater in 1929, in a classic paper on the theory of complex spectra.[1] The argument will only be summarized here. For the reason given in § 2.1, it will be expressed in

[1] J. C. Slater, *Phys. Rev.*, **34**, 1293 (1929); see also G. H. Shortley, *Phys. Rev.*, **50**, 1072 (1936).

terms of the variation principle rather than in terms of perturbation theory.

If spin-orbit interaction is neglected, the components in any one direction (say the $z$ direction) of the total "orbital" moment of momentum and the total "spin" moment of momentum are both conserved, and can be quantized separately. Their quantum values (in atomic units) are $M_L = \Sigma m_l$ and $M_S = \Sigma m_s$, respectively. For an $(LS)$ term, $M_L$ takes all values from $-L$ to $+L$ at unit intervals and $M_S$ takes all values from $-S$ to $+S$ at unit intervals.

We list all the possible determinants containing the specified numbers of wave functions of the incomplete group or groups, obtain the values of $M_L$, $M_S$ for them, and record, for each $(M_L, M_S)$, how many different determinants give that $(M_L, M_S)$. Consider again a $(3p)^2$ configuration, and let a determinant be indicated by the $(3p, m_l, m_s)$ wave functions involved in it, $m_l$ being indicated by its numerical value (negative values being indicated by bars, as $\bar{1}$ for $-1$ as in § 3.4) and $m_s = \pm \frac{1}{2}$ by $+$ or $-$. The 15 different pairs are shown in Table 6.

**Table 6**

| | | $M_L$ | $M_S$ |
|---|---|---|---|
| (1) | $(3p1+)(3p0+)$ | $M_L = 1$ | $M_S = 1$ |
| (2) | $\bar{1}+$ | 0 | 1 |
| (3) | $1-$ | 2 | 0 |
| (4) | $0-$ | 1 | 0 |
| (5) | $\bar{1}-$ | 0 | 0 |
| (6) | $(3p0+)(3p\bar{1}+)$ | $\bar{1}$ | 1 |
| (7) | $1-$ | 1 | 0 |
| (8) | $0-$ | 0 | 0 |
| (9) | $\bar{1}-$ | $\bar{1}$ | 0 |
| (10) | $(3p\bar{1}+)(3p1-)$ | 0 | 0 |
| (11) | $0-$ | $\bar{1}$ | 0 |
| (12) | $\bar{1}-$ | $\bar{2}$ | 0 |
| (13) | $(3p1-)(3p0-)$ | 1 | $\bar{1}$ |
| (14) | $\bar{1}-$ | 0 | $\bar{1}$ |
| (15) | $(3p0-)(3p\bar{1}-)$ | $\bar{1}$ | $\bar{1}$ |

Only one pair of wave functions gives $M_L = 2$, $M_S = 0$; namely that numbered (3) in Table 6; and only one gives $M_L = 1$, $M_S = 1$; namely that numbered (7); three give $M_L = 0$, $M_S = 0$: namely those numbered (5), (8), and (10). The result of the whole count can be represented diagrammatically as in Fig. 6.2, in which each number in a circle at a grid point of the $(M_L, M_S)$ plane is the number of determinants giving those values of $(M_L, M_S)$. Although the wave function of a state may not be a single determinant, the *number* of distinct wave functions with given $(M_L, M_S)$ will not be affected by linear combination of the determinants with those values of $(M_L, M_S)$; hence the count of the number of single determinants with given $(M_L, M_S)$, as illustrated in Fig. 6.2, is also a count of the number of states.

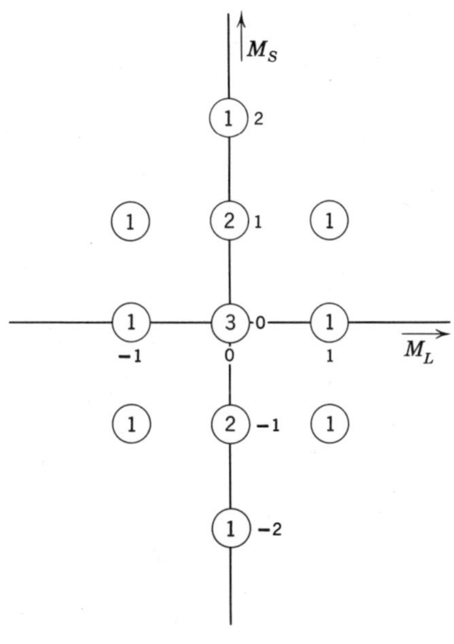


Fig. 6.2.

Since in this example the greatest value of $M_L$ is 2, there can be no term with $L > 2$, for a term with $L > 2$ would have at least one state with $M_L > 2$; furthermore, for $M_L = 2$ there is no determinant with $M_S > 0$, so that by a similar argument the term with $L = 2$ must have $S = 0$. That is, it must be a $^1D$ term, and the single determinant with $M_L = 2$, $M_S = 0$ is an approximate wave function for one state of this term. The other states must have $M_S = 0$ and $M_L = 1, 0, \bar{1}, \bar{2}$; their wave functions may not be single determinants. Similarly there is no determinant with both $M_L > 1$ and $M_S > 1$; so the single determinant with $M_L = 1$, $M_S = 1$ must be an approximate wave function of a state of a term with $L = 1$, $S = 1$; that is, a $^3P$ term. This will have nine states, with $M_L = 1, 0, \bar{1}$, and $M_S = 1, 0, \bar{1}$ for each value of $M_L$. The states of the $^1D$ and $^3P$ terms together account for all the wave functions with the various values of $(M_L, M_S)$ shown in Fig. 6.2 except for one with $M_L = 0$, $M_S = 0$, which must by a similar argument be the wave function of the single state of a $^1S$ term. Thus the terms arising from a $(3p)^2$ configuration are $^1D$, $^3P$, and $^1S$, as already quoted in § 6.1.

The same argument applies to any configuration consisting of a $(np)^2$ group in addition to complete groups.

Tables of the terms arising from a single incomplete group of $p$, $d$, or $f$ wave functions are given by Condon and Shortley[2] and by Slater[3] and such tables for some combinations of two and three incomplete groups are given in the National Bureau of Standards volumes on *Atomic Energy Levels*.[4]

### 6.3. DERIVATION OF THE FORMULA FOR $E'$

In the absence of spin-orbit interaction and of an external magnetic field, all states of a single term have the same energy. So although the wave functions for most of the states of this term may not be single determinants, yet, if the wave function for *any one* of these states *is* a single determinant, the formula for $E'$ in terms of integrals over radial wave functions can be obtained in the same way as for a complete group (see § 3.4). For example, for a configuration consisting of closed groups and a $(3p)^2$ group considered in § 6.2, we have seen that the determinant written $(3p1\,+)(3p1\,-)$, in the notation there used, is an approximate wave function for a state of the $^1D$ term, and the determinant $(3p1\,+)$ $(3p0\,+)$ an approximate wave function for a state of the $^3P$ term.

For a single incomplete group, the formula for $E'$ for the state of highest $S$, and among such states, if there is more than one, that of highest $L$ can always be obtained in this way. For a number of other cases, including all terms arising from a single incomplete $(np)^q$ group, the formulae for $E'$ can be found by an argument due to Slater. This will be explained here in its application to the $^1S$ state of a $(3p)^2$ configuration, and its generalization then sketched.

As pointed out in § 6.1, there are three determinants containing two $(3p)$ wave functions for which $M_L = 0$, $M_S = 0$: namely those represented in the notation of Table 6 by

$$(3p1\,+)(3p\bar{1}\,-),\qquad (3p0\,+)(3p0\,-),\qquad (3p\bar{1}\,+)(3p1\,-).$$

Let these be written for short

$$\Phi_1,\qquad \Phi_2,\qquad \Phi_3.$$

[2] E. U. Condon and G. H. Shortley, *Theory of Atomic Spectra*, Cambridge, Table 1[7] (1935).

[3] J. C. Slater, *Quantum Theory of Matter*, Table 7.3.4, p. 180 ($p$ and $d$ groups only).

[4] Vol. I, Tables 5–22, vol. II, Tables 1–17.

Any linear combination

$$\Phi = a\Phi_1 + b\Phi_2 + c\Phi_3 \tag{1}$$

has the same values of $M_L$ and $M_S$; we can appeal to the variation principle and ask for the "best" values, in the sense of the variation principle, of the coefficients $a$, $b$, $c$ to use in such an approximate wave function (1), with given functions $\Phi_1$, $\Phi_2$, and $\Phi_3$, and what are the corresponding expressions for $E'$ in terms of these functions $\Phi_1$, $\Phi_2$, and $\Phi_3$. Slater showed how in many cases these expressions for $E'$ can be obtained without explicitly solving for the coefficients $a$, $b$, $c$ in the linear combination (1).

Let $\Phi_1$, $\Phi_2$, and $\Phi_3$ in (1) be normalized. Any two of these functions differ in at least one function $\psi$ in the determinants, and these are orthogonal through the properties of the spherical harmonic and spin factors in them, independently of their radial variations; so $\Phi_1$, $\Phi_2$, and $\Phi_3$ are orthogonal, and therefore

$$\int \Phi^2 \, d\tau = a^2 + b^2 + c^2.$$

Let $H_{mn}$ be written for $\int \Phi_m H \Phi_n \, d\tau$ ($m = 1, 2, 3$; $n = 1, 2, 3$). Then substitution of (1) into $E' = \int \Phi H \Phi \, d\tau / \int \Phi^2 \, d\tau$ gives

$$(a^2 + b^2 + c^2)E' = a^2 H_{11} + b^2 H_{22} + c^2 H_{33} + 2ab H_{12} + 2bc H_{23} + 2ca H_{31}.$$

For a variation $\Delta a$ of $a$, the first-order variation $\Delta_a E'$ of $E'$ is given by

$$a^2 \, \Delta_a E' - 2aE' \, \Delta a = (2aH_{11} + 2bH_{12} + 2cH_{13}) \, \Delta a,$$

and, for the "best" wave function (1) in the sense of the variation principle, $\Delta_a E' = 0$; hence

$$(H_{11} - E')a + H_{12}b + H_{13}c = 0; \tag{2}$$

similarly by considering the variations of $E'$ with $b$ and $c$

$$H_{12}a + (H_{22} - E')b + H_{23}c = 0, \tag{3}$$

$$H_{13}a + H_{23}b + (H_{33} - E')c = 0. \tag{4}$$

To give a significant wave function (1), $a$, $b$, and $c$ must not all be zero; hence we require a solution of equations (2), (3), (4) other than $a = b = c = 0$; and these equations have such a solution only of

$$\begin{vmatrix} H_{11} - E' & H_{12} & H_{13} \\ H_{12} & H_{22} - E' & H_{23} \\ H_{13} & H_{23} & H_{33} - E' \end{vmatrix} = 0.$$

Expanded and expressed as a polynomial in $E'$, this gives

$$-(E')^3 + (H_{11} + H_{22} + H_{33})(E')^2 - BE' + C = 0 \tag{5}$$

(we do not need the expressions for $B$ and $C$ in terms of the quantities $H_{mn}$). Hence

$$\text{Sum of roots } E' = H_{11} + H_{22} + H_{33}. \tag{6}$$

This is a special case of a result termed by Slater the "diagonal sum rule."

Now two of the roots $E'$ of (5) are the values of $E'$, in terms of the functions $\Phi_1$, $\Phi_2$, and $\Phi_3$, for the $M_L = 0$, $M_S = 0$ states of the $^1D$ and $^3P$ terms. These can be determined separately since each of these terms has another state whose wave function is a single determinant. Hence the expression for $E'$ for the $^1S$ term can be obtained from the sum (6) without either solving the cubic (5), or finding the coefficients $a$, $b$, $c$ in (1). Also it is not necessary to evaluate the quantities $H_{mn}$ for $n \neq m$; the only quantities required are the integrals $H_{11}$, $H_{22}$, and $H_{33}$, and, since $\Phi_m (m = 1, 2, 3)$ is a single determinant, these integrals can be evaluated as in § 3.4.

This is about the simplest example of Slater's general treatment, expressed in terms of the variation principle rather than in terms of perturbation theory. The following is an outline of the general treatment.

Consider *all* the determinants arising from a given configuration, for example the 15 for $(3p)^2$, not only those for a single $(M_L, M_S)$. Let these be $\Phi_A$, where $A$ stands for the set of one-electron wave functions in a single determinant, and consider the linear combination

$$\Phi = \Sigma a_A \Phi_A. \tag{7}$$

Then:

(*a*) $\int \Phi^* H \Phi \, d\tau$ contains only those terms $\int \Phi^*_{A'} H \Phi_A \, d\tau$ for which the sets $A$ and $A'$ have the same values of $M_L = \Sigma m_l$ and $M_S = \Sigma m_s$.

(*b*) It follows from (*a*) that application of the variation principle to determine the coefficients gives a set of linear equations

$$\left.\begin{aligned} (H_{11} - E')a_1 + H_{12}a_2 + \cdots &= 0 \\ H_{12}a_1 + (H_{22} - E')a_2 + \cdots &= 0 \end{aligned}\right\}, \tag{8}$$
$$\text{etc.}$$

in which the matrix of the elements $H_{AA'}$ splits up into submatrices each referring to a single $(M_L, M_S)$ only; for example for a $(3p)^2$ configuration, a matrix in which the nonzero elements are indicated by crosses in Fig. 6.3.

(*c*) A submatrix of one row and column represents a state whose wave function is (in this approximation) a single determinant, and the expression for $E'$ for the term of which it is a state can be derived as in § 3.4.

(*d*) The sum of the diagonal elements of each submatrix is the sum of those integrals $\int \Phi^*_A H \Phi_A \, d\tau$ with the appropriate $(M_L, M_S)$.

(*e*) In the absence of a magnetic field the value for $E'$ for an $(L, S)$ term is independent of $(M_L, M_S)$, so that we can get expressions for $E'$ for individual terms from diagonal sums, as illustrated in the case of $(3p)^2$.

| | | | Ref. No. | (3) | (1) | (6) | (4) | (2) | (5) | (8) | (10) | . . . |
|---|---|---|---|---|---|---|---|---|---|---|---|---|
| | | | $(m_l m_s)\alpha$ | (1+) | (1+) | (0+) | (1+) | (1+) | (1+) | (0+) | ($\bar{1}$+) | . . . |
| | | | $(m_l m_s)\beta$ | (1−) | (0+) | (1−) | (0−) | ($\bar{1}$+) | ($\bar{1}$−) | (0−) | (1−) | . . . |
| | | | $M_L$ | 2 | 1 | 1 | 1 | 0 | 0 | 0 | 0 | . . . |
| | | | $M_S$ | 0 | 1 | 0 | 0 | 1 | 0 | 0 | 0 | . . . |
| $(m_l m_s)\alpha$ | $(m_l m_s)\beta$ | $M_L$ | $M_S$ | | | | | | | | | |
| (1+) | (1−) | 2 | 0 | × | | | | | | | | |
| (1+) | (0+) | 1 | 1 | | × | | | | | | | |
| (0+) | (1−) | 1 | 0 | | | × | × | | | | | |
| (1+) | (0−) | 1 | 0 | | | × | × | | | | | |
| (1+) | ($\bar{1}$+) | 0 | 1 | | | | | × | | | | |
| (1+) | ($\bar{1}$−) | 0 | 0 | | | | | | × | × | × | |
| (0+) | (0−) | 0 | 0 | | | | | | × | × | × | |
| ($\bar{1}$+) | (1−) | 0 | 0 | | | | | | × | × | × | |
| ⋮ | ⋮ | ⋮ | ⋮ | | | | | | | | | ⋱ |

Fig. 6.3. Part of matrix $H_{AA'}$ for $(3p)^2$ configuration; nonzero elements indicated by crosses. Numbers in brackets refer to the list of determinants in Table 6 (p. 104).

When a configuration gives two or more terms of the same $L$ and same $S$, the use of diagonal sums alone does not give the expression for $E'$ for each separate one of these terms, but only the sum for all such terms. Furthermore, the expression for $E'$ for such terms is not a sum of $I$, $F_k$, and $G_k$ integrals with numerical coefficients which are independent of the radial wave functions, but contains square roots of quadratic expressions involving $F_k$ and $G_k$ integrals. These contributions to $E'$ would complicate the process of deriving and solving the equations for the radial wave functions, and, as far as I am aware, no complete calculation for such a case has been carried out.

Another method of deriving the expressions for $E'$ in terms of the radial wave function has been developed by Racah.[5] This uses matrix transformation methods and, in effect, determines the characteristic values $E'$ of the matrix $H_{AA'}$ without use of the diagonal sum property. This method is more general and more widely applicable than Slater's use of diagonal sums, in that, when a configuration gives two or more terms with the same $(LS)$, it provides expressions for $E'$ for these terms individually. However, it is a good deal more elaborate algebraically, and, if results for a few particular cases only are required, the method of diagonal sums appears much the simpler, provided that it will produce the results required; and, as already mentioned, terms for which $E'$ is not given by the diagonal sum rule involve the other complications also.

### 6.4. STRUCTURE OF THE FORMULA FOR $E'$

For a configuration comprising one or more incomplete groups, it is convenient to divide the terms in the whole expression for $E'$ into three groups, namely:

(i) Those involving wave functions of the complete groups only.

(ii) The $I$ integrals for the wave functions of incomplete groups, and $J$, $K$ integrals, or $F_k$, $G_k$ integrals, involving one wave function of a complete group and one wave function of an incomplete group.

(iii) $J$ and $K$ integrals, or $F_k$ and $G_k$ integrals, in which both the wave functions involved belong to the incomplete group or groups.

The contributions (i) to $E'$ are independent of the presence of the incomplete groups. Of the contributions (ii), the $I$ integrals depend only on $(nl)$ and so are the same whether the wave functions belong to a complete or an incomplete group. The sums $\Sigma_\alpha J(\alpha\beta)$, $\Sigma_\alpha K(\alpha\beta)$ of the integrals $J(\alpha\beta)$, $K(\alpha\beta)$ (see § 3.3) over the wave functions $\alpha$ of a complete $(n'l')$ group and any one wave function $\beta$ of another group, complete or incomplete, are independent of the $m_l$, $m_s$ of the wave function $\beta$ of the second group.[6] Hence, if an incomplete $(nl)$ group contains $q(nl)$ occupied wave functions, the contribution to $E'$ from this incomplete $(nl)$ group and a *complete* $(n'l')$ group is $q(nl)/2(2l+1)$ times that from complete $(nl)$ and $(n'l')$ groups. Hence for a single incomplete $(nl)$ group the total contribution to $E'$ from terms of group (ii) is

$$q(nl)[I(nl) + \Sigma'_{n'l'}q(n'l')F_0(nl, n'l')] - \frac{q(nl)}{2(2l+1)}[\Sigma_{n'l'k}B_{ll'k}G_k(nl, n'l')], \quad (1)$$

the coefficients $B_{ll'k}$ being those for complete groups (see Table 3). If

[5] G. Racah, *Phys. Rev.*, **62**, 438 (1942).

[6] See E. U. Condon and G. H. Shortley, *Theory of Atomic Spectra*, § 9[6], formula (11), Cambridge (1935).

there is more than one incomplete group, each gives a contribution to $E'$ expressed by (1).

Only the contributions of group (iii) need special evaluation by Slater's or Racah's method. For a single incomplete $(nl)$ group, the contributions to $E'$ are of the form

$$-\Sigma_k A_{lk} F_k(nl, nl). \tag{2}$$

The coefficients $A_{lk}$ are generalizations of those introduced in § 3.4 for configurations of complete groups. Their values for all terms of $(np)^q$ configurations[7] and the lowest terms of $(nd)^q$ configurations[8] are given in Table 7; values of $4A_{lk}/q(nl)$ are also given for a reason that will appear

**Table 7**

| $l = 1$ | | $A_{p2}$ | $4A_{p2}/q(np)$ | $l = 2$ | | $A_{d2}$ | $A_{d4}$ | $4A_{d2}/q(nd)$ | $4A_{d4}/q(nd)$ |
|---|---|---|---|---|---|---|---|---|---|
| $(np)^2$ | $^3P$ | 1/5 | 2/5 | $(nd)^2$ | $^3F$ | 8/49 | 1/49 | 16/49 | 2/49 |
| | $^1D$ | − 1/25 | − 2/25 | $(nd)^3$ | $^4F$ | 15/49 | 8/49 | 20/49 | 32/147 |
| | $^1S$ | − 2/5 | − 4/5 | $(nd)^4$ | $^5D$ | 3/7 | 3/7 | 3/7 | 3/7 |
| $(np)^3$ | $^4S$ | 3/5 | 4/5 | $(nd)^5$ | $^6S$ | 5/7 | 5/7 | 4/7 | 4/7 |
| | $^2P$ | 6/25 | 8/25 | $(nd)^6$ | $^5D$ | 5/7 | 5/7 | 10/21 | 10/21 |
| | $^2D$ | 0 | 0 | $(nd)^7$ | $^4F$ | 43/49 | 36/49 | 172/343 | 144/343 |
| $(np)^4$ | $^3P$ | 3/5 | 3/5 | $(nd)^8$ | $^3F$ | 50/49 | 43/49 | 25/49 | 43/98 |
| | $^1D$ | 9/25 | 9/25 | $(nd)^9$ | $^2D$ | 8/7 | 8/7 | 32/63 | 32/63 |
| | $^1S$ | 0 | 0 | $(nd)^{10}$ | $^1S$ | 10/7 | 10/7 | 4/7 | 4/7 |
| $(np)^5$ | $^2P$ | 4/5 | 16/25 | | | | | | |
| $(np)^6$ | $^1S$ | 6/5 | 4/5 | | | | | | |

in § 6.5. Only a few results for more than one incomplete group have been worked out.[9]

### 6.5. EQUATIONS FOR THE RADIAL WAVE FUNCTIONS

For a configuration with one incomplete group, we require first the equation for the radial wave function of the incomplete group and second the contributions of the incomplete group to the equations for the radial wave functions of the complete groups. Let $(nl)$ refer to the incomplete group, $(n''l'')$ to a particular complete group for which the equation for the radial wave function is to be obtained, and $(n'l')$ to the complete groups generally.

The equation for the radial wave function $P(nl; r)$ for the incomplete

[7] See D. R. Hartree, W. Hartree, and B. Swirles, *Phil. Trans. Roy. Soc.*, **238**, 229, Table I (1939).

[8] See D. R. Hartree, *Proc. Cambridge Phil. Soc.*, **51**, 126, Table I (1955). The coefficients $A_{lk}$ are written $\beta_{lk}$ in this paper.

[9] See for example E. U. Condon and G. H. Shortley, *Theory of Atomic Spectra*, ch. 7, Cambridge (1935), and G. Racah, *Phys. Rev.*, **62**, 438 (1942).

group is obtained by considering the variation of $E'$ with $P(nl; r)$, and for this purpose we need only consider the terms in $E'$ that depend on $P(nl; r)$. These are given in § 6.4(1) and (2). The terms (1) are just $q(nl)/2(2l+1)$ times the corresponding terms for a complete $(nl)$ group, so that, on taking the variation of these terms with $P(nl; r)$ and multiplying by $-1/q(nl)$ to reduce the coefficient of $d^2P(nl; r)/dr^2$ to unity, they give exactly the same terms in the equation for $P(nl; r)$ that one would get for a complete $(nl)$ group. The variation of the expression § 6.4(2) with $P(nl; r)$ is

$$-(4/r)\Sigma_k A_{lk} Y_k(nl, nl; r) P(nl; r)\, \Delta P(nl; r); \tag{1}$$

the coefficient of $\Delta P(nl; r)$ in (1), multiplied by $-1/q(nl)$, gives the contribution from this term to the left-hand side of the equation (see § 5.7(1))

$$\left[\frac{d^2}{dr^2} + \frac{2}{r}\, Y(nl; r) - \varepsilon_{nl,nl} - \frac{l(l+1)}{r^2}\right] P(nl; r) = X(nl; r). \tag{2}$$

Thus, for the radial wave function of the incomplete group, the function $2Y(nl; r)$ in equation (2) is

$$\begin{aligned} 2Y(nl; r) = 2N &- \Sigma_{n'l'} 2q(n'l') Y_0(n'l', n'l'; r) \\ &- 2[q(nl) - 1] Y_0(nl, nl; r) + \Sigma_k [4A_{lk}/q(nl)] Y_k(nl, nl; r), \end{aligned} \tag{3}$$

the sum $\Sigma_{n'l'}$ being over the complete groups, and the sum $\Sigma_k$ being over values of $k > 0$. The last term in (3) is the only difference from the equation for $P(nl; r)$ in a configuration with a complete $(nl)$ group. The coefficients $[4A_{lk}/q(nl)]$ which occur in this term are given in Table 7. Since the coefficients $A_{lk}$ in formula (4), and perhaps some of the coefficients in contributions to the function $X(nl; r)$ in equation (2), are different for different $(LS)$ terms arising from a single configuration, it follows that the radial wave functions for these terms are also slightly different.

In obtaining the equation for the radial wave function for the complete $(n''l'')$ group, the contributions § 6.4(2) to $E'$ play no part, and the contributions § 6.4(1) which depend on $P(n''l''; r)$ are

$$q(nl)\left[q(n''l'') F_0(nl, n''l'') - \frac{1}{2(2l+1)}\, \Sigma_k B_{ll''k} G_k(nl, n''l'')\right].$$

These are $q(nl)/2(2l+1)$ times the contributions to $E'$ from complete $(nl)$ and $(n''l'')$ groups. Since in deriving the equation for $P(n''l''; r)$ these terms are treated in exactly the same way whether the $(nl)$ group is complete or not, the only difference in equation (2) for $P(n''l''; r)$ from that for a configuration with a complete $(nl)$ group is that the contributions from the $(nl)$ group are reduced by the factor $q(nl)/2(2l+1)$. This leaves unaltered the expression § 3.6(11) for $Y(n''l''; r)$, and only the contributions from the $(nl)$ group to the exchange term $X(n''l''; r)$ have explicitly to be reduced by the factor $q(nl)/2(2l+1)$.

Once the equations for the radial wave functions have been obtained, the process of evaluating the solution of them is the same as for a configuration of complete groups only.

If there are two or more incomplete groups, the only terms in $E'$ that involve the wave functions of two of the incomplete groups are those of the third group of terms mentioned in § 6.4. These contribute to the exchange terms $X(r)$ only in the equations for the radial wave functions for the incomplete groups; the expression (3) for $Y(nl; r)$ stands, with the appropriate coefficient $[4A_{lk}/q(nl)]$ for each incomplete group.

## 6.6. ONE WAVE FUNCTION IN ADDITION TO COMPLETE GROUPS

Some of the general relations for configurations comprising incomplete groups become particularly simple for a configuration consisting of a single $(nl)$ wave function only in addition to complete groups. Such a configuration gives a $^2L$ term, and each state of this term has a wave function which is a single determinant. Furthermore, of the contributions to $E'$ of the three kinds mentioned in § 6.4, there are none of the third kind, so that in the expression § 6.5(3) for the function $Y(nl; r)$ in equation § 6.5(2) there are no terms involving the $Y_k(nl, nl; r)$ functions. Hence equation § 6.5(2) becomes

$$\left\{\frac{d^2}{dr^2}+\frac{2}{r}[N-\Sigma_{n'l'}q(n'l')Y_0(n'l', n'l'; r)]-\varepsilon_{nl,nl}-\frac{l(l+1)}{r^2}\right\}P(nl; r) = X(nl; r), \quad (1)$$

and, by the argument already used in § 6.5, the exchange term $X(nl; r)$ in this equation is the same as for a complete $(nl)$ group.

This exchange term is linear in $P(nl; r)$, and, since the coefficient of $P(nl; r)$ does not now involve any function $Y_k(nl, nl; r)$ which depends on $P(nl; r)$, equation (1) is now strictly linear in $P(nl; r)$. Hence a normalized solution can be obtained, if it is convenient so to obtain it, by first evaluating an unnormalized solution and later multiplying it by a normalizing factor $1\Big/\left[\int_0^\infty P^2\,dr\right]^{\frac{1}{2}}$.

## 6.7. DIFFERENT RADIAL WAVE FUNCTIONS WITHIN A SINGLE GROUP

Slater has suggested that, for a configuration comprising incomplete groups, the approximation could be improved by relaxing the restriction that the radial wave function shall be taken the same for all wave functions of the same group.

An example is provided by the $(3d)^5(4s)^2\ {}^6S$ term of neutral Mn. For the state $M_L = 0$, $M_S = 3$ of this term, the five $(3d)$ wave functions all have the same spin; one $(4s)$ wave function has the same spin as the five $(3d)$ wave functions, and one has the opposite spin. In the expression for $E'$ there are exchange integrals $K(\alpha\beta)$ involving wave functions $\alpha$, $\beta$ of the same spin but no such integrals involving wave functions of opposite spin. Hence, if $P(4s+)$ and $P(4s-)$ are the radial wave functions occurring in the two $(4s)$ wave functions, and these are both left free to be determined by the variation principle, the equations for them would be different, and these radial wave functions themselves would be different.[10]

[10] For a development of this approximation, see G. W. Pratt, *Phys. Rev.*, **102,** 1303 (1956).

# 7. THE VARIATION OF ATOMIC WAVE FUNCTIONS AND FIELDS WITH ATOMIC NUMBER

## 7.1. THE NEED FOR A PROCEDURE FOR INTERPOLATION WITH RESPECT TO ATOMIC NUMBER

Calculations of self-consistent fields, either with or without exchange, have been carried out for a number of atoms and ions. However, atomic fields or wave functions may be required for an atom or ion for which no such calculations have been carried out. The required information can then be obtained, approximately, by interpolation with respect to atomic number $N$ between the results for atoms or ions for which results of such calculations are already available.

Whether the results of such an interpolation are going to be used directly for the calculation of other atomic properties, or adopted as initial estimates in a new self-consistent field calculation, it is important to make the interpolation as good as is practicable. If the results of it are going to be used as they stand, this is obvious. The importance of a good interpolation procedure is scarcely less when the results of it are going to be used as initial estimates for a self-consistent field calculation. As explained in § 5.1, such a calculation is carried out by a process of successive approximation, and the process of refining an already good approximation to the solution is likely to be much quicker and less troublesome than the process of reaching even a moderate approximation from bad initial estimates. If an interpolation procedure can be made to produce good initial estimates, the time and labor of computation can be considerably reduced; it is probably not an exaggeration to say that two man-days spent in getting good initial estimates may save anything from two man-weeks to two man-months of computation if the numerical work is done by hand, and a corresponding period of machine time if the numerical work is done by an automatic digital calculating machine. Thus it is worth taking some trouble to obtain good initial estimates, and the time taken in this preliminary stage is likely to be repaid many times over in the subsequent numerical work.

As explained in Chapter 5, in calculations with exchange, what are wanted are estimates of the radial wave functions themselves; in calculations without exchange, estimates of the contributions to $Z$. The former are considered in § 7.4; the latter in § 7.7. The next two sections are concerned with some aspects common to results calculated with and without exchange.

### 7.2. PURE SCALING

Let $R$ be a typical length, defining the linear scale of the $(nl)$ wave function; $R$ might, for example, be taken to be the mean radius

$$\bar{r}_{nl} = \int_0^\infty r P^2(nl;\, r)\, dr, \tag{1}$$

or the radius $r_M$ of the main maximum of $P(nl;\, r)$, or the median radius $r_m$ such that

$$\int_0^{r_m} P^2(nl;\, r)\, dr = \tfrac{1}{2}; \tag{2}$$

that is, the radius $r_m$ such that the probability of an electron in an $(nl)$ wave function lying inside a sphere of radius $r_m$ is $\frac{1}{2}$. The scale radius $R$ will be written $R_{nl}$ when it is necessary to specify the values of $(nl)$ to which it applies; but this will not usually be necessary.

If, for a given $(nl)$, the normalized radial wave functions $P(nl;\, r)$ for atoms of different atomic number $N$ are geometrically similar, that is to say, they are replicas of the same function on different linear scales, then they would be related in the way expressed by

$$R^{1/2} P(nl;\, r) \text{ is a function of } (r/R) \text{ only,} \tag{3}$$

independent of the atomic number (the factor $R^{1/2}$ in (3) is a normalizing factor).

Let $P(N;\, nl;\, r)$ be written for the $(nl)$ radial wave function of an atom of atomic number $N$, and similarly $Z_0(N;\, nl, nl;\, r)$ for the function $Z_0(nl, nl;\, r)$ for such an atom. Then, if relation (3) holds, the wave functions and contributions to $Z$ for two atoms of atomic number $N_0$ and $N$ are related by

$$P(N;\, nl;\, r) = (R_0/R)^{1/2} P(N_0;\, nl;\, R_0 r/R), \tag{4}$$

$$Z_0(N;\, nl, nl;\, r) = Z_0(N_0;\, nl, nl;\, R_0 r/R). \tag{5}$$

The process of deriving wave functions and contributions to $Z$ for an atom of atomic number $N$ from known results for an atom of atomic number $N_0$ by means of relations (4) and (5) will be called "pure scaling" from atomic number $N_0$ to atomic number $N$.

Further, if $R_{(\mathrm{H})}$ is the value of $R$ for the $(nl)$ wave function of the hydrogen atom, then in the Coulomb field of a point charge $(N - \sigma)$

$$R = R_{(\mathrm{H})}/(N - \sigma), \tag{6}$$

so that $(N - \sigma) = R_{(H)}/R$ can be regarded as the "effective nuclear charge for $R$," in the sense that replacement of $N$ by $(N - \sigma)$, in the formula $R = R_{(H)}/N$ for a hydrogen-like atom of atomic number $N$, gives the correct value of $R$. And

$$\sigma = N - R_{(H)}/R \tag{7}$$

expresses the effect, on the value of $R$ for the $(nl)$ wave function, of the screening of the nucleus by the electrons in the other occupied wave functions. $\sigma$ will be called a "screening number" for $R$ (it is sometimes called a "screening constant," but this usage is undesirable, as $\sigma$ is not a constant). It will be written $\sigma_{nl}$ when it is necessary to specify the wave function to which it refers.

If the $(nl)$ wave function for an atom were a scaled hydrogen $(nl)$ wave function, the value of $\sigma$ would be the same whatever choice were made for the scale radius $R$. But departures from scaled hydrogen wave functions may be considerable (see § 7.5), and the value of $\sigma$ depends on the property taken to define the scale radius $R$, whether, for example, this is taken as the radius of the main maximum of $|P(nl; r)|$, the mean radius, the root-mean-square radius, the median radius, etc. This variation of $\sigma$ may be quite considerable, up to 2 or 3 units; thus there is no one screening number (or "screening constant"), even for a given $(nl)$ wave function in a given atom; the appropriate screening number depends on what is the atomic property which it is intended to represent in terms of a screening number.

For each complete $(nl)$ group, $\sigma$ is likely to vary only slowly with atomic number, so that, for atoms of neighboring atomic numbers $N_0$ and $N$,

$$(R/R_0) = (N_0 - \sigma)/(N - \sigma)$$

and (4) and (5) become

$$P(N; nl; r) = \left(\frac{N - \sigma}{N_0 - \sigma}\right)^{1/2} P(N_0; nl; r_0), \tag{8}$$

$$Z_0(N; nl, nl; r) = Z_0(N_0; nl, nl; r_0), \tag{9}$$

where

$$r_0 = [(N - \sigma)/(N_0 - \sigma)]r. \tag{10}$$

For neighboring values of $N_0$ and $N$, the scaling ratio $(N - \sigma)/(N_0 - \sigma)$ is not sensitive to the value of $\sigma$ adopted. For heavy atoms, the results for $Hg^{+2}$ $(N = 80)$ indicated[1] the following set of values as useful working values of $\sigma$:

| $nl$ | (1s) | (2s) | (2p) | (3s) | (3p) | (3d) | (4s) | (4p) | (4d) | (4f) | (5s) | (5p) |
|---|---|---|---|---|---|---|---|---|---|---|---|---|
| $\sigma_{nl}$ | 0.3 | 3.6 | 4.2 | 10.3 | 11.6 | 16.2 | 21 | 25 | 31 | 47 | 40 | 46 |

[1] A. S. Douglas, D. R. Hartree, and W. A. Runciman, *Proc. Cambridge Phil. Soc.*, **51**, 486 (1955).

Pure scaling provides one method for estimating both radial wave functions and contributions to $Z$. Another process, based on pure scaling, is to derive wave functions (or contributions to $Z$) for an atom of atomic number $N$ by pure scaling from two or more atoms with different values of $N_0$, and then interpolate, in the results of this scaling process, for the value $N_0 = N$. This takes into account the departures from pure scaling. Another, and more convenient, process, depending on interpolation of the departures from pure scaling, is considered in § 7.4.

### 7.3. LIMITING BEHAVIOR OF THE EQUATIONS AND THEIR SOLUTIONS AS $N \to \infty$

In considering how the $(nl)$ wave functions of an atom vary with atomic number $N$, it is helpful to consider the asymptotic form of their dependence on $N$ as $N \to \infty$. We have regarded these wave functions as obtained from equations like § 5.7(1) (with exchange) or §5.1(3) (without exchange), which are in turn derived from the nonrelativistic Hamiltonian § 1.8(5). Relativistic effects become predominant for large $N$; so the equations we have so far considered, such as § 5.7(1) and § 5.1(3), are not physically significant for large $N$. Nevertheless we can inquire, as a mathematical rather than a physical question, how the solutions of these equations behave as $N \to \infty$.

Consider, for example, the equations for the radial wave functions for the normal configuration of a ten-electron system, with exchange (see § 3.6.1). From the definition of the $Y_k$ functions [§ 3.5(1)] it follows that $|Y_k(nl, n'l'; r)| \leqslant 1$. Hence, for large $N$, equations § 3.6.1(2) for the $(2p)$ wave function has the form

$$\left\{\frac{d^2}{dr^2} + \frac{2}{r}[N + O(1)] - \varepsilon_{2p,2p} - \frac{2}{r^2}\right\} P(2p; r) + \frac{1}{r}[O(1)P(1s; r) + O(1)P(2s; r)] = 0,$$

the $O(1)$ indicating a quantity that remains finite as $N \to \infty$. Divide by $N^2$ and put $Nr = \rho$; then

$$\left\{\frac{d^2}{d\rho^2} + \frac{2}{\rho}\left[1 + O\left(\frac{1}{N}\right)\right] - \frac{1}{N^2}\varepsilon_{2p,2p} - \frac{2}{\rho^2}\right\} P\left(2p; \frac{\rho}{N}\right) + \frac{1}{N\rho}\left[O(1)\, P\left(1s; \frac{\rho}{N}\right) + O(1) P\left(2s; \frac{\rho}{N}\right)\right] = 0. \quad (1)$$

Let $P_{(\mathrm{H})}(nl; r)$ be the $(nl)$ radial wave function for hydrogen; then in the Coulomb field of a point charge $N$ the normalized $(nl)$ wave function is $N^{1/2}P_{(\mathrm{H})}(nl; Nr)$. For large $N$, the leading terms in equation (1) are just those for a $(2p)$ wave function in such a Coulomb field, and similarly for the equations for the $(1s)$ and $(2s)$ functions. It follows from these equations that

$$P(nl; \rho/N) = N^{1/2}[P_{(\mathrm{H})}(nl; \rho) + O(1/N)];$$

that is

$$P(nl; r) = N^{1/2}[P_{(\mathrm{H})}(nl; Nr) + O(1/N)], \tag{2}$$

and, furthermore,

$$\varepsilon_{nl,nl}/N^2 = 1/n^2 + O(1/N). \tag{3}$$

Hence, if $R$ is a scale radius of the $(nl)$ wave function and $R_{(\mathrm{H})}$ its value for hydrogen,

$$NR = R_{(\mathrm{H})} + O(1/N); \tag{4}$$

this can be written in the alternative form [compare § 7.2(4)]

$$R = R_{(\mathrm{H})}/(N - \sigma), \tag{5}$$

where $\sigma$ is $O(1)$ in $N$. Hence from formula (2)

$$R^{1/2}P(nl; r) = R_{(\mathrm{H})}{}^{1/2}P_{(\mathrm{H})}(nl; R_{(\mathrm{H})}r/R) + O(R), \tag{6}$$

$O(R)$ meaning a quantity $Q$ which, as $N \to \infty$, tends to zero in such a way that $Q/R$ remains finite.

It is convenient to write

$$r/R = s \tag{7}$$

and

$$R^{1/2}P(nl; r) = P^*(nl; s); \tag{8}$$

then (6) can be written

$$P^*(nl; s) = P^*_{(\mathrm{H})}(nl; s) + O(R). \tag{9}$$

$P^*(nl; s)$ will be called the "reduced wave function" for the value $s = r/R$ of the "reduced radius."

The result (9) indicates the form of the departures from pure scaling. For pure scaling, $P^*(nl; s)$ is independent of $N$, and so of $R$. The second term in (9) shows that the departures from pure scaling are such that, for a given value of the reduced radius $s = r/R$, the asymptotic behavior of the variation of the reduced wave function $R^{1/2}P(nl; r)$ with atomic number is such that it can be expressed as a linear variation with $R$. It is clear from formula (9) that in this context the values for hydrogen are to be regarded as the limiting values as $R \to 0$; that is, $N \to \infty$.

### 7.4. VARIATION OF REDUCED WAVE FUNCTION WITH $R$ FOR FIXED $s$

The results of the previous section suggest that a good process for interpolating wave functions would be to use the variation of the reduced wave function $P^*(nl; s) = R^{1/2}P(nl; r)$ with atomic number for fixed $s$, expressing this variation with atomic number in terms of the variation with some scale radius $R$. For each value of $s$, this variation will usually be small compared with the maximum of $|P^*(nl; s)|$ itself, and so can be plotted on a relatively open scale; use of such a plot may be the most convenient way of carrying out the interpolation.[2]

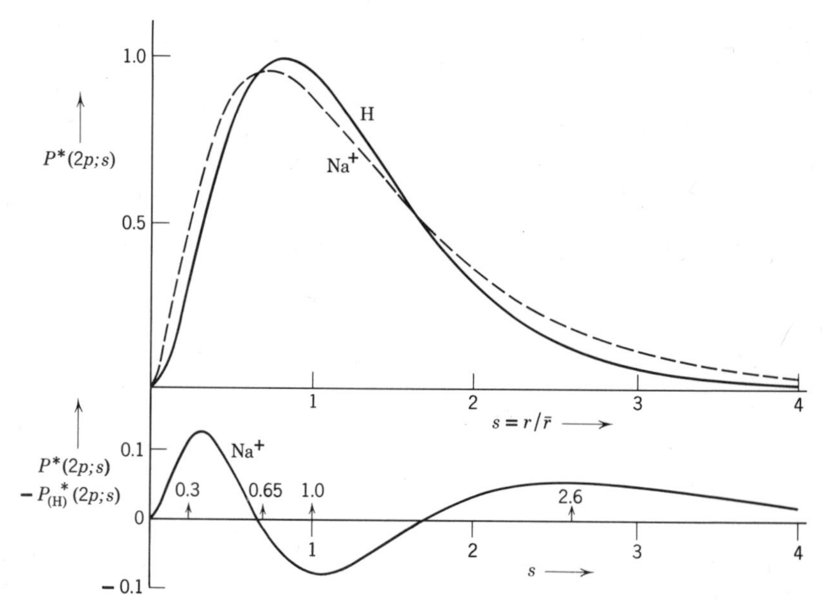


Fig. 7.1. Reduced $(2p)$ wave function $P^*(2p; s)$ against $s = r/\bar{r}$ for H and $Na^+$, and difference between these functions.

Consider, for example, the variation of the reduced $(2p)$ wave function $P^*(2p; s)$ with atomic number. Figure 7.1 shows $P^*(2p; s)$ as a function of $s$ for H and $Na^+$, the scale radius $R$ being taken as the mean radius $\bar{r} = \int_0^\infty rP^2\,dr$ [see § 7.2(1)]; it also shows the difference between these functions. The variation of $P^*(2p; s)$ with atomic number has maxima at about $s = 0.30$, 1.0, and 2.6, and is small at $s = 0.65$. For these values of $s$, the variation with $\bar{r}$ of $P^*(2p; s)$, calculated with exchange for various atoms and ions in which the $(2p)$ group is complete, is shown in Fig. 7.2; these values of $s$ are marked by arrows in Fig. 7.1.

[2] See D. R. Hartree, *Proc. Cambridge Phil. Soc.*, **51,** 684 (1955).

In Fig. 7.2, the results for different values of $s$ have been plotted from different zeros of $P^*$, so that they can be plotted on an open scale and still included in a single diagram. Straight lines have been drawn joining the points for H ($\bar{r} = 0$) and $Na^+$ ($\bar{r} = 0.796$). These lines must not be taken as implying that a linear relation is to be expected over such a large range of atomic number; they are shown only as the best means

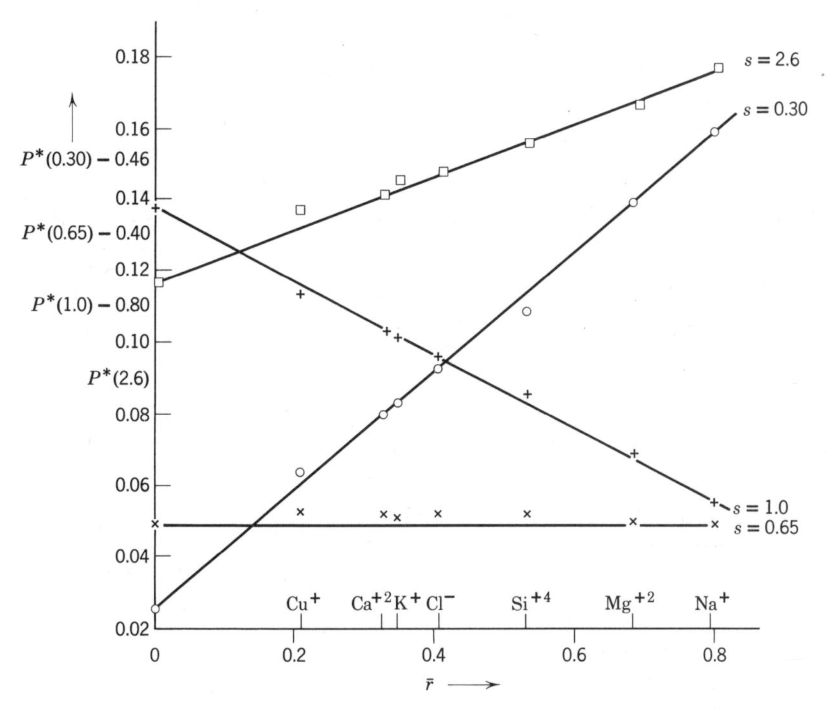


Fig. 7.2. Reduced $(2p)$ wave function, for four values of $s$, against mean radius $r$ for atoms and ions with complete $(2p)$ groups.

of exhibiting the departures from a linear relation. These departures are of the order of 0.003, the maximum value of $P^*(2p; s)$ being about 1. Thus it appears that, for a configuration in which the $(2p)$ group is complete, it should be possible to interpolate $P(2p; r)$ to about 1 part in 300 of the maximum of the wave function, or better; such estimates would provide an excellent start for a self-consistent field calculation.

It is not to be expected that the close approach to a linear variation with $R$, illustrated by Fig. 7.2, will extend to those configurations in which the $(2p)$ group is incomplete. Figure 7.3 shows an extension of

Fig. 7.2, for $s = 0.30$ only, to include results, calculated with exchange, for such configurations. As already mentioned in § 6.3, when a configuration comprising an incomplete group or incomplete groups gives more than one $(LS)$ term, the radial wave functions for different terms are slightly different. Consequently both the scale radius $\bar{r}$ and the reduced wave function $P^*(nl; s)$ are slightly different for the different $(LS)$ terms, and the points for the lowest terms of different configurations may not

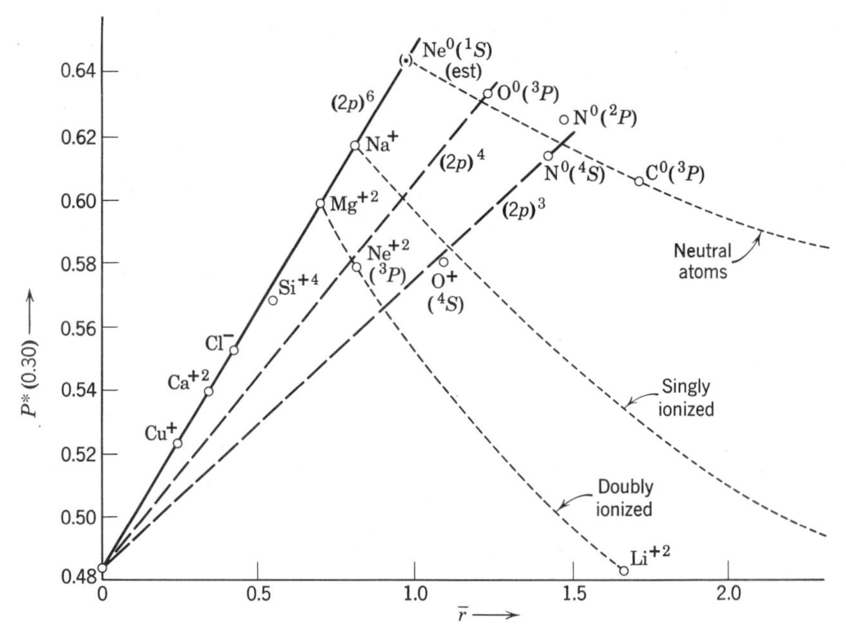


Fig. 7.3. Reduced $(2p)$ wave function for $s = 0.30$ only, against mean radius $r$ for atoms and ions with complete and incomplete $(2p)$ groups.

lie on a smooth curve. This is illustrated in Fig. 7.3. Nevertheless, a series of plots such as Fig. 7.3, for different values of $s$, would still be valuable in providing initial estimates for a self-consistent field calculation.

Similar diagrams can be drawn[3] for other values of $(nl)$, though the $(1s)$ wave function differs so little from a scaled hydrogen wave function that the other methods of estimating it are more convenient (see § 7.4.1), and the data available for drawing such diagrams for wave functions with $n = 3$ are much fewer than for $n = 2$. Some results for the $(3d)$

[3] Data for drawing such diagrams are given in Tables A1 to A7 of Appendix 2. See Appendix 3 for further notes on use of such diagrams.

wave function for various singly ionized atoms are shown in Fig. 7.4; the reduced wave functions $\bar{r}^{1/2}P(3d; r)$ for $Ti^+(3d)^3$, $Mn^+(3d)^6$, and $Cu^+(3d)^{10}$ are so nearly the same that the curves for these ions cannot be

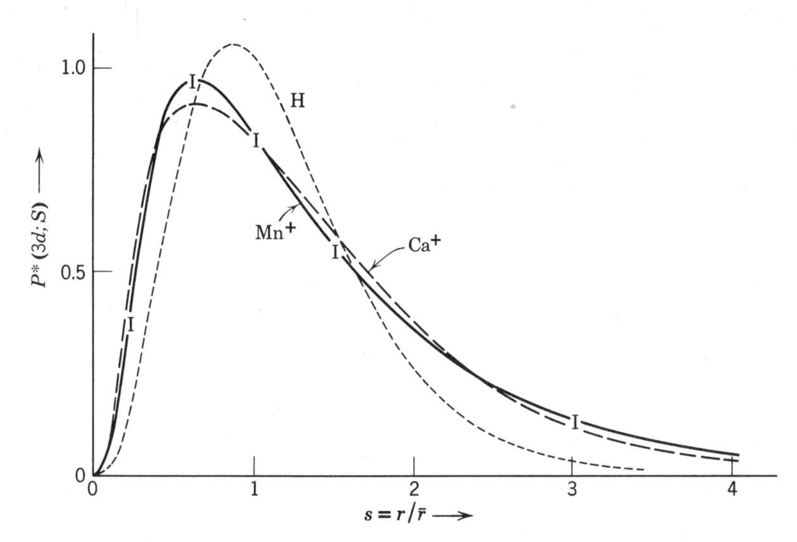


**Fig. 7.4.** Reduced (3*d*) wave function against *s* for singly ionized atoms. The results for $Ti^+$, $Mn^+$ and $Cu^+$ are all included in the range indicated by the marks I.

drawn distinctly separate on the scale of the figure; they are, however, very considerably different from the curve for hydrogen.

### 7.4.1. THE (1*s*) WAVE FUNCTION

Except for the lightest atoms, the (1*s*) wave function is so nearly hydrogen-like that for it a different method of interpolation, based on the departure from a scaled hydrogen wave function, is more convenient than the method of § 7.4.

Formula § 7.3(2) suggests that for such nearly hydrogen-like functions

$$N^{1/2}[P(nl; r) - N^{1/2}P_{(\mathrm{H})}(nl; Nr)] \tag{1}$$

is approximately the same function of $Nr$, independent of the atomic number. A more convenient function to work with is obtained by replacing $N$ by $N - \sigma$, where $\sigma$ is a screening number whose exact value is unimportant so long as the same value is taken in reducing the known results of previous calculations and in obtaining the estimates for the new calculation; 0.3 or 0.4 is a good working value. Also for small ranges of

$N$ the variation of the factor $N^{1/2}$ outside the square bracket in (1) is small, and its omission saves a certain amount of calculation. Thus the most convenient procedure is to carry out the interpolation in terms of the quantity

$$[P(1s; r) - (N - \sigma)^{1/2} P_{(\mathrm{H})}(1s; (N - \sigma)r)] \tag{2}$$

regarded as a function of $(N - \sigma)r$. For the $(1s)$ wave function the greatest value of the difference (2) may be only 1 per cent of the maximum value of $|P|$, and no great refinement in carrying out the interpolation is necessary. Examples of plots of the function (2) are shown in Fig. 7.5.

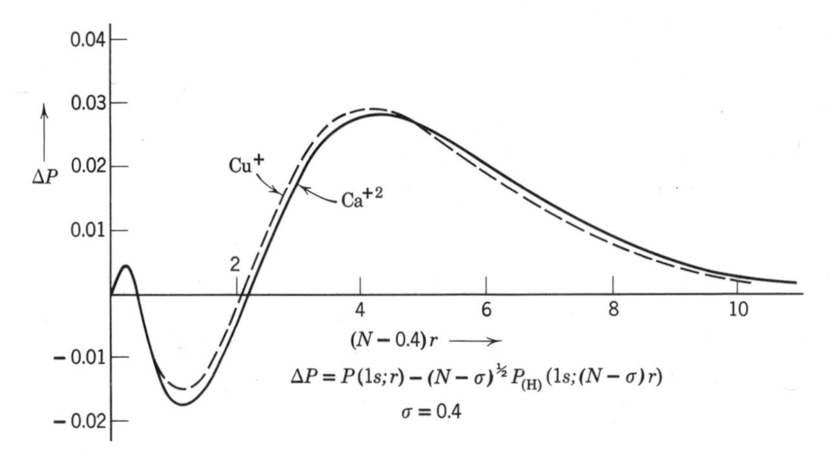


Fig. 7.5. Difference $\Delta P$ between $(1s)$ wave functions for Ca and Cu and screened hydrogen-like $(1s)$ wave function.

## 7.5. VARIATION OF THE SCREENING NUMBERS WITH ATOMIC NUMBER

The argument of § 7.3, carried to one higher order in $(1/N)$ (see § 7.6), indicates that for a given $(nl)$ the screening number $\sigma$ tends to a limiting value, $\sigma_0$ say, as $N \to \infty$, and that, asymptotically in $N$,

$$\sigma = \sigma_0 + O(1/N) = \sigma_0 + O(R). \tag{1}$$

This suggests that a useful interpolation for $\sigma$ might be based on a plot of $\sigma$ against $R$. Since, by definition of $\sigma$,

$$R = R_{(\mathrm{H})}/(N - \sigma), \tag{2}$$

the points in such a diagram fall on hyperbolas $(N - \sigma)R = R_{(\mathrm{H})}$, which correspond to the ordinates of a plot of $\sigma$ against $N$ or against $(1/N)$. The purpose of plotting against $R$ rather than $(1/N)$ is to get a nearly linear variation over a larger range of atomic number.

If the mean radius $\bar{r}$ is taken as the scale radius $R$, the values for hydrogen are given by the simple formula[4]

$$\bar{r}_{(\mathrm{H})} = \tfrac{1}{2}[3n^2 - l(l+1)] \tag{3}$$

which gives

$$\left.\begin{array}{lccccccccc} (nl) = & (1s) & (2s) & (2p) & (3s) & (3p) & (3d) & (4s) & (4p) & (4d) \\ \bar{r}_{(\mathrm{H})} = & 1.5 & 6 & 5 & 13.5 & 12.5 & 10.5 & 24 & 23 & 21 \end{array}\right\} \tag{4}$$

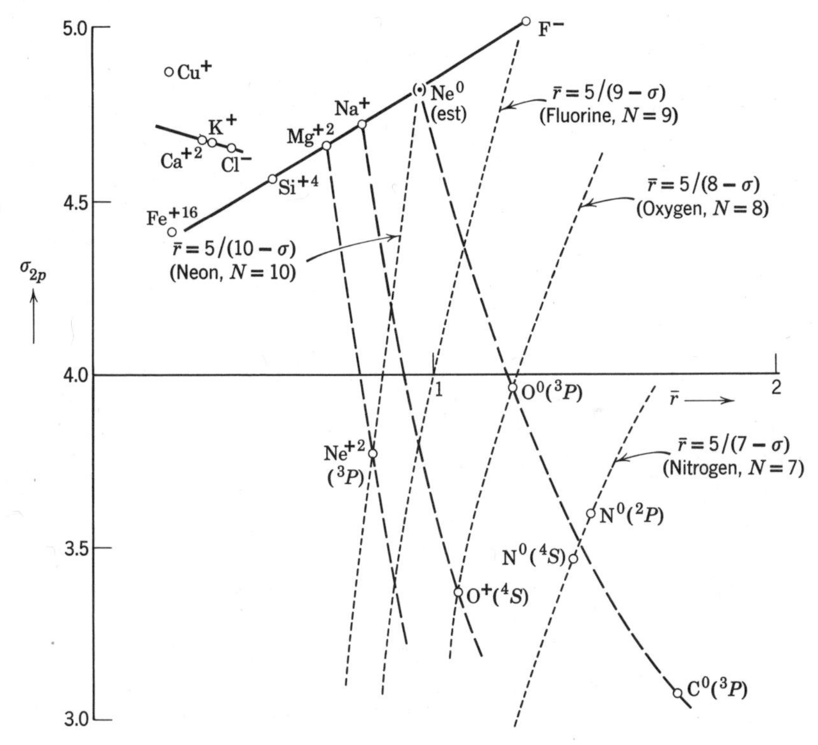


Fig. 7.6. Screening numbers $\sigma_{2p}$ for $(2p)$ wave function, against $\bar{r}$.

Figure 7.6 shows a plot of $\sigma_{2p}$ against $\bar{r}$, for the solutions of Fock's equations of a number of atoms, both with complete and with incomplete $(2p)$ groups. A qualitative interpretation can be given of some of the features of the results for atoms and ions with complete $(2p)^6$ groups. In the ten-electron isoelectronic sequence, the $(2p)$ wave function contracts

[4] E. U. Condon and G. H. Shortley, *Theory of Atomic Spectra*, Table $2^5$, Cambridge (1935).

relatively to the ($2s$) wave function as the atomic number increases, so that the screening effect of the electrons in the $(2s)^2$ group on the ($2p$) wave function decreases; this is represented by the decrease of $\sigma_{2p}$ with $\bar{r}$ in the sequence $Na^+$, $Mg^{+2}$, $Si^{+4}$. Although the ($3s$), ($3p$), and ($3d$) wave functions lie mainly outside the ($2p$) wave function, the ($3s$) and ($3p$) have subsidiary maxima in the region where the ($2p$) wave function is large, and these subsidiary maxima increase in prominence as the atomic number increases and these wave functions become more hydrogen-like; this is represented by the increasing contribution to $\sigma_{2p}$ from the $(3s)^2(3p)^6$ group as $\bar{r}$ decreases in the 18-electron isoelectronic sequence. And the value of $\sigma_{2p}$ for $Cu^+$ indicates that the $(3d)^{10}$ group, although lying mainly outside the ($2p$) wave function, still exerts a small but appreciable screening on it.

For the light atoms, the loci of constant $N$, namely

$$\bar{r} = 5/(N - \sigma) \tag{5}$$

[see (2) and (4)] are drawn dotted, and approximate loci for different degrees of ionization are drawn as broken curves. From the intersections of these two sets of curves, approximate values of $\sigma$ for atoms and ions for which calculations have not been carried out can be estimated, and $\bar{r}$ then found from (5). Similar diagrams can be drawn up for other ($nl$) values. Data for drawing such diagrams are given in Table A1 of Appendix 2.

Slater[5] has given some rough rules for estimating screening numbers for the different ($nl$) groups in different configurations. The values given in Table A1 can be regarded as improvements on the values given by these rules. One feature in which the results given in Table A1 differ from those given by Slater's rules is the difference $\sigma_{2p} - \sigma_{2s}$ between the screening numbers for the ($2s$) and ($2p$) wave functions, which, for atoms in which both these groups are complete, lies between 1.0 and 1.45, whereas Slater's rules make $\sigma_{2p} = \sigma_{2s}$.

It has already been mentioned in § 7.2 that, since the ($nl$) wave functions in a many-electron atom are not hydrogen-like, the appropriate screening number $\sigma$, for a given wave function in a given atom, depends on the particular atomic property which one wishes to express by its value for a hydrogen-like wave function for atomic number $(N - \sigma)$. The ($3d$) wave function for atoms of the first long period provides a striking example. If $r_M$ is the radius of the maximum of $|P|$, then $r_M/\bar{r}$ is about 0.63 for the ($3d$) wave function of $Ti^+$, $Mn^+$, and $Cu^+$, whereas for hydrogen it is 6/7; that is, about 0.86. Let $\bar{\sigma}$ be the screening number for $\bar{r}$ and $\sigma_M$ that for $r_M$; then

$$(N - \bar{\sigma})\bar{r} = 10.5, \qquad (N - \sigma_M)r_M = 9,$$

[5] J. C. Slater, *Phys. Rev.*, **36**, 57 (1930); see also J. C. Slater, *Quantum Theory of Matter*, Appendix 13, McGraw-Hill, New York (1951).

so that

$$(N - \sigma_M)/(N - \bar{\sigma}) = (6/7)/0.63 = 1.36;$$

that is,

$$\bar{\sigma} - \sigma_M = 0.36(N - \bar{\sigma}).$$

For $Mn^+$ this gives $\bar{\sigma} - \sigma_M = 3$ approximately. So large a difference between the screening numbers appropriate to different atomic properties

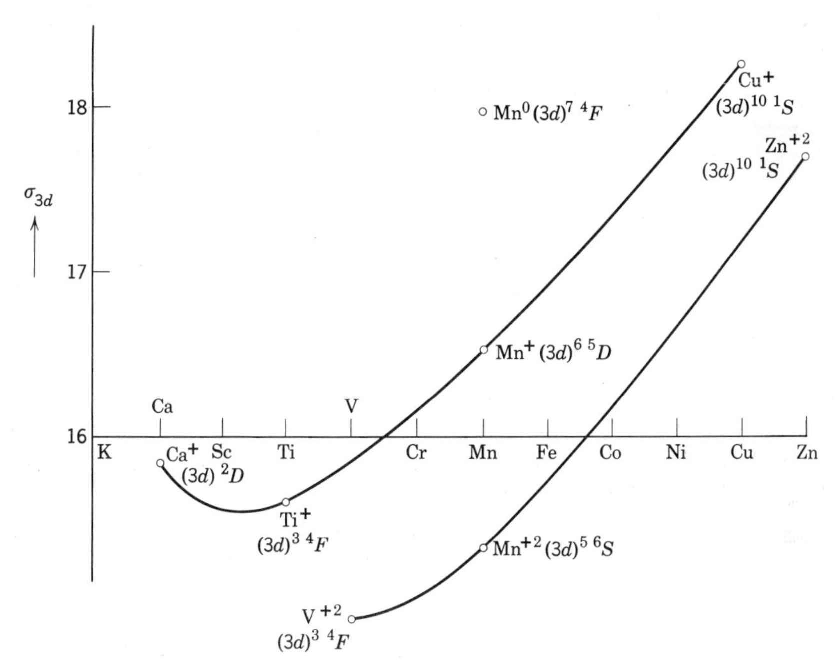


Fig. 7.7. Screening numbers $\sigma_{3d}$ for $(3d)$ wave function, against atomic number for first long period.

may be unusual. However, in comparing values of $\sigma$ obtained by different methods or from different atomic properties, it is as well to remember that such differences may occur. The values of $\sigma$ given in Table A1, or interpolated from them, are intended explicitly for the purpose of obtaining values of $\bar{r}$, and not for obtaining values of other properties of the wave functions.

Figure 7.7 shows the variation of $\sigma_{3d}$, defined by formula § 7.2(7) with $R = \bar{r}$, for some atoms and ions of the first long period. In these atoms the $(3d)$ group is incomplete, and no approach to the asymptotic variation with $\bar{r}$ as $N \to \infty$ is to be expected [compare Fig. 7.6 for the $(2p)$ group];

so the values of $\sigma_{3d}$ are plotted against the atomic number $N$ rather than against $\bar{r}$. The points for the singly and doubly ionized atoms are joined by continuous curves, but there is no significance in points on these curves other than those for integral values of $N$; furthermore the points for integral values of $N$ refer to different $(LS)$ states, so that, if they were all known, the curves through them might not be as smooth as those shown in Fig. 7.7. However, these curves should be useful for interpolation purposes.

The decrease of $\sigma_{3d}$ with increasing atomic number $N$ at the calcium end of the sequence of singly ionized atoms may seem surprising at first sight. It results from the considerable contraction of the $(3d)$ wave function relative to the $(3s)^2$ and $(3p)^6$ wave functions as $N$ increases, so that for the $(3d)$ wave function the decrease of the screening of the nucleus by the $(3s)^2$ and $(3p)^6$ groups more than compensates, at first, for the contribution to the screening from the electrons added in the $(3d)$ group.

This shows that although, asymptotically for large $N$, $\sigma_{nl}$ can be regarded as the sum of contributions from the occupied $(n'l')$ wave function, these contributions depending on $(nl)$ and $(n'l')$ only, such a treatment of the screening numbers may give only a rough approximation when applied to the outer wave functions of neutral and slightly ionized atoms.

## 7.6. FURTHER EXAMINATION OF THE BEHAVIOR OF THE RADIAL WAVE FUNCTIONS AS $N \to \infty$

The value of diagrams such as Figs. 7.2–7.4, 7.6, and 7.7 for interpolating wave functions, especially for the higher stages of ionization, would be increased if there were available the limiting values $\sigma_0$ of $\sigma$ as $N \to \infty$ ($\bar{r} \to 0$) in Fig. 7.6 and in similar diagrams for other values of $(nl)$, and the slopes at $\bar{r} = 0$ of the curves of $P^*(nl; s)$ against $\bar{r}$ for different configurations.

These results can be obtained[6] by extending the analysis of § 7.3, by considering $N^{-1/2}P(nl; r)$ expanded in inverse powers of $N$,

$$P(nl; r) = N^{1/2}[P_{(\mathrm{H})}(nl; \rho) + (1/N)Q(nl; \rho) + O(1/N^2)], \tag{1}$$

and determining the functions $Q(nl; \rho)$. For, in terms of such an expansion

$$\begin{aligned} N\bar{r} = N\int_0^\infty rP^2\,dr &= \int_0^\infty \rho\left[P_{(\mathrm{H})}(nl; \rho) + \frac{1}{N}Q(nl; \rho)\right]^2 d\rho + O\left(\frac{1}{N^2}\right) \\ &= \bar{r}_{(\mathrm{H})} + \frac{2}{N}\int_0^\infty \rho P_{(\mathrm{H})}(nl; \rho)Q(nl; \rho)\,d\rho + O\left(\frac{1}{N^2}\right). \end{aligned} \tag{2}$$

[6] See C. Froese, *Proc. Roy. Soc.* (in press). Figs. 7.6, 7.7 were drawn before the results of this work were available.

Also by definition of $\sigma$, $\bar{r} = \bar{r}_{(\mathrm{H})}/(N-\sigma)$; so

$$N\bar{r} = \bar{r}_{(\mathrm{H})}/(1-\sigma/N) = \bar{r}_{(\mathrm{H})}[1+\sigma_0/N + O(1/N^2)], \tag{3}$$

and, by comparison of (2) and (3),

$$\sigma_0 = \frac{2}{\bar{r}_{(\mathrm{H})}} \int_0^\infty \rho P_{(\mathrm{H})}(nl;\rho) Q(nl;\rho)\, d\rho. \tag{4}$$

We shall see later that $Q(nl;\rho)$ is the sum of contributions from the different $(nl)$ groups; so $\sigma_0$ can similarly be regarded as the sum of such contributions.

Furthermore, the reduced radius $s$ is

$$s = r/\bar{r} = Nr/N\bar{r} = \rho(1-\sigma/N)/\bar{r}_{(\mathrm{H})},$$

so that

$$\rho = \bar{r}_{(\mathrm{H})}s + \sigma_0\rho/N + O(1/N^2) \tag{5}$$

and

$$P_{(\mathrm{H})}(nl;\rho) = P_{(\mathrm{H})}(nl;\bar{r}_{(\mathrm{H})}s) + (\sigma_0\rho/N)P'_{(\mathrm{H})}(nl;\rho) + O(1/N^2). \tag{6}$$

Also, from formula (3),

$$(N\bar{r})^{1/2} = [\bar{r}_{(\mathrm{H})}]^{1/2}[1+\tfrac{1}{2}(\sigma_0/N) + O(1/N^2)]. \tag{7}$$

From formula (1), the reduced wave function $P^*(nl;s) = \bar{r}^{1/2}P(nl;r)$ has for large $N$ the form

$$P^*(nl;s) = (N\bar{r})^{1/2}[P_{(\mathrm{H})}(nl;\rho) + (1/N)Q(nl;\rho) + O(1/N^2)],$$

and substitution of expressions (6) and (7) gives

$$P^*(nl;s) = [\bar{r}_{(\mathrm{H})}]^{1/2}P_{(\mathrm{H})}(nl;\bar{r}_{(\mathrm{H})}s)$$
$$+ (1/N)[r_{(\mathrm{H})}]^{1/2}\{\sigma_0[\tfrac{1}{2}P_{(\mathrm{H})}(nl;\rho) + \rho P'(nl;\rho)] + Q(nl;\rho)\} + O(1/N^2). \tag{8}$$

Also, from formula (3),

$$\bar{r}/\bar{r}_{(\mathrm{H})} = 1/N + O(1/N^2),$$

so that, if we extend formula § 7.3(9), with $R = \bar{r}$, by writing

$$P^*(nl;s) = P^*_{(\mathrm{H})}(nl;s) + \bar{r}Q^*(nl;s) + O(\bar{r}^2), \tag{9}$$

it follows from (8) that

$$Q^*(nl;s) = (1/r_{(\mathrm{H})})^{1/2}\{\sigma_0[\tfrac{1}{2}P_{(\mathrm{H})}(nl;\rho) + \rho P'_{(\mathrm{H})}(nl;\rho)] + Q(nl;\rho)\}, \tag{10}$$

the relation between $\rho$ and $s$ being given by formula (5) which, to the order required here, becomes $\rho = \bar{r}_{(\mathrm{H})}s$. The function $Q^*(nl;s)$, for a fixed $s$, gives the slope, at $\bar{r} = 0$, of the curve of $P^*(nl;s)$ against $\bar{r}$ for that value of $s$. Thus formulae (4) and (10) give, in terms of the function $Q(nl;\rho)$, the information required for improving the information, for large $N$, contained in diagrams such as Figs. 7.2–7.4, 7.6, 7.7.

The equations satisfied by the functions $Q(nl; r)$ are obtained by substituting the asymptotic forms (1) for $P(nl; r)$ in the equations for the radial wave functions, dividing out a factor $N^{1/2}$, and then separating out the terms of order $1/N$.

Consider the equation for $P(2p; r)$ in a ten-electron configuration [see § 3.6.1(2)], which in full is

$$\left\{\frac{d^2}{dr^2}+\frac{2}{r}\left[N-\Sigma_{n'l'}q(n'l')Y_0(n'l',n'l';r)+Y_0(2p,2p;r)+\tfrac{2}{5}Y_2(2p,2p;r)\right]\right.$$
$$\left.-\varepsilon_{2p,2p}-\frac{6}{r^2}\right\}P(2p;r)+\frac{2}{r}\left[Y_1(1s,2p;r)P(1s;r)+Y_1(2s,2p;r)P(2s;r)\right]=0. \tag{11}$$

Following the notation of § 7.2, let $Y_k(\mathrm{H}; nl, n'l'; r)$ be the function $Y_k(nl, n'l'; r)$ calculated from hydrogen $(nl)$ and $(n'l')$ wave functions. Then substitution of formula (1) in the integral for $Y_k(nl, n'l'; r)$ gives

$$Y_k(nl, n'l'; r) = Y_k(\mathrm{H}; nl, n'l'; Nr) + O(1/N). \tag{12}$$

Furthermore, let

$$\varepsilon_{nl,nl}/N^2 = 1/n^2 + \Delta\varepsilon/N + O(1/N^2). \tag{13}$$

Substitution of (1), (12), and (13) in (11) gives, in terms of $\rho = Nr$ as independent variable,

$$\left\{\frac{d^2}{dr^2}+\frac{2}{\rho}\left[1-\frac{1}{N}\left(\Sigma_{n'l'}q(n'l')Y_0(\mathrm{H};n'l',n'l';\rho)-Y_0(\mathrm{H};2p,2p;\rho)\right.\right.\right.$$
$$\left.\left.\left.-\tfrac{2}{5}Y_2(\mathrm{H};2p,2p;\rho)\right)\right]-\left(\frac{1}{4}+\frac{\Delta\varepsilon}{N}\right)-\frac{6}{\rho^2}\right\}\left[P_{(\mathrm{H})}(2p;\rho)+\frac{1}{N}Q(2p;\rho)\right]$$
$$+\frac{2}{\rho}\frac{1}{N}\left[Y_1(\mathrm{H};1s,2p;\rho)P_{(\mathrm{H})}(1s;\rho)+Y_1(\mathrm{H};2s,2p;\rho)P_{(\mathrm{H})}(2s;\rho)\right]$$
$$+O\left(\frac{1}{N^2}\right)=0.$$

The terms of zero order in $(1/N)$ vanish identically, and the terms of first order in $(1/N)$ give

$$\left(\frac{d^2}{d\rho^2}+\frac{2}{\rho}-\frac{1}{4}-\frac{6}{\rho^2}\right)Q(2p;\rho)=\frac{2}{\rho}\{[\Sigma_{n'l'}q(n'l')Y_0(\mathrm{H};n'l',n'l';\rho)$$
$$-Y_0(\mathrm{H};2p,2p;\rho)-\tfrac{2}{5}Y_2(\mathrm{H};2p,2p;\rho)]\,P_{(\mathrm{H})}(2p;\rho)$$
$$-Y_1(\mathrm{H};1s,2p;\rho)P_{(\mathrm{H})}(1s;\rho)-Y_1(\mathrm{H};2s,2p;\rho)P_{(\mathrm{H})}(2s;\rho)\}$$
$$+\Delta\varepsilon P_{(\mathrm{H})}(2p;\rho). \tag{14}$$

The required solution of equation (14) is that for which $Q = 0$ at $\rho = 0$ and $Q \to 0$ as $\rho \to \infty$, and for which $P(nl; r)$ given by formula (1) is normalized. The parameter $\Delta\varepsilon$ is adjustable to enable the boundary conditions to be satisfied, but a solution satisfying the boundary conditions is not unique, since the complementary function of equation (14) is just $P_{(\mathrm{H})}(nl; \rho)$ which also satisfies them. However, the normalization condition on $P(nl; r)$ defines a unique solution. This condition is

$$\begin{aligned} 1 &= \int_0^\infty P^2(nl; r)\, dr \\ &= \int_0^\infty \left[ P^2(nl; \rho) + \left(\frac{2}{N}\right) P_{(\mathrm{H})}(nl; \rho) Q(nl; \rho) + O\left(\frac{1}{N^2}\right)\right] d\rho, \end{aligned}$$

and the terms of order $(1/N)$ can only vanish if

$$\int_0^\infty P_{(\mathrm{H})}(nl; \rho) Q(nl; \rho)\, d\rho = 0; \tag{15}$$

that is, we require the solution of equation (14) which satisfies the boundary conditions and which is orthogonal to $P_{(\mathrm{H})}(nl; \rho)$.

From equation (14) it follows that $Q(nl; \rho)$ can be regarded as a sum of contributions from the separate terms in the braces {} on the right-hand side, $\Delta\varepsilon$ being also a sum of such contributions. For example,[7] we can consider the effect of the exchange terms alone as being a function $Q_x(2p; \rho)$ satisfying the equation

$$\begin{aligned} &\left(\frac{d^2}{d\rho^2} + \frac{2}{\rho} - \frac{1}{4} - \frac{6}{\rho^2}\right) Q_x(2p; \rho) \\ &\quad = -\frac{2}{\rho}[Y_1(\mathrm{H}; 1s, 2p; \rho) P_{(\mathrm{H})}(1s; \rho) + Y_1(\mathrm{H}; 2s, 2p; \rho) P_{(\mathrm{H})}(2s; \rho)] \\ &\qquad + \Delta\varepsilon_x P_{(\mathrm{H})}(2p; \rho), \end{aligned} \tag{16}$$

with the boundary conditions $Q_x = 0$ at $\rho = 0$ and $Q \to 0$ as $\rho \to \infty$, and orthogonal to $P_{(\mathrm{H})}(2p; \rho)$.

The value of $\Delta\varepsilon$ in (14), or $\Delta\varepsilon_x$ in (16), can be found as follows. Consider equation (16) as an example. $P_{(\mathrm{H})}(2p; \rho)$ satisfies the homogeneous equation

$$\left(\frac{d^2}{d\rho^2} + \frac{2}{\rho} - \frac{1}{4} - \frac{6}{\rho^2}\right) P_{(\mathrm{H})}(2p; \rho) = 0 \tag{17}$$

corresponding to equation (16). Multiply equation (16) by $P_{(\mathrm{H})}(2p; \rho)$

[7] See D. R. Hartree and W. Hartree, *Proc. Roy. Soc.*, **166**, 450, text following equation (6) (1938). See further C. Froese, *loc. cit.*

and equation (13) by $-Q_x(2p;\rho)$, add, and integrate from 0 to $\infty$ in $\rho$. The terms on the left-hand side cancel on integration; also

$$\int_0^\infty Y_1(\mathrm{H};\,1s,2p;\rho)P_{(\mathrm{H})}(1s;\rho)P_{(\mathrm{H})}(2p;\rho)\,d\rho = G_1(\mathrm{H};\,1s,2p), \quad (18)$$

and similarly for the integral resulting from the second term on the right of (16); and $\int_0^\infty P_{(\mathrm{H})}(2p;\rho)\,d\rho = 1$. Hence

$$\Delta\varepsilon_x = 2[G_1(\mathrm{H};\,1s,2p) + G_1(\mathrm{H};\,2s,2p)]. \quad (19)$$

The equation for $P(2p;r)$ in a ten-electron configuration has been taken as an example here; the equations for other radial wave functions, and in other configurations, can clearly be treated similarly.

### 7.7. INTERPOLATION OF CONTRIBUTIONS TO $Z$

For calculations without exchange, the required starting point is a set of estimates of contributions to $Z$. These can be obtained by a

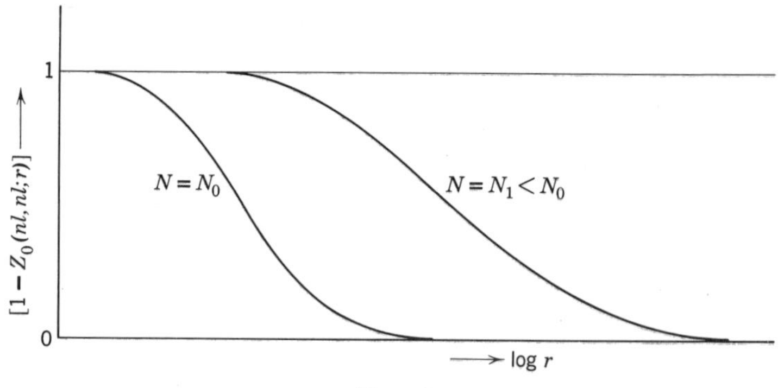


Fig. 7.8

process similar to that of § 7.4, but the following alternative process, due to Mrs. E. C. Ridley,[8] seems simpler.

If the functions $[1 - Z_0(nl, nl;r)]$ for different atomic numbers were related by the pure-scaling relation § 7.2(5), the graphs of $[1 - Z_0(nl,nl;r)]$ against $\log r$ would all consist of the same curve displaced in the direction of the axis of $\log r$. Actually the graph for smaller $N$ is appreciably less steep than that for greater $N$ (Fig. 7.8). This departure from pure scaling can be expressed approximately by a change in scale of $\log r$.

[8] E. C. Ridley, *Proc. Cambridge Phil. Soc.*, **51**, 693 (1955).

Let $r(z)$ stand for the radius at which the function $[1 - Z_0(nl, nl; r)]$ has the value $z$; that is, $r(z)$ is the function inverse to the function $[1 - Z_0(nl, nl; r)]$. And, as before, let subscript (H) indicate a value for the hydrogen atom.

A shift of the curve of $[1 - Z_0]$ against $\log r$, without change in scale, can be represented by

$$\log r(0.5) = -\beta + \log r_{(\mathrm{H})}(0.5), \tag{1}$$

and a change of scale of $\log r$ can be represented by

$$\log r(z) - \log r(0.5) = \alpha[\log r_{(\mathrm{H})}(z) - \log r_{(\mathrm{H})}(0.5)]. \tag{2}$$

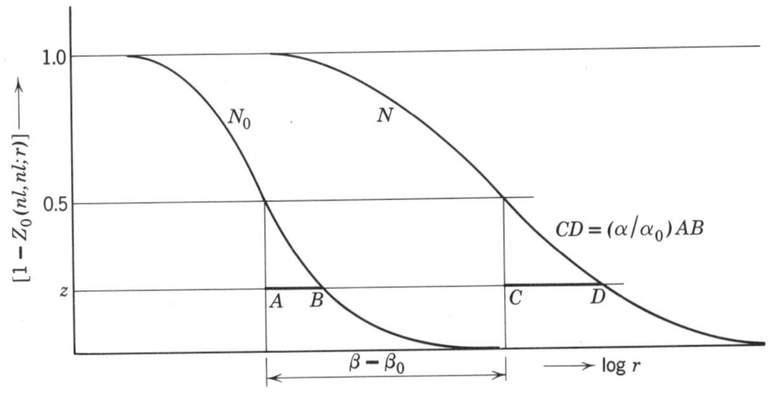


Fig. 7.9

It is found that the value of $\alpha$ determined from (2) varies little over the range $z = 0.2$ to $0.8$; a good working value is given by

$$\log r(0.6) - \log r(0.4) = \alpha[\log_{(\mathrm{H})}(0.6) - \log_{(\mathrm{H})}(0.4)]. \tag{3}$$

Then, if as in § 7.2 subscript 0 refers to an atom for which results are known,

$$\log r(0.5) = (\beta_0 - \beta) + \log r_0(0.5),$$

$$\log r(z) - \log r(0.5) = (\alpha/\alpha_0)[\log r_0(z) - \log r_0(0.5)],$$

(the latter only being approximate), whence

$$\log r(z) = (\beta_0 - \beta) + \log r_0(0.5) + (\alpha/\alpha_0)[\log r_0(z) - \log r_0(0.5)]. \tag{4}$$

The significance of this formula is illustrated graphically in Fig. 7.9. The values of $\alpha$ and $\beta$, for each $(nl)$, are interpolated from the values for neighboring atoms. Then, on the right-hand side everything is known, and formula (4) gives (approximately) $r(z)$ as a function of $z$, from which $Z_0(nl, nl; r)$ as a function of $r$ follows by inverse interpolation. This process aims at determining $Z_0(nl, nl; r)$ well where it is changing most rapidly, and has been found to give very satisfactory estimates.

In using this method, the median radius $r(0.5)$ is a more convenient quantity than $\bar{r}$ to take as the scale radius $R$, for the value of $r(0.5)$ can be obtained by interpolation in a table of $[1 - Z_0(nl, nl; r)]$ whereas evaluation of $\bar{r}$ requires a further integration; and the value of $r(0.5)$ is required in the work in any case. If the scale radius $R$ is taken as $r(0.5)$, the relation § 7.2(6) defining $\sigma$ becomes

$$\log r(0.5) = \log r_{(\mathrm{H})}(0.5) - \log (N - \sigma),$$

and comparison with (1) gives

$$\beta = \log (N - \sigma);$$

so the term $\beta_0 - \beta$ in (4) can be written alternatively,

$$\beta_0 - \beta = \log [(N_0 - \sigma_0)/(N - \sigma)],$$

and the most convenient way to obtain a value of this term is through an interpolation for $\sigma$.

Data for using this method of estimating contributions to $Z$ are given in Mrs. Ridley's paper.[8]

### 7.8. THOMAS–FERMI APPROXIMATION

An approximation to the total potential of the atomic field can be obtained by an argument given independently by Thomas and by Fermi.[9] This is based on the application of Fermi–Dirac statistics to the assembly of electrons in the field of the nucleus and of their own change distribution. It leads to an equation for the potential $V(r)$ of this field, which has the property that, for neutral atoms of different atomic numbers $N$, $rV(r)/N$ is the same function of $N^{1/3}r$ for all values of $N$. A table of this function is given in Condon and Shortley.[10]

The Thomas–Fermi approximation can be used in two ways. First, the tables of the solution of the Thomas–Fermi equation can be used to give

[9] L. H. Thomas, *Proc. Cambridge Phil. Soc.*, **23**, 542 (1927); E. Fermi, *Z. Physik*, **48**, 73 (1928). See also L. Brillouin, L'Atome de Thomas–Fermi, *Actualités sci. et ind.*, **160** (1934); E. U. Condon and G. H. Shortley, *Theory of Atomic Spectra*, § 2[14], Cambridge (1935). For a very full account of the Thomas–Fermi approximation and developments of it, see P. Gombas, *Die Statistische Theorie des Atomes and ihre Anwendungen*, Springer, Vienna (1949).

[10] *Loc. cit.*

$V(r)$ or, second, the Thomas–Fermi relation $rV(r)/N = f(N^{1/3}r)$ can be used as a scaling relation for the *total* potential, in the place of estimates of contributions to the potential from the different $(nl)$ groups.

However, in the Thomas–Fermi approximation in its simple form, the potential of the field acting on each electron is taken to be the potential of the field of the nucleus and of *all* the electrons, whereas in the self-consistent field process the contribution to the potential from one electron in an $(nl)$ wave function is omitted from the potential used in calculating that wave function. For this reason a set of estimates of contributions to the field from different $(nl)$ groups is a more appropriate starting point for such a calculation than an estimate of the total potential $V(r)$ only.

The Thomas–Fermi approximation can be expected to be most accurate for atoms with many electrons and for values of $r$ not too large. It does not seem to give a good approximation in the outer regions of atoms, even with many electrons.

The solution of the Thomas–Fermi equation for positive ions has been considered by Baker[11] and the argument has been extended by Vallarta and Rosen[12] to include the relativistic variation of mass with velocity.

[11] E. B. Baker, *Phys. Rev.*, **36**, 630 (1930); see also discussion of this paper by E. Guth and R. E. Peierls, *Phys. Rev.*, **37**, 217 (1931).

[12] M. Vallarta and M. Rosen, *Phys. Rev.*, **41**, 708 (1932).

# 8. ENERGY RELATIONS

## 8.1. THE TOTAL ENERGY AND CONTRIBUTIONS TO IT

Two aspects of the quantity $E' = \int \Phi^* H \Phi \, d\tau / \int \Phi^* \Phi \, d\tau$ have already been pointed out in Chapter 2. One is the aspect of $E'$ as an approximate energy value for the whole atomic system, derived from the approximate wave function $\Phi$, another is the aspect of $E'$ as a functional of $\Phi$ whose stationary character is used to determine the "best" approximate wave function among functions of a specified class. This second aspect is the more prominent in the evaluation of atomic structures. However, given a function $\Phi$ so determined, it may be required to evaluate the corresponding approximate energy $E'$, or a contribution to it.

Except perhaps for the light atoms, the total energy is not a quantity of much interest. Even though the value of $E'$ has been specified as the criterion by which we assess whether one approximate wave function is "better" than another, this assessment on the basis of this criterion must be used with discretion. For example, since the electrons in the $(1s)^2$ group are relatively tightly bound, a small improvement of the wave function as far as this group is concerned (for example, by including the dependence of $\Phi$ on the distance $r_{ij}$ between the electrons of this group only) might have a much greater influence on the total energy than a similar improvement for the wave function of an outer group (say the $(4s)^2$ group of natural calcium) which would be much more important for many atomic properties, such as transition probabilities in the optical spectrum.

However, what are usually required are energy differences within the set of terms for a single degree of ionization, or between a term of one degree of ionization and the normal state of some higher degree of ionization, usually one having a configuration of complete groups. For example, for calcium we might require the energies of the $(4s)\ {}^2S$ term of $Ca^+$, and the $(4s)^2\ {}^1S$, $(4s)(4p)\ {}^3P$ and ${}^1P$, and $(4p)^2\ {}^3P$, ${}^1D$ and ${}^1S$ terms of neutral Ca, relative to the normal state of $Ca^{+2}$.

Let $E_{(i)}$, $E_{(ii)}$, and $E_{(iii)}$ stand for the three kinds of contributions to $E'$ listed in § 6.4. The wave functions of the core of complete groups are usually only slightly affected by the addition of electrons in wave functions lying mainly outside the core; also for the core alone, $E' = E_{(i)}$, and the wave functions of the ion consisting of the core alone are determined by making $E_{(i)}$ stationary with respect to variations in them. Hence the variations of $E_{(i)}$ with degree of ionization are small, and may well be negligible, and then the only energy differences that have to be calculated are those arising from the contributions $E_{(ii)}$ and $E_{(iii)}$ to $E'$. We shall see in § 8.2 that this simplifies the calculation of $E'$ considerably.

### 8.2. SUBSTITUTION IN THE $I$ INTEGRALS

Whether the total energy or only the contribution of $E_{(ii)}$ and $E_{(iii)}$ to it from the outer groups is required, this quantity could be calculated from the solutions $P(nl; r)$ of Fock's equations by evaluating the integrals $I$, $F_k$, and $G_k$ which occur in the expression for $E'$, and substituting the values in this expression. However, the integrand of the $I$ integral

$$I(nl) = -\frac{1}{2}\int_0^\infty P(nl; r)\left[\frac{d^2}{dr^2} + \frac{2N}{r} - \frac{l(l+1)}{r^2}\right] P(nl; r)\, dr \qquad (1)$$

[see § 3.4(2)] involves the second derivative of $P(nl; r)$. In the process of determining the solution of the radial wave equation which satisfies the boundary conditions and is normalized, this second derivative of the final solution $P(nl; r)$ need never be evaluated. It could be evaluated numerically by substitution of this solution in the radial wave equation, but it is more satisfactory, and leads to a simpler formula to evaluate, to carry out the substitution for $d^2P/dr^2$ from the radial wave equation algebraically.

Whether or not the $(nl)$ group is complete, the terms in $E'$ depending on $P(nl; r)$ are of four types, given in the first column of Table 8 and, in

**Table 8**

| Term in $E'$ | Contribution to $Q(r)$ in Formula § 3.6(6) |
|---|---|
| $q(nl)I(nl)$ | $-q(nl)\left[\frac{d^2}{dr^2} + \frac{2N}{r} - \frac{l(l+1)}{r^2}\right] P(nl; r)$ |
| $A_kF_k(nl, nl)$ | $+A_k\frac{4}{r}Y_k(nl, nl; r)\,P(nl; r)$ |
| $A'_kF_k(nl, n'l')$ $(n'l') \neq (nl)$ | $+A'_k\frac{2}{r}Y_k(n'l', n'l'; r)\,P(nl; r)$ |
| $-B_kG_k(nl, n'l')$ | $-B_k\frac{2}{r}Y_k(nl, n'l'; r)\,P(n'l'; r)$ |

the expression for the variation $\Delta E'$ of $E'$ for a variation $\Delta P(nl; r)$, they give the coefficients of $\Delta P(nl; r)$ given in the second column of Table 8; the coefficients, here written $A_k$, $A'_k$, $B_k$ for short, have the values $A_0 = \frac{1}{2}q(nl)[q(nl) - 1]$, $A'_0 = q(nl)q(n'l')$, $A_k = -A_{lk}$ $(k \neq 0)$,

$B_k = B_{ll'k}$ (see §§ 3.6, 6.5). Hence, if the terms in $E'$ depending on $P(nl; r)$ are

$$q(nl)I(nl) + \Sigma_k A_k F_k(nl, nl) + \Sigma'_{n'l'k} A'_k F_k(nl, n'l') - \Sigma_{n'l'k} B_k G_k(nl, n'l'), \quad (2)$$

the equation for $P(nl; r)$ is

$$-q(nl)\left[\frac{d^2}{dr^2} + \frac{2N}{r} - \frac{l(l+1)}{r^2}\right] P(nl; r) + \frac{1}{r}\{\Sigma_k 4A_k\, Y_k(nl, nl; r)P(nl; r)$$
$$+ \Sigma'_{n'l'k}[2A'_k Y_k(n'l', n'l'; r)P(nl; r) - 2B_k\, Y_k(nl, n'l'; r)\, P(n'l'; r)]\}$$
$$+ q(nl)[\varepsilon_{nl,nl}\, P(nl; r) + \Sigma_{n' \neq n} \varepsilon_{nl,n'l}\, P(n'l; r)] = 0; \quad (3)$$

the terms in the last square bracket have been written so that the $\varepsilon$ parameters in them are the same as in the radial wave equation as written in the form § 3.6(9).

On multiplying equation (3) by $\frac{1}{2}P(nl; r)$ and integrating from 0 to $\infty$ in $r$, the first term in equation (3) gives $q(nl)I(nl)$, which is just the first term in the expression (2). Also

$$\int_0^\infty \frac{1}{r}\, Y_k(n'l', n'l'; r)P^2(nl; r)\, dr = F_k(nl, n'l'),$$

$$\int_0^\infty \frac{1}{r}\, Y_k(nl, n'l'; r)P(nl; r)P(n'l'; r)\, dr = G_k(nl, n'l'),$$

and from the orthonormal properties of the radial wave functions

$$\int_0^\infty P(nl; r)P(n'l; r)\, dr = \delta_{nn'};$$

so the whole equation (3) gives

$$q(nl)I(nl) + \Sigma_k 2A_k F_k(nl, nl) + \Sigma'_{n'l'k}[A'_k F_k(nl, n'l')$$
$$- B_k G_k(nl, n'l')] + \tfrac{1}{2} q(nl)\varepsilon_{nl,nl} = 0.$$

Hence on substitution for $q(nl)I(nl)$ in expression (2), this contribution to $E'$ becomes simply

$$-\tfrac{1}{2} q(nl)\varepsilon_{nl,nl} - \Sigma_k A_k F_k(nl, nl), \quad (4)$$

all the terms involving integrals $F_k(nl, n'l')$ and $G_k(nl, n'l')$ with $(n'l') \neq (nl)$ having disappeared. This is a result of substituting for *only one* $I$ integral from the equation satisfied by the corresponding radial wave function; if such a substitution is made for *two* $I$ integrals, say $I(nl)$ and $I(n''l'')$, then terms involving $F_k(nl, n''l'')$ and $G_k(nl, n''l'')$ reappear and would have to be evaluated. It also depends on the radial wave functions $P(nl; r)$ being determined by solution of Fock's equations;

if they were calculated from the equations of the self-consistent field without exchange, the formula for the contribution to $E'$ corresponding to (4) would contain several more terms.

### 8.3. ONE INCOMPLETE GROUP

For one incomplete group in addition to a core of closed groups, § 8.2(4) gives

$$E'[\text{core} + (nl)^q] = E_{(i)} - \tfrac{1}{2}q(nl)\varepsilon_{nl,nl} - \Sigma_k A_k F_k(nl, nl), \tag{1}$$

whereas

$$E'(\text{core}) = E_{(i)}.$$

If the variation in $E_{(i)}$ arising from the small perturbation of the radial wave functions of the core by the $(nl)^q$ group is neglected, this gives

$$2E'[\text{core} + (nl)^q] - 2E'(\text{core}) = -q(nl)\varepsilon_{nl,nl} - 2\Sigma_k A_k F_k(nl, nl). \tag{2}$$

This result is expressed as a formula for $2E'$, which is the energy expressed in terms of the ionization energy of hydrogen ($\frac{1}{2}$ atomic unit) as unit.

The quantity of the left-hand side of (2) is the energy of the configuration [core + $(nl)^q$] relative to the energy of the core alone as zero. Its negative is the ionization energy of the whole $(nl)^q$ group.

### 8.4. ENERGY DIFFERENCES BETWEEN *(LS)* TERMS OF A SINGLE INCOMPLETE GROUP

Let I and II refer to two terms arising from a single configuration consisting of complete $(n'l')$ groups and a single incomplete $(nl)$ group. In the expression § 8.2(2) the only coefficients that depend on the $(LS)$ values of a particular term are the $A_k$'s; let these be $A_k(\text{I})$, $A_k(\text{II})$ for the two terms.

Then, if the differences between the $(nl)$ wave functions for the different terms of the same configuration are neglected, it follows from § 8.2(2) that

$$E'(\text{II}) - E'(\text{I}) = \Sigma_k[A_k(\text{II}) - A_k(\text{I})]F_k(nl, nl), \tag{1}$$

and an expression of this kind is customarily used in studying interterm separations and their relations.

However, from § 8.3(1)

$$E'(\text{II}) - E'(\text{I}) = -\tfrac{1}{2}q(nl)[\varepsilon_{nl,nl}(\text{II}) - \varepsilon_{nl,nl}(\text{I})] - \Sigma_k[A_k(\text{II}) - A_k(\text{I})]F_k(nl, nl), \tag{2}$$

and it might be argued that, since the difference between the functions $P(nl; r)$ for the terms I and II is being neglected, the difference between the values of $\varepsilon_{nl,nl}$ for the two terms should also be neglected. Then the energy differences given by formula (2) would be the same in magnitude as those given by (1) but of the opposite sign. The reason for this apparent discrepancy is that, as already pointed out, the substitution leading to formula § 8.3(1), and so to the formula (2), depends on the radial wave function $P(nl; r)$ being a solution of equation § 8.2(3), and this requires that both $\varepsilon_{nl,nl}$ *and* the radial wave function $P(nl; r)$ shall be different for the different terms.

A calculation of differences between terms of the same configuration, including the differences between the radial wave function for different terms, has been carried out for the normal configurations of the oxygen in various degrees of ionization.[1]

## 8.5. ONE WAVE FUNCTION IN ADDITION TO CLOSED GROUPS

If the incomplete group consists of a single $(nl)$ wave function only, there are no $F_k(nl, nl)$ terms on the expression for $E'$, and then § 8.3(2) becomes simply

$$2E'[\text{core} + (nl)] - 2E'(\text{core}) = -\varepsilon_{nl,nl}, \tag{1}$$

so that the parameter $\varepsilon_{nl,nl}$ in Fock's equation for the $(nl)$ wave function is the calculated value, in this approximation, for the corresponding term, reckoned from the energy of the core as zero; for example, for $Ca^+(4s)$. $\varepsilon_{4s,4s}$ is the calculated value, in Rydbergs (1 Rydberg $= \frac{1}{2}$ atomic unit), of the $(4s)$ term in the spectrum Ca II. Thus, for a set of configurations consisting of a core of complete groups and an $(nl)$ wave function with a given value of $l$, the variation of $\varepsilon_{nl,nl}$ with $n$ corresponds to the variation of term value with $n$ in a single series of terms in a spectrum which can be described by transition of a single "valency" or "series" electron in the field of the core regarded as fixed.

For such a configuration, the equation for the $(nl)$ wave function is, in integrodifferential form (see equation § 6.6(1) and § 3.7),

$$\left[\frac{d^2}{dr^2} + \frac{2Y_0(r)}{r} - \varepsilon_{nl,nl} - \frac{l(l+1)}{r^2}\right] P(nl; r) + \frac{2}{r}\int_0^\infty K(r, s) P(nl; s)\, ds = 0, \tag{2}$$

where the kernel $K(r, s)$ is

$$\begin{aligned} K(r, s) &= \Sigma_{n'l'k} B_k P(n'l'; r) P(n'l'; s)(s/r)^k \quad \text{for} \quad s < r \\ &= \Sigma_{n'l'k} B_k P(n'l'; r) P(n'l'; s)(r/s)^{k+1} \quad \text{for} \quad s > r, \end{aligned}$$

and the function $Y_0(r)$ does not involve the function $P(nl; r)$ and is independent of $n$. The charge of the "core" consisting of the nucleus and complete groups will be written $C$, so that, for values of $r$ large enough

[1] D. R. Hartree, W. Hartree, and B. Swirles, *Phil. Trans. Roy. Soc.*, **238**, 229 (1939).

for departures from a Coulomb field to be negligible, the function $Y_0(r)$ has the constant value $C$. Then, as mentioned in § 6.6, equation (2) is strictly linear and homogeneous in $P(nl; r)$, and a normalized solution can in principle be obtained by first evaluating an un-normalized solution satisfying the boundary conditions, and later multiplying by appropriate normalizing factor. This normalization does not affect the value of $\varepsilon_{nl,nl}$.

For any value of $\varepsilon_{nl,nl}$, equation (2) has a solution satisfying the condition at the origin. It is convenient for the present argument to suppose that, for each $l$, the multiplying constants in the solutions of (2) for different values of $\varepsilon_{nl,nl}$ are chosen so that the value of $(P/r^{l+1})_{r=0}$ is the same for all these solutions. This defines a relation between solutions with different values of $n$, and we can write

$$P(nl; r) = P_0(l; r) + \varepsilon_{nl,nl}P_1(l; r) + (\varepsilon_{nl,nl})^2 P_2(l; r) + \cdots, \tag{3}$$

the functions $P(l; r)$ satisfying the equations

$$\left[\frac{d^2}{dr^2} + \frac{2Y_0(r)}{r} - \frac{l(l+1)}{r^2}\right] P_0(l; r) + \frac{2}{r}\int_0^\infty K(r, s)P_0(l; s)\, ds = 0,$$

and, for $m \neq 0$,

$$\left[\frac{d^2}{dr^2} + \frac{2Y_0(r)}{r} - \frac{l(l+1)}{r^2}\right] P_m(l; r) + \frac{2}{r}\int_0^\infty K(r, s)P_m(l; s)\, ds = P_{m-1}(l; r), \tag{4}$$

with the conditions $[P_0(l; r)/r^{l+1}]_{r=0} = A \neq 0$, $[P_m(l; r)/r^{l+1}]_{r=0} = 0$.

Consider now the process of determining a solution, and the corresponding value of $\varepsilon_{nl,nl}$, by matching a solution satisfying the conditions at the origin and one satisfying the conditions at infinity, the match being made at a radius $r_0$ such that exchange terms, expressed by the integral in equation (2), and the departures from a Coulomb field are negligible. Then the function satisfying the boundary condition at $\infty$ is the solution of

$$\left[\frac{d^2}{dr^2} + \frac{2C}{r} - \varepsilon_{nl,nl} - \frac{l(l+1)}{r^2}\right] P(nl; r) = 0 \tag{5}$$

satisfying this condition.

It is convenient to write

$$\varepsilon_{nl,nl} = C^2\varepsilon^* = C^2/(n^*)^2;$$

for a spectroscopic term of energy $\varepsilon_{nl,nl}$, $n^*$ is called the "effective quantum number" and $q = n - n^*$ the "quantum defect."

For small values of $\varepsilon$, the solution of equation (2) which is zero at the origin can be regarded as a variation on the solution with $\varepsilon = 0$, as represented by formula (3). For the solution of equation (5) which is zero at infinity, we shall see that $[P'(r_0)/P(r_0)]$ varies rapidly with $n$, covering the range $-\infty$ to $\infty$ for a change of $n$ of approximately unity, however small $\varepsilon_{nl,nl}$ is. Hence the matching process always gives a good determination of $n^*$ and of the quantum defect.

The solution of equation (5) which is zero at infinity can be expressed in terms of the confluent hypergeometric function of Whittaker,

$$P = AW_{n^*,l+1/2}(2Cr/n^*), \tag{6}$$

and we are concerned with such functions for integral values of $l$, and values of $n^*$ which may not be integral but which may be large. Moreover, we are concerned with the variation with $n^*$ of the function (6) *at a fixed value of* $r$, and *not* at a fixed value of $2Cr/n^*$, for it is at a fixed value of $r$ that we propose to match the solutions, one satisfying the boundary condition at the origin and the other the condition at infinity, and can express the behavior of the former by (3) and (4). For this reason the usual analytical treatment of the complementary hypergeometic function, which involves an examination of the expressions for $e^{\frac{1}{2}z}W_{k,m}(z)$ as power series in $z$, is inappropriate in the present context; indeed, emphasis on $z = 2Cr/n^*$, rather than on $r$ or $2Cr$, as the independent variable obscures a feature of the behavior of these functions which is of some importance in this context.

Similarly, for numerical work, a tabulation of the function $W_{k,m}(z)$ as a function of $z$ for different values of $k$ as a parameter is of little use here; what is wanted is a tabulation[2] of the function (6) as a function of $2Cr$ for different values of $\varepsilon^*$; that is, a tabulation of $W_{k,m}(z)$, or auxiliary functions, as functions of $z/k$ for parameter $1/k^2$. Furthermore, such a tabulation can be made smooth through $\varepsilon^* = 0$, that is through $1/k^2 = 0$, so that the function values appropriate to calculations on bound states join smoothly with those appropriate to calculations involving states of the continuum (e.g., calculations of collision cross sections); this cannot be done if $k$ is taken as the parameter of the tabulation.

To match solution (6) to solution (2) at a fixed value of $r$, however large the value of $n^*$, we require the behavior near the origin of the function $W_{n^*,l+1/2}(2Cr/n^*)$. Let $\sigma = 2Cr$; then equation (5) becomes

$$\left[\frac{d^2}{d\sigma^2} + \frac{1}{\sigma} - \frac{1}{4}\varepsilon^* - \frac{l(l+1)}{\sigma^2}\right] P = 0. \tag{7}$$

When $2l$ is not an integer, the relations between the expressions for the solutions of this equation in asymptotic series and in ascending power

[2] Such a tabulation of the solutions of equation (5), as functions of $2Cr$ and $\varepsilon^*$, is being carried out by the Mathematics Division of the National Physical Laboratory.

series have been given by Whittaker; however, in the present context $2l$ is always an integer, and Whittaker's results are inapplicable. His analysis has been extended[3] to the relevant case of integral $l$. The analytical details are some what long and complicated; only the main results are given here.

Equation (7) has one solution regular at the origin; let it be written $G_l(\sigma, \varepsilon^*)$. It is convenient to take the multiplying constant to be defined by

$$(2l+1)!\,G_l(\sigma, \varepsilon^*) = \sigma^{l+1}(1 + a_1\sigma + a_2\sigma^2 + \cdots). \tag{8}$$

The second solution is singular at the origin, and of the form

$$H_l(\sigma, \varepsilon^*) = \sigma^l(b_0 + b_1\sigma + b_2\sigma^2 + \cdots) + \alpha G_l(\sigma, \varepsilon^*) \log \sigma, \tag{9}$$

$\alpha$ and $b_{2l+1}$ being arbitrary. It is convenient to take $\alpha = 1/\pi$, and $b_{2l+1}$ given by a formula which for a general value of $l$ is rather elaborate, but for $l = 0$ gives

$$\pi b_1 = -\psi(1) - \psi(2) + \left(\psi(n^*) - \log n^* + \frac{1}{2n^*}\right), \tag{10}$$

$\psi(z)$ being the logarithmic derivative of the gamma function. The recurrence relations for the successive coefficient $a_m$ in (8) and $b_m$ in (9) involve integral powers of $\varepsilon^*$ only; furthermore,

$$\psi(n^*) - \log n^* + \frac{1}{2n^*} = \sum_{q=1}^{\infty}(-1)^q\left(\frac{B_q}{2q}\right)(n^*)^{2q}$$

$$= \sum_{q=1}^{\infty}(-1)^q\left(\frac{B_q}{2q}\right)(\varepsilon^*)^q$$

and also involves integral powers of $\varepsilon^*$ only. So the dependence of $G_l(\sigma, \varepsilon^*)$ and $H_0(\sigma, \varepsilon^*)$ on $\varepsilon^*$ for a given value of $\sigma$ is expressed by a series in integral powers of $\varepsilon^*$; there are no odd powers of $(\varepsilon^*)^{1/2}$.

It can be shown that, with this particular choice of standard solutions $G_l(\sigma, \varepsilon^*)$ and $H_l(\sigma, \varepsilon^*)$, the Whittaker function $W_{n^*,l+1/2}(\sigma/n^*)$ can be expressed as

$$\frac{(-n^*)^{l+1}}{\Gamma(n^*+l+1)} W_{n^*,l+1/2}\left(\frac{\sigma}{n^*}\right) = G_l(\sigma, \varepsilon^*) \cos \pi n^* + H_l(\sigma, \varepsilon^*) \sin \pi n^*. \tag{11}$$

The functions $G$ and $H$ are both regular in $\varepsilon^*$ for a given $\sigma$, and for small $\sigma$ they vary only slowly with $\varepsilon^*$; the main variation with $\varepsilon^*$ comes from the circular functions on the right-hand side of (11). This form of the variation with $n^*$, for given $\sigma$, is quite unrecognizable from the usual expression obtained by working with $z = \sigma/n^*$ as independent variable.

[3] D. R. Hartree, *Proc. Cambridge Phil. Soc.*, **24**, 428 (1928).

That $H_l(\sigma, \varepsilon^*)$ is regular in $\varepsilon^*$ for a given $\sigma$ has so far only been established for $l = 0$. The result can be extended to any $l$ by the use of the recurrence relations with respect to $l$ satisfied by the various functions.[4] From the definition of the function $G_l(\sigma, \varepsilon^*)$ it follows that

$$G_{l+1}(\sigma, \varepsilon^*) = -\frac{1}{1-(l+1)^2\varepsilon^*}\left\{2(l+1)\frac{d}{d\sigma}G_l(\sigma, \varepsilon^*) + \left[1 - \frac{2(l+1)^2}{\sigma}\right]G_l(\sigma, \varepsilon^*)\right\}, \quad (12)$$

and it can be shown that $W_{n^*,l+1/2}(\sigma/n^*)$ satisfies the same recurrence relation. It follows from (11) that $H_l(\sigma, \varepsilon^*)$ also satisfies such a relation, and, since the coefficients in the relation (12) involve only integral powers of $\varepsilon^*$, and $H_0(\sigma, \varepsilon^*)$ is regular in $\varepsilon^*$, so also is $H_l(\sigma, \varepsilon^*)$.

We can now dispense with the inconvenient form (6) of the solution which satisfies the boundary condition at infinity, and write it instead

$$P = A[G_l(2Cr, \varepsilon^*)\cos \pi n^* + H_l(2Cr, \varepsilon^*)\sin \pi n^*]. \quad (13)$$

The matching condition, that the value of $P'(r_0)/P(r_0)$ for the solution satisfying the boundary condition at the origin should be same as for the solution satisfying the condition at infinity, then becomes

$$\frac{P'(r_0)}{P(r_0)} = 2C\left[\frac{G'_l(2Cr_0, \varepsilon^*)\cos \pi n^* + H'_l(2Cr_0, \varepsilon^*)\sin \pi n^*}{G_l(2Cr_0, \varepsilon^*)\cos \pi n^* + H_l(2Cr_0, \varepsilon^*)\sin \pi n^*}\right].$$

Now $n^* = n - q$ and $n$ is integral; so

$$\tan \pi q = -\tan \pi n^* = \frac{2CP(r_0)G'_l(2Cr_0, \varepsilon^*) - P'(r_0)G_l(2Cr_0, \varepsilon^*)}{2CP(r_0)H'_l(2Cr_0, \varepsilon^*) - P'(r_0)H_l(2Cr_0, \varepsilon^*)}. \quad (14)$$

Furthermore, $P(r_0)$ and $P'(r_0)$ are expressible in power series in $\varepsilon^*$, and so are the functions $G$ and $H$ and their derivatives. So, therefore, is $q$; that is

$$q = q_0 + q_1\varepsilon^* + q_2(\varepsilon^*)^2 + \cdots,$$

which is the extended Ritz formula for the terms of an optical spectrum.

For $\varepsilon^* = 0$, the functions $G$ and $H$ are the Bessel functions

$$G_l(\sigma, 0) = J_{2l+1}(2\sigma^{1/2}),$$
$$H_l(\sigma, 0) = Y_{2l+1}(2\sigma^{1/2});$$

the function $P$ is the solution $P_0$ of the first of equations (4), and formula (14) then gives the limiting value $q_0$ of the quantum defect in a series of terms.

[4] D. R. Hartree, *Proc. Cambridge Phil. Soc.*, **25**, 310, § 2 (1929).

### 8.6 TWO INCOMPLETE GROUPS

If there are two incomplete groups, say $(n_1l_1)$ and $(n_2l_2)$ with $\varepsilon_{nl,nl} = \varepsilon_1$ and $\varepsilon_2$, respectively, the expression for $E'$ contains contributions like § 8.2(2) for each separate incomplete group and also one or more terms of the form

$$\Sigma_k[A''_k F_k(n_1l_1, n_2l_2) - B''_k G_k(n_1l_1, n_2l_2)]. \tag{1}$$

On substituting for $dP/dr$ in *either* $I(n_1l_1)$ or $I(n_2l_2)$ from the differential equation, these terms will disappear, their contributions to $E'$ being incorporated in the $\varepsilon$ values $\varepsilon_1$ or $\varepsilon_2$. But, if substitution is made for *both* $d^2P(n_1l_1; r)/dr^2$ and $d^2P(n_2l_2; r)/dr^2$, these terms (1) reappear with the opposite sign. Hence the contribution to $E'$ from $(n_1l_1)^{q_1}(n_2l_2)^{q_2}$ is

$$- \tfrac{1}{2}q_1\varepsilon_1 - \tfrac{1}{2}q_2\varepsilon_2 - \Sigma_k[A_{1k}F_k(n_1l_1, n_1l_1) + A_{2k}F_k(n_2l_2, n_2l_2) \\ - \Sigma_k[A''_k F_k(n_1l_1, n_2l_2) - B''_k G_k(n_1l_1, n_2l_2)].$$

# 9. RELATIVISTIC EXTENSION

## 9.1. DIRAC'S RELATIVISTIC WAVE EQUATION

For a single particle, Schrödinger's equation in its general form (that is, not necessarily for a stationary state) is, in atomic units,

$$[-(1/2m)\nabla^2 + V]\psi = -i\,\partial\psi/\partial t, \tag{1}$$

and the wave equation § 1.5(1) for a stationary state is obtained by taking functions $\psi$ having a time dependence $\exp(iEt)$. However, equation (1) does not satisfy the special principle of relativity, for a Lorentz transformation transforms it to an equation with first-order space derivatives and second-order time derivatives, so that, if for any one frame of reference the wave equation did have the form (1), then this frame of reference would be distinguished from all others, in motion relative to it, by the specially simple form the wave equation took for this frame of reference. But one aspect of the special principle of relativity is just that there is no preferred frame of reference distinguished by specially simple forms of general physical laws when that frame is used.

Dirac showed that it is possible to obtain a wave equation satisfying the special principle of relativity and equivalent to equation (1) in the formal limit $c \to \infty$. Dirac's equation is an equation for a function $\psi$ having not one but four components ($\psi_1$, $\psi_2$, $\psi_3$, $\psi_4$) at each point of space, and this equation can be written as a set of four coupled first-order equations for these four components.

He also showed that the phenomena which, in nonrelativistic mechanics, are ascribed to electron spin and to spin-orbit interaction are covered by the properties of these equations and their solutions, and that there is now no need to include explicitly a "spin coordinate" $s$, though the variable which takes four discrete values to distinguish the four components of $\psi$ can be regarded as taking its place.

The rest of this chapter is concerned with those aspects of Dirac's equations and Dirac wave functions that are relevant to the calculation of structures of many-electron atoms; more general aspects of relativistic quantum mechanics will not be considered here.

## 9.2. FORM OF SOLUTION OF DIRAC'S EQUATIONS FOR STATIONARY STATES OF AN ELECTRON IN A CENTRAL FIELD

Dirac[1] and Darwin[2] showed, that, for a stationary state of an electron in a central field, a solution $(\psi_1, \psi_2, \psi_3, \psi_4)$ of Dirac's equations is expressible in terms of two functions of $r$ and spherical harmonics. In Darwin's notation, $F(r)$ is the function of $r$ occurring in $\psi_1$ and $\psi_2$, and $G(r)$ that in $\psi_3$ and $\psi_4$. There are two classes of solution. Let $W$ be the total energy (including the rest energy $m_0c^2$ of the electron) of the stationary state. Then in one of these classes of solution $F(r)$ and $G(r)$ satisfy the equations, in atomic units ($m_0 = 1$, $e = -1$, $c = 137$; see § 1.4),

$$\frac{dF}{dr} + \frac{l+2}{r} F - \left[\frac{W - V(r)}{c} - c\right] G = 0, \tag{1}$$

$$\frac{dG}{dr} - \frac{l}{r} G + \left[\frac{W - V(r)}{c} + c\right] F = 0; \tag{2}$$

in the other class $F(r)$ and $G(r)$ satisfy the equations

$$\frac{dF}{dr} - \frac{l-1}{r} F - \left[\frac{W - V(r)}{c} - c\right] G = 0, \tag{3}$$

$$\frac{dG}{dr} + \frac{l+1}{r} G + \left[\frac{W - V(r)}{c} + c\right] F = 0. \tag{4}$$

The number $l$ (Darwin's $k$) is integral, and is the order of the spherical harmonics multiplying $G(r)$ in the expression for the wave function $\psi$; the notation $l$ is used for this number, because of its close relation to the quantity $l$ which occurs in the nonrelativistic equations, as will appear shortly. For equations (1) and (2), $l \geqslant 0$ and the order of the spherical harmonics multiplying $F(r)$ is *greater* by unity than the order of those multiplying $G(r)$; for equations (3) and (4), $l \geqslant 1$, and the order of the spherical harmonics multiplying $F(r)$ is *less* by unity than the order of those multiplying $G(r)$.

Since $W$ is of order $m_0c^2$, that is, $c^2$ atomic units, and $c = 137$, it follows that, except for a range of $r$ near $r = 0$ where $V(r)/c^2$ is of numerical order of magnitude 1 or greater, $F(r)$ is small compared with $G(r)$.

The wave functions $(\psi_1, \psi_2, \psi_3, \psi_4)$ for which the functions $F(r)$ and $G(r)$ satisfy equations (1) and (2) give states in which the total moment of momentum quantum number $j$ has the value $j = l + \frac{1}{2}$, and those for which $F(r)$ and $G(r)$ satisfy equations (3) and (4) give states in which $j = l - \frac{1}{2}$. For any solution $F(r)$, $G(r)$, there are $(2j + 1)$ different sets of spherical harmonics which give solutions of Dirac's equations.

[1] P. A. M. Dirac, *Proc. Roy. Soc.*, **117**, 610 (1928).

[2] C. G. Darwin, *Proc. Roy. Soc.*, **118**, 654 (1928).

For a given value of $l$, equations (1) and (2) have a set of solutions satisfying the conditions $rG \to 0$ as $r \to 0$, $G \to 0$ as $r \to \infty$, and similar conditions of $F$, each solution having a different value of $E$. These solutions can be distinguished by a classificatory number $n$, and written $F(nl; r)$, $G(nl; r)$. And, since equations (3), (4) can be obtained from equations (1), (2) by writing $-(l+1)$ for $l$, they could be indicated by $F(n, -(l+1); r)$, $G(n, -(l+1); r)$. However, this notation is rather awkward, and it seems more convenient to indicate a solution of equations (3), (4) with a specified value of $l$ by the symbol $\bar{l}$ (written $\bar{p}, \bar{d}, \bar{f}, \cdots$ for $\bar{l} = 1, 2, 3 \cdots$).

It is convenient in handling these equations to write

$$\begin{aligned} r\,G(nl; r) &= P(nl; r), & r\,G(n\bar{l}; r) &= P(n\bar{l}; r), \\ r\,F(nl; r) &= Q(nl; r), & r\,F(n\bar{l}; r) &= Q(n\bar{l}; r), \end{aligned} \tag{5}$$

and also to write

$$W = c^2 + E, \tag{6}$$

so that $E$ is the energy of a stationary state reckoned from the rest energy of the electron, in a region where $V(r) = 0$, as zero. Then equations (1) and (2) become

$$\frac{d}{dr} P(nl; r) = \frac{l+1}{r} P(nl; r) - \left[2c + \frac{E - V(r)}{c}\right] Q(nl; r), \tag{7}$$

$$\frac{d}{dr} Q(nl; r) = -\frac{l+1}{r} Q(nl; r) + \frac{E - V(r)}{c} P(nl; r), \tag{8}$$

and (3), (4) become

$$\frac{d}{dr} P(n\bar{l}; r) = -\frac{l}{r} P(n\bar{l}; r) - \left[2c + \frac{E - V(r)}{c}\right] Q(n\bar{l}; r), \tag{9}$$

$$\frac{d}{dr} Q(n\bar{l}; r) = +\frac{l}{r} Q(n\bar{l}; r) + \frac{E - V(r)}{c} P(n\bar{l}; r). \tag{10}$$

These equations are closely related to the equations obtained in § 5.9 from breaking down the second-order nonrelativistic equation for the radial wave function into two first-order equations. If in equations (7), (8) we write

$$2cQ(nl; r) = -Q^*(nl; r),$$

they become

$$\frac{d}{dr} P(nl; r) = \frac{l+1}{r} P(nl; r) + \left(1 + \frac{E - V}{2c^2}\right) Q^*(nl; r), \tag{11}$$

$$\frac{d}{dr} Q^*(nl; r) = -\frac{l+1}{r} Q^*(nl; r) - 2(E - V) P(nl; r), \tag{12}$$

and these differ from the equations § 5.9(3) only by the term $(E - V)/2c^2$ in equation (11) and the exchange term $X$ in equation § 5.9(3), which is zero for a single electron in a given central field. For light atoms the term $(E - V)/2c^2$ is small compared with unity except for very small $r$. For example, for atomic number $N = 20$, $|V/2c^2| = 1/2000r$ approximately, and so is already only 1/10 at $r = 0.005$, which might be the end of the first integration interval in the integration of the nonrelativistic equation.

There is a similar close relation between equations (9), (10) and equations § 5.9(2). However, in the nonrelativistic equations § 5.9(2) and (3), the functions $Q_1$ and $Q_2$ are different auxiliary functions which might be used in the calculation of the *same* solution $P$ of equation § 5.9(1), whereas the solutions $P(nl; r)$, $P(n\bar{l}; r)$ of equations (7), (8) and equations (9), (10) are not the same. The value of $E$ in equations (9), (10) is also different from that in equations (7), (8) for the same value of $n$, the difference corresponding to the spin-doublet separation of the two levels.

### 9.3. MANY-ELECTRON ATOM

The treatment of a many-electron atom, starting from the approximation of regarding each electron in a stationary state in the field of the nucleus and of some average of the charge distribution of the other electrons, can be extended to the use of Dirac wave functions for these one-electron wave functions to express Pauli's principle in this approximation, with the understanding that each of these one-electron functions is a function of four variables, the space coordinates $x$, $y$, $z$ of the electron and a fourth, discrete, variable which distinguishes the components of the four-component function $(\psi_1, \psi_2, \psi_3, \psi_4)$.

We can further restrict the one-electron wave functions to be of central-field type, and consider the whole structure as being composed of subgroups of wave functions, the wave functions in a subgroup having the same radial variations $F(r)$, $G(r)$ but different variations with direction; an $(nl)$ subgroup and an $(n\bar{l})$ subgroup have different radial variations, and together form an $(nl)$ group of the nonrelativistic approximation. The number of linearly independent wave functions in an $(nl)$ or $(n\bar{l})$ subgroup is $(2j + 1)$, that is, $2(l + 1)$ for an $(nl)$ subgroup and $2l$ for an $(n\bar{l})$ subgroup; and each complete subgroup can be divided into two halves, each of which gives a spherically symmetrical charge distribution.[3]

The complete relativistic theory of a many-electron atom would start from the appropriate many-particle wave equation which would include the relativistic interactions of the electrons; but the correct expressions for these are not known. However, for heavy atoms it seems probable

[3] D. R. Hartree, *Proc. Cambridge Phil. Soc.*, **25**, 225 (1929).

that the main effects which depend on the finiteness of the velocity of light are (i) those arising from the relativistic variation of mass with velocity and (ii) those which, in terms of nonrelativistic mechanics, are ascribed to spin-orbit interaction. Both these may be included if we use Dirac wave functions, and take for the interaction energy of two electrons either the simple electrostatic form $(1/r_{ij})$, or better the formula[4] $[1 - \boldsymbol{\alpha}(i) \cdot \boldsymbol{\alpha}(j)]/r_{ij}$ (where $\boldsymbol{\alpha}$ is the Dirac matrix vector), and write the total interaction as the sum of these two-particle interactions. This omits retardation effects—the fact that the presence of an electron at $P$ at time $t_0$ does not affect the field at $Q$ until a time $t_0 + r_{PQ}/c$—but these may be small, since (in the approximation we are contemplating) an atomic configuration consists mainly of complete subgroups, and the net current and the magnetic moment of each complete subgroup is zero, so that its contribution to the field on another electron is, in this approximation, closely that of a static distribution of charge.[5]

Bertha Swirles showed that Dirac's equation for the stationary states of an electron in a given field can be derived from a variation principle, and she carried through, for an approximate wave function $\Phi$ consisting of a determinant of one-electron wave functions $\psi$ of Dirac central-field type, an analysis similar to that of §§ 3.3, 3.4, 3.6.[6] The equations obtained for the "best" radial wave functions $P(nl; r)$, $Q(nl; r)$ and $P(n\bar{l}; r)$, $Q(n\bar{l}; r)$ are of the form of equations § 9.2(7), (8) and (9), (10), with additional "exchange" terms corresponding to the term $X(r)$ in equations § 5.9(2), (3), but now occurring in both equations (7), (8) or (9), (10).

Since for each $P(nl; r)$ function with $l \neq 0$ in the nonrelativistic approximation there are two different functions $P(nl; r)$ and $P(n\bar{l}; r)$, each with its associated $Q$ function, in the relativistic case, the amount of work involved in solving the equations in the relativistic case is considerably greater than in the nonrelativistic case; the number of $Y_k$ functions to be evaluated is about four times as great, and the wave equation is no longer a second-order equation with first derivatives absent, the most convenient form for numerical solution. Further, relativistic effects are most important for heavy atoms for which even nonrelativistic calculations with exchange would be lengthy.

A solution of the relativistic equations without exchange for $Cu^+$ has been carried out by Williams.[7]

[4] See G. E. Brown, *Phil. Mag.*, **43**, 467 (1952).

[5] For a further discussion of retardation effects, see B. Swirles, *Proc. Roy. Soc.*, **157**, 680 (1936), and Brown, *loc. cit.*

[6] B. Swirles, *Proc. Roy. Soc.* **152**, 625 (1935). See corrections in Hartree, *Repts. Progr. Phys.*, **11**, 113, appendix (1948).

[7] A. O. Williams, *Phys. Rev.*, **58**, 723 (1940). See further Appendix 3.

## 9.4. SOLUTION OF THE RADIAL WAVE EQUATIONS

Solution of a pair of first-order linear differential equations such as § 9.2(7) and (8), or the corresponding equations which would occur in calculations with exchange, can be obtained by means of an extension of the Fox–Goodwin process given in § 4.7; such an extension is given in the paper by Fox and Goodwin.[8]

Brenner, Brown, and Woodward[9] have suggested the following procedure for reducing the solution of a pair of homogeneous linear equations like § 9.2(7), (8) to the solution of a single, nonlinear, equation. Let $u$ be the variable

$$u = Q/P \tag{1}$$

Then equations § 9.2(7), (8) give

$$\begin{aligned}\frac{du}{dr} &= \frac{1}{P}\frac{dQ}{dr} - \frac{Q}{P^2}\frac{dP}{dr} = \frac{1}{P}\left(\frac{dQ}{dr} - u\frac{dP}{dr}\right)\\ &= \frac{E-V}{c} - \frac{2(l+1)}{r}u + \left(2c + \frac{E-V}{c}\right)u^2.\end{aligned}$$

This equation is closely related to equation § 5.9(9). This can be seen by writing

$$\xi = 2cQ/P = 2cu \tag{3}$$

when equation (2) becomes

$$d\xi/dr = 2(E-V) - [2(l+1)/r]\xi + [1 + (E-V)/2c^2]\xi^2, \tag{4}$$

which, in the formal nonrelativistic limit $c \to \infty$, becomes equation § 5.9(9) [in equation (4), $V$ is the potential energy of an electron which is $-Y/r$ in the notation of § 5.9; and $\varepsilon$ in equation § 5.9(9) is positive for a stationary state, whereas $E$ is negative; $\varepsilon = -2E$].

Equation (4) can clearly not be integrated through a zero of $P$. But, in the neighborhood of a zero of $P$, $Q$ is not zero, and one can use as an alternative the variable

$$\zeta = 1/\xi \tag{5}$$

which satisfies a similar equation with the first and third terms interchanged; namely,

$$-d\zeta/dr = [1 + (E-V)/2c^2] - [2(l+1)/r]\zeta + 2(E-V)\zeta^2. \tag{6}$$

When the solution of equation (4) satisfying the conditions at $r = 0$ and $r = \infty$ has been found by adjustment of $E$, the function $P$ can be

[8] L. Fox and E. T. Goodwin, *Proc. Cambridge Phil. Soc.*, **45**, 373 (1949).

[9] S. Brenner, G. E. Brown, and J. B. Woodward, *Proc. Roy. Soc.*, **227**, 59, equation (13) (1954).

obtained by substituting $Q = (\xi/2c)P$ in equation § 9.2(7), $\xi$ being now a known function of $r$. Then log $P$ is given by a quadrature.

This procedure might have advantages in the integration of equations § 9.2(7), (8) without exchange. It would have no advantage in the integration of the corresponding equations with exchange, as the "exchange" term in the equation for $d\xi/dr$ would have a factor $1/P$, so that the solution for $P$ would have to be carried out simultaneously with that for $\xi$ for each trial value of $E$, instead of being carried out just once after the solution of the equation for $\xi$ satisfying the boundary conditions has been determined.

# 10. BETTER APPROXIMATIONS

## 10.1. TWO KINDS OF IMPROVEMENT IN THE APPROXIMATION

The basic approximation in the calculation of atomic structures by the methods of Chapters 5, 6, and 7 is the adoption of an approximate wave function $\Phi$ representing a single configuration, and consisting of a single determinant of one-electron wave functions $\psi_\alpha$ for a configuration of complete groups, or a linear combination of such determinants for a configuration comprising incomplete groups. The determinant is a formal expression of a model of the atom in which each electron is regarded as in a stationary state in the field of the nucleus and the other electrons, but in which it is indeterminate *which* electron is in which of the states represented by the wave functions $\psi_\alpha$.

There are several ways in which attempts have been made to improve on this approximation; these can be illustrated by the simple example of the normal state of a two-electron system such as $H^-$, He, $Li^+$, · · ·. The wave function $\Psi$ for an $S$ state of such a system is a function not of the two variables $r_1$ and $r_2$ alone, but depends also on the mutual distance $r_{12} = |\mathbf{r}_1 - \mathbf{r}_2|$ between the electrons; an alternative third variable is $\theta_{12}$, the angle between the vectors $\mathbf{r}_1$ and $\mathbf{r}_2$. Most of the ways of improving the approximation are concerned with ways of including a dependence on this third variable, explicitly or implicitly, in the approximate wave function $\Phi$.

The representation of an atomic state by a single configuration is a useful and simple approximation and one that it is easy to visualize; but it is only an approximation. One way of improving the approximation is to use approximate wave functions $\Phi$ involving $r_{12}$ or $\theta_{12}$ explicitly, such as

$$\Phi = e^{-k(r_1+r_2)}(1 + \alpha r_{12}) \tag{1}$$

or

$$\Phi = \Sigma_n u_n(r_1, r_2) P_n(\cos \theta_{12}). \tag{2}$$

Use of such approximate wave functions involves the rejection of the idea of "configurations." Some such approximations are considered in § 10.2. They have given important results for two-electron systems, but the difficulties of extending this kind of approximation to a many-electron system appear formidable. The number of interelectronic distances $r_{ij}$ (or corresponding angles $\theta_{ij}$) in an $N$-electron system is $\frac{1}{2}N(N-1)$; for quite small values of $N$ this is comparable with $N$ itself, and moreover for $N = 2$ and $N = 3$ the $r_{ij}$'s are independent (subject to inequalities such as $|r_1 - r_2| \leqslant r_{12} \leqslant r_1 + r_2$) and so can be used as the additional independent variables; whereas for large values of $N$, say 20 or 30, the number of $r_{ij}$'s becomes considerable, and for $N \geqslant 4$ they are no longer independent.

Another way of attempting to improve the approximation is to retain the idea of configurations but to represent an atomic state not by a function representing a single configuration but by the superposition of a set of functions, each of which has the form of the wave function for a single configuration. This is called "configuration mixing," "superposition of configurations," or "configuration interaction" (the last of these terms seems unfortunate, in view of the different sense in which the term "interaction" is used in related contexts). For example, let $\Phi_A$ be an approximate wave function for the $(1s)^2$ configuration of He, and $\Phi_B$ such a function for the $^1S$ state of the $(2p)^2$ configuration. Then we might examine whether the wave function of the normal state could be improved (in the sense of the variation principle) by use of

$$\Phi = \Phi_A + \beta\Phi_B \tag{3}$$

as an approximate wave function.

Here we could proceed in two ways. We could either determine the best radial wave function $P(1s)$ for the $(1s)^2$ configuration alone and $P(2p)$ for the $^1S$ state of the $(2p)^2$ configuration alone, and then, taking these radial wave functions as given, determine the best value of $\beta$ to be used in the linear combination (3). Or we could regard both $\beta$ and the radial wave functions in (3) as free to be determined by application of the variation principle to our approximate wave function of the form (3), with the radial wave functions in $\Phi_A$ and $\Phi_B$ not specified in advance. And whichever way was adopted, we could either restrict the radial wave functions to be of specified analytical form (such as sums of products of exponentials and polynomials) or leave them unspecified and determine them numerically from the differential equations which arise from application of the variation principle.

In the example of the normal state of the two-electron system, a qualitative argument suggests that a considerably greater improvement would probably be obtained if the radial wave function in $\Phi_B$ were *not* restricted to be that for the $(2p)^2$ configuration by itself. For $P(1s)$ of a $(1s)^2$ configuration has a maximum at about $r = 0.6$, and a greater improvement in $E'$ is likely to come from an improvement in the wave function where it is large than from one where it is small. But the maximum of $P(2p)$ for $(2p)^2$ is outside $r = 2$, where $\Phi_A$ is quite small, whereas, if the radial wave function in $\Phi_B$ is unspecified, there is more scope, in the application of the variation principle, for obtaining such a function having its largest values just where the improvement it produces matters most.

This expectation is confirmed by the work of Taylor and Parr[1] using hydrogen-like one-electron functions in an approximate wave function of this kind. The functions

$$\Phi_A = e^{-N_1(r_1+r_2)}, \tag{4}$$

$$\Phi_B = r_1 r_2 e^{-\frac{1}{2}N_2(r_1+r_2)} \cos\theta_{12} \tag{5}$$

are approximate wave functions for the $(1s)^2$ configuration and for the $^1S$ term of the $(2p)^2$ configuration [see § 10.3 below, formula (1)], respectively, constructed from hydrogen-like radial wave functions for atomic numbers $N_1$ and $N_2$. Taylor and Parr found that, if they used these functions in an approximate wave function (3) without imposing the condition $N_2 = N_1$, then for helium the "best" values of $N_1$ and $N_2$ are approximately 1.6 and 5.0, respectively.

The same conclusion is suggested by the results of Green and others[2] on an analysis of one of Hylleraas's wave functions, in $r_1$, $r_2$, and $r_{12}$ as independent variables, into central-field wave functions which can be interpreted in terms of configurations.

The use of a radial wave function in $\Phi_B$ different, and perhaps considerably different, from that for the $^1S$ term of the $(2p)^2$ configuration can be expressed in different ways. We may regard $\Phi_B$ as the wave function of a $(2p)^2$ configuration modified by being superposed on a $(1s)^2$ configuration; then the notation $P(2p)$ for this radial wave function is valid, and the terminology of superposition of configurations can still be used, with the understanding that the wave functions may be modified, perhaps considerably, by this superposition. Or we can avoid the language of configurations altogether, and also use a notation such as $P(1p)$ or $P(ap)$ for the radial wave function in $\Phi_B$ to emphasize that it is not regarded as having any necessary relation to the $P(2p)$ function of the $(2p)^2$ configuration.

This approach, and developments of it, are considered further in § 10.3.

## 10.2. APPROXIMATE WAVE FUNCTIONS INVOLVING $r_{ij}$ OR $\theta_{ij}$ EXPLICITLY

Most of the work on wave functions involving $r_{ij}$ or $\theta_{ij}$ explicitly has been done for two-electron systems, and in most of it analytic wave functions have been used.

[1] G. R. Taylor and R. G. Parr, *Proc. Natl. Acad. Sci.*, **38**, 154 (1952).

[2] L. C. Green and others, *Phys. Rev.*, **96**, 319 (1954).

The classical work in this field is that of Hylleraas.[3] In this work analytical wave functions were used with a dependence on the space coordinates given by a finite number of terms in the triple series in the expression

$$\Phi = e^{-k(r_1+r_2)}\Sigma_{lmn}a_{lmn}(r_1 + r_2)^l (r_1 - r_2)^{2m}r_{12}{}^n, \tag{1}$$

the coefficient $k$ in the exponent and the coefficients $a_{lmn}$ in the triple series being determined by application of the variation principle. This work has been extended, by the inclusion of more terms in the triple series, by Chandrasekhar and others.

Two important results have come from this work. First, the work of Hylleraas[3] showed that the extension of Schrödinger's equation to a two-particle system, expressed by equation § 1.8(1), leads to a value of the total energy of the normal state of helium in close agreement with experiment; and the more recent work of Chandrasekhar and Herzberg[4] has shown that, with the appropriate small corrections for relativistic effects and the finite mass of the nucleus, the difference between the calculated and observed values of this energy is less than the residual uncertainty arising from uncertainties in the calculation (for example, Lamb shift for a two-electron system) and uncertainties of experimental origin in the observed value. The second important result is Chandrasekhar's work on the $H^-$ ion,[5] which led to the identification of $H^-$ in the solar atmosphere.

James and Coolidge[6] have shown that the approximation of $E'$ to $E$ could be increased indefinitely by increasing the number of terms taken in an approximate wave function $\Phi$ of the form (1). However, this leaves open the question how good an approximation to the solution $\Psi$ of Schrödinger's equation such an approximate wave function $\Phi$ is. First, the adoption of such a form for $\Phi$ leaves aside the nature of the singularity, if any, in $\Psi$ at $r_1 = r_2 = r_{12} = 0$; and, second, it seems that use of a finite number of terms in an expression of the form (1) may give $\Phi$ quite the wrong asymptotic behaviour for large values of $r_1$ or $r_2$. Consider, for example, the behavior of $\Phi$ for $r_2$ given and $r_1 \gg r_2$. The term with coefficient $a_{lmn}$ will behave like $e^{-kr_1}r_1{}^{l+2m+n}$, and if (for example) the highest-degree term retained has $l = 2$, $m = 2$, $n = 4$, then, for large $r_1$, $\Phi$ behaves asymptotically like $r_1{}^{10}e^{-kr_1}$, which seems unlikely to represent the behavior of $\Psi$ at all closely.

[3] Summarized in *Norske Videnskaps-Akad. Skrifter*, **1**, *Math. u. Naturw. Klasse*, **6** (1932).

[4] S. Chandrasekhar and G. Herzberg, *Phys. Rev.*, **98**, 1050 (1955).

[5] S. Chandrasekhar, *Revs. Mod. Phys.*, **16**, 301 (1944).

[6] H. M. James and A. S. Coolidge, *Phys, Rev.*, **51**, 855, 860 (1937).

These features of the approximate wave function given by (1) may be related to a result found by James and Coolidge.[6] They showed how it is possible to obtain an approximation to the mean square residual, $\int(\Psi - \Phi)^2\, d\tau$, for an approximate wave function $\Phi$, without knowing the function $\Psi$ to which it is an approximation, and found that for an approximate wave function (1) the value of this mean square residual, which is one criterion of an approximate wave function, decreases only slowly with increase of the number of terms included in the series in (1), despite the considerable improvement in the energy value.

Another criterion of an approximate wave function $\Phi$ is the range of the ratio $(H\Phi)/\Phi$, which is constant for a solution $\Psi$ of Schrödinger's equation. Bartlett has shown[7] that, even for Hylleraas's best approximation of the form (1), the value of this ratio takes all values from 0 to $\infty$, though the values which differ considerably from $E(= -2.90$ atomic units) occur in regions of coordinate space in which $\Phi$ is small.

Thus, although a satisfactory approximation to the energy of the normal state of a two-electron atom has been attained, there is still room for improvement in the approximation to the wave function.

Another kind of approximate wave function has been studied by Luke, Meyerott, and Clendinin:[8] namely, one obtained by taking a finite number of terms of the series

$$\Phi = \Sigma_n u_n(r_1, r_2)\, P_n(\cos\theta_{12}). \tag{2}$$

Use of such an expansion has also been suggested by Lennard-Jones and Pople.[9] In this case, appeal to the variation principle is not necessary; the expression (2) is substituted into the wave equation in $r_1$, $r_2$, and $\theta_{12}$, and the coefficient of each $P_n(\cos\theta_{12})$ separately equated to zero. The result is a set of coupled second-order partial differential equations in the two variable $r_1$ and $r_2$, which can be solved numerically by a process of successive approximation.

Baber and Hassé[10] attempted to find an approximate wave function for the normal state of He of the form

$$\Phi = \psi(r_1)\, \psi(r_2)\, g(r_{12}),$$

and Green, in extending this work, has shown that little improvement is obtained by leaving the function $g(r_{12})$ to be determined rather than taking it to be linear in $r_{12}$.

Another approach to the treatment of a two-electron system is through

[7] J. H. Bartlett, *Phys. Rev.*, **98**, 1067 (1955).
[8] P. J. Luke, R. Meyerott, and W. W. Clendinin, *Phys. Rev.*, **85**, 401 (1952).
[9] J. E. Lennard-Jones and J. A. Pople, *Phil. Mag.*, **43**, 581 (1952).
[10] T. D. Baber and H. R. Hassé, *Proc. Cambridge Phil. Soc.*, **33**, 253 (1937).

a transformation of the coordinate system. Gronwall[11] has shown that in terms of the independent variables,[12]

$$\left.\begin{aligned}\xi &= \tfrac{1}{2}r_1r_2\cos\theta_{12},\\ \eta &= \tfrac{1}{4}(r_1{}^2 - r_2{}^2),\\ \zeta &= \tfrac{1}{2}r_1r_2\sin\theta_{12},\end{aligned}\right\} \qquad (3)$$

the differential operator in the two-particle wave equation for an $S$ state reduces to the simple form

$$\partial^2/\partial\xi^2 + \partial^2/\partial\eta^2 + \partial^2/\partial\zeta^2 + (1/\zeta)(\partial/\partial\zeta) \qquad (4)$$

and then further transforms the equation by use of polar coordinates in the ($\xi$, $\eta$, $\zeta$) space. The use of Gronwall's variables has been developed by Bartlett[13] who has obtained an approximate solution of the resulting equation in the three variables $\xi$, $\eta$, $\zeta$ by a numerical process. Bartlett's function $\Phi$ gives values of $(H\Phi)/\Phi$ which vary over a relatively small range, and only differ by more than a few per cent from the value $E = -2.90$ (atomic units) in regions of coordinate space where $\Phi$ is small, whereas, as already mentioned, even for Hylleraas's best approximation the range of values of $|(H\Phi)/\Phi|$ over all coordinate space is from 0 to $\infty$.

Fock[14] has suggested the use of a set of four independent variables, namely Gronwall's $\xi$, $\eta$ given by formulae (3) and two others (say $u$ and $v$) related to Gronwall's $\zeta$, in terms of which the differential operator (4) becomes

$$\partial^2/\partial\xi^2 + \partial^2/\partial\eta^2 + \partial^2/\partial u^2 + \partial^2/\partial v^2.$$

This makes possible the use of a set of functions related to the Laplacian operator in four dimensions in the same way as the spherical harmonics are related to the Laplacian operator in three dimensions. He does not, however, give a solution of the resulting equation.

All the above methods of improving the approximation from which Fock's equations are derived refer to a two-electron system, and as mentioned in § 10.1 their full extension to a many-electron system appears a formidable undertaking. However, it may be possible to make a partial extension of some of them. For example, we may regard the

[11] T. H. Gronwall, *Phys. Rev.*, **51**, 655 (1937).

[12] In Gronwall's paper these variable are written $x$, $y$, $z$; I have avoided this notation which may lead to confusion with the use of $x$, $y$, $z$ for Cartesian coordinates in physical space.

[13] J. H. Bartlett, *Phys. Rev.*, **51**, 661 (1937); **98**, 1067 (1955).

[14] V. Fock, *Izvest. Akad. Nauk. SSSR. Ser. Fiz.*, **18**(2), 161 (1954). English translation by G. Belkov, *Natl. Research Council Can., Tech. Trans.* TT–503 (1954).

$(4s)^2$ configuration of neutral calcium as a state of a two-electron system in the field of the $Ca^{+2}$ ion, regarded as given, and attempt to find wave functions depending on $r_{ij}$ for the electrons in the $(4s)^2$ group only. Stevenson[15] has suggested a treatment of such a two-electron system by a method somewhat similar to that of Baber and Hassé, but using $r_1$, $r_2$, and $\cos\theta_{12}$ as independent variables, and it seems that the method of Luke and Meyerott might also be applied to such a system. Williams[16] has applied Stevenson's method to the $H^-$ ion, but came to the conclusion that it has little advantage over a treatment based on superposition of configurations [see § 10.3(1)].

Only a little work with approximate wave functions depending on $r_{12}$ has been done for the excited states of helium.[17] The doubly excited states such as $(2p)^2$ lie well up in the continuum above the $(1s)$ state of $He^+$. On the other hand, in other atoms with states which, in terms of configurations, can be described as consisting of a system of two electrons in the field of a configuration of complete groups, some of the doubly excited states, such as $(4p)^2$ and $(3d)^2$ of neutral calcium, are below the ionization limit, and transitions involving such states give some of the strong lines of the spectrum; and for such states it might well be worth improving on the approximation of Fock's equations by including the dependence of $\Phi$ on $r_{ij}$ for the electrons in these outer wave functions.

## 10.3. SUPERPOSITION OF CONFIGURATIONS

In constructing an approximate wave function by superposing functions representing different configurations, the only ones we need include, in Russell–Saunders coupling, are those that correspond to terms of the same $L$, $S$, and parity.[18]

As mentioned in § 10.1, there are two ways of carrying out calculations of atomic structure including superposition of configurations. One is to carry out a solution of Fock's equations for each configuration separately and then, in superposing the configurations, to regard the radial wave functions as given by these solutions for the separate configurations, and only the coefficients in the linear combination as adjustable to minimize the value of $E'$. The other is to regard the radial wave functions in the wave function for each configuration as being free to be modified by the superposition of the other configuration. The former is considerably the

[15] A. F. Stevenson, *Proc. Roy. Soc.*, **160**, 588 (1937); *Phys. Rev.*, **56**, 586 (1939).

[16] A. O. Williams, *Phys. Rev.*, **90**, 803 (1953).

[17] E. A. Hylleraas and B. Undheim, *Z. Physik*, **65**, 759 (1930); A. Eriksson, *Nova Acta Regiae Soc. Sci. Upsaliensis*, **11**, no. 9 (1942).

[18] See E. U. Condon and G. H. Shortley, *Theory of Atomic Spectra*, ch. 15, § 1, Cambridge (1935).

simpler to work out; the latter may give a considerably greater degree of improvement in the wave function for the whole system.

A thorough examination of superposition of configurations, and its effect on transition probabilities, for the low terms of neutral Mg and neutral Ca, has been made by Biermann and Trefftz,[19] taking the radial wave functions of the various configurations as unaffected by the superposition.

The derivation of the formula for $E'$, and of Fock's equations, when superposition of configurations is taken into account in obtaining the radial wave functions, has been given by Hartree, Hartree, and Swirles[20] for superposition of $(2s)^2(2p)^{q-2}$ and $(2p)^q$ configurations. The resulting equations are somewhat elaborate, but the nature of the problem of evaluating a solution of them can be illustrated by the simpler case of the superposition of $(1s)^2$ and $(2p)^2\,{}^1S$ for the normal state of a two-electron system.

The wave function for the $(1s)^2$ configuration is

$$(1/r_1r_2)P(1s; r_1)P(1s; r_2).$$

That for the ${}^1S$ state of the $(2p)^2$ configuration must be isotropic in the sense of § 1.9; that is, its value at any point must be unaffected by rotation of the whole wave function relative to the frame of reference. Also it must be a linear combination of products of a $p$ wave function of electron 1 and a $p$ wave function of electron 2. The only such function is

$$(1/r_1r_2)P(2p; r_1)P(2p; r_2)[\cos\theta_1\cos\theta_2 + \sin\theta_1\sin\theta_2\cos(\phi_2 - \phi_1)]$$
$$\equiv (1/r_1r_2)P(2p; r_1)P(2p; r_2)\cos\theta_{12}.$$

Hence the approximate wave function § 10.1(3), written more fully, is

$$\Phi = (1/r_1r_2)[P(1s; r_1)P(1s; r_2) + \mu P(2p; r_1)P(2p; r_2)\cos\theta_{12}]. \quad (1)$$

This shows a relation to Luke and Meyerott's treatment mentioned in § 10.2, for formula § 10.2(2) reduces to formula (1) if the functions $u_n(r_1, r_2)$ in § 10.2(2) are supposed separable in $r_1$, $r_2$.

The expression for $E'$ and the equations for $P(1s)$, $P(2p)$ and $\mu$ can be written down from the corresponding expressions for $P(2s)$ and $P(2p)$ for the configurations $(2s)^2$ and $(2p)^2\,{}^1S$, and are

$$\left\{\frac{d^2}{dr^2} + \frac{2}{r}[N - Y_0(2s, 1s; r)] - \varepsilon_{1s,1s}\right\} P(1s; r)$$
$$- \frac{2\gamma\mu}{r} Y_1(1s, 2p; r)P(2p; r) = 0 \quad (2)$$

[19] L. Biermann and E. Trefftz, *Z. Astrophys.*, **26**, 213 (1949); E. Trefftz, *ibid.*, **26**, 240 (1949); **28**, 67 (1951); **29**, 287 (1952).

[20] D. R. Hartree, W. Hartree, and B. Swirles, *Phil. Trans. Roy. Soc.*, **238**, 229 (1939).

$$\left\{\frac{d^2}{dr^2} + \frac{2}{r}[N - Y_0(2p, 2p; r) - \tfrac{1}{5}Y_2(2p, 2p; r)] - \varepsilon_{2p,2p} - \frac{2}{r^2}\right\} P(2p; r)$$

$$- \frac{2\gamma}{\mu r} Y_1(1s, 2p; r)P(1s; r) = 0 \qquad (3)$$

$$\frac{\mu}{1-\mu^2} = \gamma G_1(1s, 2p) \Big/ \Big[ \varepsilon_{1s,1s} - \varepsilon_{2p,2p} + F_0(1s, 1s) - F_0(2p, 2p)$$

$$- \tfrac{2}{5}F_2(2p, 2p) + 2\gamma \left(\mu - \frac{1}{\mu}\right) G_1(1s, 2p) \Big] \qquad (4)$$

$$\gamma = 1/\sqrt{3}.$$

The process of solution consists in estimating a value of $\mu$, solving equations (2), (3) with this value of $\mu$, and then evaluating a "final" value of $\mu$ for this stage of the calculation from formula (4), using in the right-hand side of (4) the estimated value of $\mu$ adopted. The estimate of $\mu$ is then modified until the "final" value of $\mu$ so obtained is in adequate agreement with the estimated value. The solution of equations (2) and (3) for a given value of $\mu$ can be carried out by the methods of Chapter 5.

Calculations for the $(2s)^2(2p)^2$ and $(2p)^4$ configurations of $O^{+2}$ have shown that in that case the modifications of the $(2s)$ and $(2p)$ wave functions arising from the superposition are quite small, too small to justify the labor of evaluating them. In this case, however, the ranges of $r$ in which the radial wave functions $P(2s)$ and $P(2p)$ are large are much the same. The argument of § 10.1 suggests that in a wave function $\Phi_A + \mu\Phi_B$ where $|\mu| < 1$ (so that $\mu\Phi_B$ can be regarded as an improving correction "superposed on" $\Phi_A$) the radial wave functions in $\Phi_B$ may often be considerably different from those for the configuration $B$ alone.[21]

A considerable development of this approach, using analytic wave functions, has been carried out by Boys and his co-workers.[22] Boys derives the formula for $E'$ for the kinds of wave functions he uses from vector-coupling arguments rather than by a development of the method of Chapters 3 and 6, and as basic functions uses a nonorthogonal set of functions $r^m e^{-kr}$ or $r^m e^{-kr^2}$. This choice is made to simplify and systematize the various integrals to be evaluated; the process of orthogonalizing

[21] See also A. P. Iustis and others, *J. Exptl. and Theoret. Physics of U.S.S.R.*, **23,** 129 (1952); **25,** 264 (1953); **27,** 425 (1954) and references 27, 29, 30 in Appendix 1.

[22] For the general theory, see S. F. Boys, *Proc. Roy. Soc.*, **206,** 489 (1951); **207** 181, 197 (1951); *Phil. Trans Roy. Soc.*, **245,** 95 (1952); M. J. M. Bernal and S. F. Boys, *Phil. Trans. Roy. Soc.*, **245,** 116 (1952); S. F. Boys and R. C. Sahni, *Phil. Trans. Roy. Soc.*, **246,** 463 (1953). For results of applications to particular atoms, see references in Appendix 1.

the wave functions is, in effect, carried out on these integrals and not on the wave functions themselves.

## 10.4. POLARIZATION

For a configuration consisting of a "core" of complete groups and one wave function of a "series" or "valency" electron, a correlation effect between the "series" electron and the core which is omitted in the self-consistent field treatment, with or without exchange, is one that can be expressed classically as "polarization" of the core by the series electron.[23]

At a large distance $r$ from the core, the electron produces at the core a field $1/r^2$; if $\alpha$ is the polarizability of the core, the induced dipole moment of the core is $\alpha/r^2$; this produces at the position of the electron an attractive field $2\alpha/r^5$, and, as far as the motion of this electron is concerned, this field can be regarded as derived from a potential

$$W(r) = \alpha/2r^4. \tag{1}$$

This expression for the "polarization potential" can only be expected to apply for large $r$. Whether correlation effects between the "series" electron and the core for small values of $r$ can be expressed approximately by means of a "polarization potential" at all is uncertain; nevertheless we may examine empirically whether the addition to the potential of a contribution $W(r)$ with the asymptotic behavior specified by (1) will improve the agreement between calculated values of atomic properties, such as energy levels and scattering cross sections, and results of observations when these are available.

Even the direction of the departure from formula (1) is uncertain. If the core, from the point of view of an electron outside it, is regarded as a conducting or dielectric sphere of radius $a$, then from the theory of images it would be expected that $W(r)$ would increase faster than $1/r^4$ with decreasing $r$, when $r$ is larger than $a$ but not large compared with $a$. However, it seems unlikely that treatment of the core as a conducting or dielectric sphere would apply for values of $r$ as small as the radius of the main maximum of the outermost wave functions of the core, and it is doubtful if it applies at all.

In a study of the effect of polarization on the distribution of intensity in a continuous spectrum beyond the series limit, Bates,[24] used a polarization potential

$$W(r) = \tfrac{1}{2}\alpha/(r^2 + a^2)^2; \tag{2}$$

[23] For a quantum mechanical treatment of this interaction between a "series" electron and the core, see J. H. van Vleck and N. G. Whitelaw, *Phys. Rev.*, **44**, 551 (1933).

[24] D. R. Bates, *Proc. Roy. Soc.*, **188**, 350 (1947).

this increases with decreasing $r$, giving an attractive force, over the whole range of $r$. Biermann and others[25] have examined the effect of polarization on the energy levels of the terms of various optical spectra, using a polarization potential

$$W(r) = \tfrac{1}{2}(\alpha/r^4)\{1 - \exp[-(r/a)^p]\} \tag{3}$$

with $p > 4$ to make $W(r)$ finite at the origin. Such a formula gives an outward force for small $r$.

Both Bates's and Biermann's formulae give a potential which increases *less* rapidly than $1/r^4$ as $r$ decreases, when $r/a$ is greater than 1 but not large compared with 1, which disagrees with what would be expected from a classical electrostatic argument if this were applicable. However, Douglas[26] has found that, if one does not restrict $W(r)$ to the limited class of functions specified by some analytical formula with adjustable parameters, but works with functions specified numerically, then good agreement with observed energy levels in an optical spectrum can be obtained by taking a function $W(r)$ which at first increases faster than $1/r^4$ as $r$ decreases, and subsequently continues to increase, though less fast than $1/r^4$, instead of decreasing as Biermann's expression (3) does. The treatment of polarization is a matter which deserves further examination.

[25] L. Biermann and E. Trefftz, *Z. Astrophys.*, **30**, 275 (1953).

[26] A. S. Douglas, *Proc. Cambridge Phil. Soc.*, **52**, 687 (1956).

# APPENDIX 1

## Results of Calculations of Atomic Structures

A table of references to results of calculations of atomic structures published up to 1947, is given in *Repts. Progr. Phy.*, **11**, 113, Table I, p. 134 (1948). The following are addenda to that list.

| Atom | Ref. No. (see below) | Atom | Ref. No. | Atom | Ref. No. | Atom | Ref. No. |
|---|---|---|---|---|---|---|---|
| $H^-$ | 9, 12 | $Ne^{+2}$ | 14 | $Cl^-$ | 8 | $Fe^{+16}$ | 28 |
| He | 2, 10, 11 | Na | 3 | Cl | 8 | $Zn^{+2}$ | 17 |
| $Li^+$ | 11, 20 | $Na^+$ | 3 | Ca | 25, 26 | $Zr^{+4}$ | 1 |
| Be | 5, 6, 30 | Mg | 4, 23, 24 | $Ti^{+2}$ | 17 | $Mo^+$ | 21 |
| B | 7, 29 | $Al^{+2}$ | 19 | $V^+$ | 17 | $In^{+3}$ | 22 |
| C | 7, 27 | $Al^{+3}$ | 19, 28 | Mn | 17 | $Sb^{+3}$ | 22 |
| $O^{+6}$ | 11 | $S^-$ | 8 | $Mn^+$ | 17 | $Au^+$ | 13, 18 |
| $F^-$ | 3, 28 | S | 8 | $Mn^{+2}$ | 16 | $Tl^+$ | 13 |
| | | | | $Fe^{+13}$ | 15 | $Tl^{+2}$ | 13 |

Of these, all up to $Mn^{+2}$, and also $Fe^{+16}$ and $Zn^{+2}$, have exchange terms included in the calculations.

## References


[1] Altmann, S., *Proc. Phys. Soc.*, **68A**, 987 (1955).

[2] Bartlett, J. H., *Phys. Rev.*, **98**, 1067 (1955).

[3] Bernal, M. J. M., and S. F. Boys, *Phil. Trans. Roy. Soc.*, **245**, 139 (1952).

[4] Bierman, L., and E. Trefftz, *Z. Astrophys.*, **28**, 213 (1949).

[5] Boys, S. F., *Proc. Roy. Soc.*, **201**, 125 (1950).

[6] Boys, S. F., *ibid*, **217**, 136 (1953).

[7] Boys, S. F., *ibid.*, **217**, 235 (1953).

[8] Boys, S. F., and V. E. Price, *Phil. Trans. Roy. Soc.*, **246**, 451 (1954).

[9] Chandrasekhar, S., *Revs. Mod. Phys.*, **16**, 301 (1944).

[10] Chandrasekhar, S., D. Elbert, and G. Herzberg, *Phys. Rev.*, **91**, 1172 (1953).

[11] Chandrasekhar, S., and G. Herzberg, *Phys. Rev.*, **98**, 1050 (1955).

[12] Chandrasekhar, S., and M. K. Klogdahl, *Astrophys. J.*, **98**, 205 (1943).

[13] Douglas, A. S., D. R. Hartree, and W. A. Runciman, *Proc. Cambridge Phil. Soc.*, **51**, 486 (1955).

[14] Garstang, R. H., *Proc. Cambridge Phil. Soc.*, **47**, 243 (1951).

[15] Gold, M. T., *Monthly Notices Roy. Astron. Soc.*, **109**, 471 (1949).

[16] Hartree, D. R., *Proc. Cambridge Phil. Soc.*, **51**, 126 (1954).

[17] Hartree, D. R., *J. Opt. Soc. Amer.*, **46**, 350 (1956).

[18] Henry, W. G., *Proc. Phys. Soc.*, **67A**, 769 (1954).

[19] Katterbach, K., *Z. Astrophys*, **33**, 165 (1953).

[20] Luke, P. J., R. Meyerott, and W. W. Clendinin, *Phys. Rev.*, **85**, 41 (1952).

[21] Ridley, E. C., *Proc. Cambridge Phil. Soc.*, **51**, 702 (1955).

[22] Ridley, E. C., *Proc. Cambridge Phil. Soc.*, **52**, 698 (1956).

[23] Trefftz, E., *Z. Astrophys.*, **26**, 240 (1947).

[24] Trefftz, E., *ibid.*, **28**, 67 (1949).

[25] Trefftz, E., *ibid.*, **29**, 287 (1950).

[26] Trefftz, E., *ibid.*, **30**, 175 (1951).

[27] Bolotin, A, B., I. B. Levinson, and L. I. Levin, *Soviet Physics JETP*, **2**, 391 (1956).

[28] Froese, C., *Proc. Cambridge Phil Soc.*, (in press).

[29] Glembotskii, I. I., V. V. Kibartas, and A. P. Iustis, *Soviet Physics JETP*, **2**, 476 (1956).

[30] Kibartas, V. V., V. I. Kavetskis, and A. P. Iustis, *Soviet Physics JETP*, **2**, 481 (1956).

# APPENDIX 2

**Mean radii $\bar{r}$, screening numbers $\sigma$, and reduced radial wave functions $P^*(nl, s)$ deduced from results of calculations of the self-consistent field with exchange** (§§ **7.4, 7.5**)

$$\bar{r} = \int_0^\infty rP^2\,dr, \qquad \bar{r} = \frac{\bar{r}_{(H)}}{N - \sigma}, \qquad s = \frac{r}{\bar{r}}, \qquad P^*(nl; s) = \bar{r}^{1/2}P(nl; r).$$

Table A1 gives mean radii $\bar{r}$ and screening numbers $\sigma$ for wave functions with $(nl) = (2s), (2p), (3s), (3p)$, and $(3d)$. Tables A2 through A7 give reduced radial wave functions $P^*(nl; s)$. The data in these tables have been derived[1] from results, either published or in course of publication, of self-consistent field calculations with exchange (for references, see Appendix 1). The accuracy of these results is not always enough to establish the third decimal in $P^*(nl; s)$ to 1 or 2 units, and for some of the results for the $(3d)$ wave function the uncertainty is larger since the radial wave functions $P(nl; r)$ from which the reduced wave functions are derived are only the results of preliminary calculations.

[1] The calculation of these tables, from the available data in the form of radial wave functions $P(nl; r)$ as functions of $r$, has been carried out on the EDSAC, the automatic digital computer at the Mathematical Laboratory of the University of Cambridge, England, using a program prepared by J. M. Watt.

## Table A1. Mean radii $\bar{r}$ and screening numbers $\sigma$

| | | | (2s) | | (2p) | |
|---|---|---|---|---|---|---|
| | | | $\bar{r}$ | $\sigma$ | $\bar{r}$ | $\sigma$ |
| | | | Atoms with complete L shells | | | |
| 29 | $Cu^+$ | | 0.2375 | 3.74 | 0.2076 | 4.89 |
| 26 | $Fe^{+16}$ | | 0.2644 | 3.30 | 0.2318 | 4.43 |
| 20 | $Ca^{+2}$ | | 0.3635 | 3.48 | 0.3267 | 4.70 |
| 19 | $K^+$ | | 0.3864 | 3.48 | 0.3494 | 4.68 |
| 17 | $Cl^-$ | | 0.4418 | 3.42 | 0.4055 | 4.67 |
| 14 | $Si^{+4}$ | | 0.5615 | 3.30 | 0.5302 | 4.57 |
| 13 | $Al^{+3}$ | | 0.6194 | 3.31 | 0.5960 | 4.61 |
| 12 | $Mg^{+2}$ | | 0.6911 | 3.32 | 0.6816 | 4.68 |
| 11 | $Na^+$ | | 0.7790 | 3.29 | 0.7964 | 4.72 |
| 9 | $F^-$ | | 1.0356 | 3.21 | 1.2553 | 5.02 |
| | | | Atoms with incomplete L shells | | | |
| 10 | $Ne^{+2}$ | $(2p)^4\ {}^3P$ | 0.8295 | 2.77 | 0.805 | 3.78 |
| 8 | $O^{+2}$ | $(2p)^2\ {}^3P$ | 1.0345 | 2.21 | 0.984 | 2.93 |
| | $O^+$ | $(2p)^3\ {}^4S$ | 1.089 | 2.49 | 1.078 | 3.36 |
| | $O^0$ | $(2p)^4\ {}^3P$ | 1.143 | 2.75 | 1.232 | 3.94 |
| 7 | $N^0$ | $(2p)^3\ {}^4S$ | 1.333 | 2.50 | 1.414 | 3.46 |
| 6 | $C^0$ | $(2p)^2\ {}^3P$ | 1.588 | 2.22 | 1.719 | 3.08 |
| 8 | $O^-$ | $(2p)^5\ {}^2P$ | 1.186 | 2.94 | 1.470 | 4.60 |
| 7 | $N^-$ | $(2p)^4\ {}^3P$ | 1.390 | 2.68 | 1.764 | 4.16 |

| | | | (3s) | | (3p) | | (3d) | |
|---|---|---|---|---|---|---|---|---|
| | | | $\bar{r}$ | $\sigma$ | $\bar{r}$ | $\sigma$ | $\bar{r}$ | $\sigma$ |
| 30 | $Zn^{+2}$ | | | | | | 0.855 | 17.72 |
| 29 | $Cu^+$ | | 0.725 | 10.38 | 0.758 | 12.51 | 0.979 | 18.28 |
| 25 | $Mn^{+4}$ | $(3d)^3\ {}^4F$ | 0.843 | 8.98 | 0.8785 | 10.77 | 0.949 | 13.94 |
| | $Mn^{+2}$ | $(3d)^5\ {}^6S$ | | | 0.911 | 11.28 | 1.082 | 15.30 |
| | $Mn^+$ | $(3d)^6\ {}^5D$ | | | | | 1.248 | 16.58 |
| | $Mn^0$ | $(3d)^7\ {}^4F$ | | | | | 1.49 | 18.0 |
| 23 | $V^{+2}$ | $(3d)^3\ {}^4F$ | | | | | 1.285 | 14.82 |
| 22 | $Ti^+$ | $(3d)^3\ {}^4F$ | | | | | 1.645 | 15.61 |
| 20 | $Ca^{+2}$ | | 1.158 | 8.34 | 1.263 | 10.10 | | |
| | $Ca^+$ | $(3d)^1\ {}^2D$ | | | | | 2.536 | 15.86 |
| 19 | $K^+$ | | 1.277 | 8.43 | 1.431 | 10.26 | | |
| 18 | $Ar^0$ | | 1.422 | 8.51 | 1.663 | 10.48 | | |
| 17 | $Cl^-$ | | 1.607 | 8.60 | 2.034 | 10.85 | | |

## Table A2. Reduced (2*s*) radial wave functions
## Atoms with complete *L* shells

| $s = r/\bar{r}$ | H | $Cu^{+}$ | $Ca^{+2}$ | $K^{+}$ | $Cl^{-}$ | $Si^{+4}$ | $Mg^{+2}$ | $Na^{+}$ |
|---|---|---|---|---|---|---|---|---|
| 0.00 | 0 | 0 | 0 | 0 | 0 | 0 | 0 | 0 |
| 0.02 | 0.184 | 0.190 | 0.192 | 0.192 | 0.192 | 0.194 | 0.197 | 0.198 |
| 0.04 | 0.324 | 0.329 | 0.330 | 0.329 | 0.330 | 0.329 | 0.331 | 0.331 |
| 0.06 | 0.427 | 0.425 | 0.422 | 0.421 | 0.420 | 0.416 | 0.413 | 0.412 |
| 0.08 | 0.497 | 0.484 | 0.476 | 0.475 | 0.472 | 0.465 | 0.457 | 0.451 |
| 0.10 | 0.539 | 0.514 | 0.500 | 0.498 | 0.493 | 0.481 | 0.466 | 0.458 |
| 0.12 | 0.557 | 0.518 | 0.499 | 0.496 | 0.488 | 0.470 | 0.451 | 0.439 |
| 0.14 | 0.554 | 0.502 | 0.478 | 0.473 | 0.463 | 0.441 | 0.416 | 0.400 |
| 0.16 | 0.535 | 0.469 | 0.440 | 0.435 | 0.422 | 0.396 | 0.365 | 0.346 |
| 0.18 | 0.501 | 0.423 | 0.390 | 0.384 | 0.369 | 0.340 | 0.305 | 0.281 |
| 0.20 | 0.456 | 0.367 | 0.330 | 0.323 | 0.307 | 0.274 | 0.235 | 0.210 |
| 0.22 | 0.402 | 0.303 | 0.263 | 0.256 | 0.238 | 0.202 | 0.160 | 0.134 |
| 0.24 | 0.340 | 0.233 | 0.191 | 0.183 | 0.165 | 0.127 | 0.082 | + 0.054 |
| 0.26 | 0.272 | 0.160 | 0.115 | 0.107 | 0.088 | + 0.049 | + 0.003 | − 0.026 |
| 0.28 | 0.201 | 0.083 | + 0.038 | + 0.029 | + 0.010 | − 0.029 | − 0.078 | − 0.107 |
| 0.30 | + 0.127 | + 0.006 | − 0.040 | − 0.049 | − 0.069 | − 0.108 | − 0.156 | − 0.186 |
| 0.35 | − 0.064 | − 0.187 | − 0.231 | − 0.239 | − 0.259 | − 0.297 | − 0.344 | − 0.372 |
| 0.40 | − 0.250 | − 0.368 | − 0.408 | − 0.416 | − 0.434 | − 0.469 | − 0.510 | − 0.536 |
| 0.45 | − 0.424 | − 0.531 | − 0.565 | − 0.572 | − 0.587 | − 0.617 | − 0.654 | − 0.675 |
| 0.50 | − 0.580 | − 0.671 | − 0.699 | − 0.705 | − 0.717 | − 0.741 | − 0.771 | − 0.789 |
| 0.55 | − 0.714 | − 0.787 | − 0.810 | − 0.813 | − 0.823 | − 0.841 | − 0.863 | − 0.877 |
| 0.60 | − 0.825 | − 0.881 | − 0.896 | − 0.898 | − 0.906 | − 0.918 | − 0.933 | − 0.942 |
| 0.65 | − 0.913 | − 0.952 | − 0.962 | − 0.964 | − 0.968 | − 0.974 | − 0.983 | − 0.988 |
| 0.70 | − 0.980 | − 1.003 | − 1.007 | − 1.008 | − 1.010 | − 1.012 | − 1.014 | − 1.017 |
| 0.75 | − 1.027 | − 1.035 | − 1.036 | − 1.036 | − 1.035 | − 1.033 | − 1.031 | − 1.030 |
| 0.80 | − 1.056 | − 1.053 | − 1.049 | − 1.048 | − 1.046 | − 1.042 | − 1.036 | − 1.031 |
| 0.9 | − 1.069 | − 1.048 | − 1.040 | − 1.038 | − 1.034 | − 1.025 | − 1.013 | − 1.005 |
| 1.0 | − 1.035 | − 1.005 | − 0.995 | − 0.993 | − 0.988 | − 0.977 | − 0.962 | − 0.953 |
| 1.1 | − 0.970 | − 0.938 | − 0.928 | − 0.926 | − 0.921 | − 0.910 | − 0.896 | − 0.886 |
| 1.2 | − 0.886 | − 0.857 | − 0.848 | − 0.846 | − 0.842 | − 0.834 | − 0.820 | − 0.811 |
| 1.3 | − 0.793 | − 0.769 | − 0.764 | − 0.761 | − 0.758 | − 0.752 | − 0.742 | − 0.734 |
| 1.4 | − 0.698 | − 0.681 | − 0.678 | − 0.677 | − 0.676 | − 0.672 | − 0.664 | − 0.659 |
| 1.5 | − 0.606 | − 0.597 | − 0.597 | − 0.596 | − 0.595 | − 0.594 | − 0.590 | − 0.586 |
| 1.6 | − 0.520 | − 0.519 | − 0.520 | − 0.519 | − 0.520 | − 0.521 | − 0.520 | − 0.518 |
| 1.8 | − 0.371 | − 0.383 | − 0.386 | − 0.387 | − 0.389 | − 0.394 | − 0.398 | − 0.400 |
| 2.0 | − 0.258 | − 0.276 | − 0.282 | − 0.283 | − 0.285 | − 0.291 | − 0.299 | − 0.304 |
| 2.2 | − 0.174 | − 0.196 | − 0.202 | − 0.203 | − 0.206 | − 0.212 | − 0.222 | − 0.228 |
| 2.4 | − 0.115 | − 0.138 | − 0.143 | − 0.144 | − 0.147 | − 0.153 | − 0.163 | − 0.170 |
| 2.6 | − 0.075 | − 0.096 | − 0.100 | − 0.102 | − 0.104 | − 0.109 | − 0.118 | − 0.125 |
| 2.8 | − 0.048 | − 0.066 | − 0.070 | − 0.071 | − 0.074 | − 0.077 | − 0.086 | − 0.092 |
| 3.0 | − 0.031 | − 0.046 | − 0.049 | − 0.050 | − 0.052 | − 0.054 | − 0.062 | − 0.069 |
| 3.2 | − 0.020 | − 0.032 | − 0.034 | − 0.035 | − 0.036 | − 0.038 | − 0.044 | − 0.050 |
| 3.4 | − 0.012 | − 0.022 | − 0.024 | − 0.024 | − 0.025 | − 0.026 | − 0.032 | − 0.036 |
| 3.6 | − 0.008 | − 0.015 | − 0.017 | − 0.017 | − 0.017 | − 0.018 | − 0.023 | − 0.026 |
| 3.8 | − 0.005 | − 0.011 | − 0.012 | − 0.012 | − 0.012 | − 0.013 | − 0.017 | − 0.019 |
| 4.0 | − 0.003 | − 0.008 | − 0.008 | − 0.008 | − 0.008 | − 0.009 | − 0.013 | − 0.014 |
| 4.2 | − 0.002 | − 0.006 | − 0.006 | − 0.006 | − 0.006 | − 0.006 | − 0.010 | − 0.010 |
| 4.4 | − 0.001 | − 0.004 | − 0.004 | − 0.004 | − 0.004 | − 0.004 | − 0.008 | − 0.008 |
| 4.6 | | − 0.002 | − 0.003 | − 0.003 | − 0.003 | − 0.003 | − 0.005 | − 0.005 |
| 4.8 | | − 0.001 | − 0.002 | − 0.002 | − 0.002 | − 0.002 | − 0.004 | − 0.004 |
| 5.0 | | − 0.001 | − 0.002 | − 0.001 | − 0.001 | − 0.001 | − 0.002 | − 0.002 |

## Table A3. Reduced (2*s*) radial wave functions Atoms with incomplete *L* shells

| $s = r/\bar{r}$ | $Ne^{+2}$ $(2p)^4$ $^3P$ | $O^{+2}$ $(2p)^2$ $^3P$ | $O^+$ $(2p)^3$ $^4S$ | $O^0$ $(2p)^4$ $^3P$ | $N^0$ $(2p)^3$ $^4S$ | $C^0$ $(2p)^2$ $^3P$ | $O^-$ $(2p)^5$ $^2P$ | $N^-$ $(2p)^4$ $^3P$ |
|---|---|---|---|---|---|---|---|---|
| 0.00 | 0 | 0 | 0 | 0 | 0 | 0 | 0 | 0 |
| 0.02 | 0.194 | 0.191 | 0.195 | 0.198 | 0.197 | 0.195 | 0.203 | 0.201 |
| 0.04 | 0.327 | 0.321 | 0.324 | 0.328 | 0.324 | 0.320 | 0.332 | 0.328 |
| 0.06 | 0.410 | 0.403 | 0.402 | 0.402 | 0.396 | 0.390 | 0.404 | 0.398 |
| 0.08 | 0.452 | 0.446 | 0.440 | 0.435 | 0.426 | 0.418 | 0.433 | 0.424 |
| 0.10 | 0.462 | 0.457 | 0.446 | 0.435 | 0.424 | 0.414 | 0.428 | 0.417 |
| 0.12 | 0.448 | 0.444 | 0.426 | 0.410 | 0.397 | 0.387 | 0.398 | 0.384 |
| 0.14 | 0.414 | 0.412 | 0.388 | 0.366 | 0.352 | 0.341 | 0.348 | 0.334 |
| 0.16 | 0.365 | 0.366 | 0.336 | 0.308 | 0.294 | 0.283 | 0.285 | 0.270 |
| 0.18 | 0.304 | 0.308 | 0.273 | 0.240 | 0.226 | 0.216 | 0.214 | 0.198 |
| 0.20 | 0.236 | 0.242 | 0.203 | 0.165 | 0.152 | 0.142 | 0.135 | 0.119 |
| 0.22 | 0.164 | 0.171 | 0.129 | 0.087 | 0.074 | 0.064 | 0.054 | 0.037 |
| 0.24 | 0.086 | 0.096 | 0.051 | 0.007 | −0.006 | −0.014 | −0.029 | −0.045 |
| 0.26 | 0.008 | 0.019 | −0.028 | −0.074 | −0.086 | −0.093 | −0.112 | −0.128 |
| 0.28 | −0.071 | −0.058 | −0.107 | −0.154 | −0.165 | −0.171 | −0.193 | −0.208 |
| 0.30 | −0.149 | −0.135 | −0.184 | −0.232 | −0.243 | −0.247 | −0.272 | −0.286 |
| 0.35 | −0.336 | −0.318 | −0.367 | −0.415 | −0.422 | −0.424 | −0.454 | −0.466 |
| 0.40 | −0.503 | −0.485 | −0.530 | −0.573 | −0.579 | −0.579 | −0.610 | −0.619 |
| 0.45 | −0.646 | −0.630 | −0.668 | −0.706 | −0.709 | −0.709 | −0.737 | −0.744 |
| 0.50 | −0.765 | −0.750 | −0.781 | −0.812 | −0.814 | −0.813 | −0.838 | −0.842 |
| 0.55 | −0.859 | −0.847 | −0.870 | −0.893 | −0.894 | −0.893 | −0.914 | −0.917 |
| 0.60 | −0.930 | −0.921 | −0.937 | −0.952 | −0.954 | −0.952 | −0.967 | −0.970 |
| 0.65 | −0.982 | −0.976 | −0.985 | −0.993 | −0.993 | −0.992 | −1.001 | −1.002 |
| 0.70 | −1.015 | −1.013 | −1.015 | −1.017 | −1.017 | −1.016 | −1.019 | −1.019 |
| 0.75 | −1.034 | −1.033 | −1.030 | −1.026 | −1.027 | −1.027 | −1.024 | −1.023 |
| 0.80 | −1.039 | −1.041 | −1.033 | −1.025 | −1.025 | −1.025 | −1.018 | −1.017 |
| 0.9 | −1.018 | −1.024 | −1.010 | −0.996 | −0.995 | −0.996 | −0.983 | −0.981 |
| 1.0 | −0.968 | −0.976 | −0.960 | −0.942 | −0.942 | −0.943 | −0.926 | −0.924 |
| 1.1 | −0.902 | −0.911 | −0.894 | −0.875 | −0.875 | −0.878 | −0.858 | −0.856 |
| 1.2 | −0.825 | −0.834 | −0.818 | −0.802 | −0.801 | −0.804 | −0.785 | −0.784 |
| 1.3 | −0.745 | −0.752 | −0.740 | −0.726 | −0.726 | −0.729 | −0.712 | −0.711 |
| 1.4 | −0.666 | −0.671 | −0.663 | −0.652 | −0.653 | −0.657 | −0.641 | −0.640 |
| 1.5 | −0.590 | −0.593 | −0.589 | −0.583 | −0.583 | −0.584 | −0.574 | −0.573 |
| 1.6 | −0.519 | −0.520 | −0.520 | −0.518 | −0.518 | −0.518 | −0.512 | −0.511 |
| 1.8 | −0.394 | −0.392 | −0.398 | −0.403 | −0.403 | −0.402 | −0.403 | −0.404 |
| 2.0 | −0.294 | −0.290 | −0.300 | −0.309 | −0.308 | −0.307 | −0.315 | −0.316 |
| 2.2 | −0.216 | −0.210 | −0.223 | −0.235 | −0.234 | −0.233 | −0.245 | −0.245 |
| 2.4 | −0.157 | −0.151 | −0.164 | −0.177 | −0.178 | −0.175 | −0.190 | −0.191 |
| 2.6 | −0.113 | −0.108 | −0.119 | −0.133 | −0.132 | −0.129 | −0.146 | −0.148 |
| 2.8 | −0.081 | −0.076 | −0.086 | −0.100 | −0.098 | −0.095 | −0.113 | −0.115 |
| 3.0 | −0.058 | −0.053 | −0.062 | −0.073 | −0.073 | −0.071 | −0.088 | −0.089 |
| 3.2 | −0.041 | −0.037 | −0.044 | −0.055 | −0.054 | −0.052 | −0.068 | −0.068 |
| 3.4 | −0.029 | −0.025 | −0.032 | −0.040 | −0.040 | −0.038 | −0.052 | −0.052 |
| 3.6 | −0.020 | −0.017 | −0.023 | −0.030 | −0.029 | −0.027 | −0.040 | −0.040 |
| 3.8 | −0.014 | −0.012 | −0.016 | −0.022 | −0.021 | −0.020 | −0.031 | −0.031 |
| 4.0 | −0.010 | −0.008 | −0.011 | −0.016 | −0.016 | −0.014 | −0.024 | −0.023 |
| 4.2 | −0.006 | −0.006 | −0.008 | −0.012 | −0.011 | −0.011 | −0.018 | −0.018 |
| 4.4 | −0.003 | −0.004 | −0.006 | −0.009 | −0.008 | −0.008 | −0.014 | −0.014 |
| 4.6 | −0.002 | −0.003 | −0.004 | −0.007 | −0.006 | −0.005 | −0.011 | −0.011 |
| 4.8 | −0.001 | −0.002 | −0.003 | −0.005 | −0.004 | −0.003 | −0.008 | −0.008 |
| 5.0 | −0.001 | −0.001 | −0.002 | −0.004 | −0.003 | −0.002 | −0.006 | −0.006 |

**Table A4. Reduced (2*p*) radial wave functions**
**Atoms with complete *L* shells**

| $s = r/\bar{r}$ | H | $Cu^+$ | $Ca^{+2}$ | $K^+$ | $Cl^-$ | $Si^{+4}$ | $Mg^{+2}$ | $Na^+$ |
|---|---|---|---|---|---|---|---|---|
| 0.00 | 0 | 0 | 0 | 0 | 0 | 0 | 0 | 0 |
| 0.02 | 0.004 | 0.005 | 0.006 | 0.006 | 0.006 | 0.006 | 0.007 | 0.008 |
| 0.04 | 0.016 | 0.020 | 0.021 | 0.022 | 0.022 | 0.024 | 0.027 | 0.030 |
| 0.06 | 0.035 | 0.042 | 0.045 | 0.046 | 0.047 | 0.051 | 0.057 | 0.061 |
| 0.08 | 0.060 | 0.070 | 0.075 | 0.076 | 0.079 | 0.085 | 0.093 | 0.100 |
| 0.10 | 0.089 | 0.104 | 0.110 | 0.111 | 0.115 | 0.123 | 0.134 | 0.144 |
| 0.12 | 0.122 | 0.140 | 0.149 | 0.151 | 0.155 | 0.165 | 0.180 | 0.192 |
| 0.14 | 0.158 | 0.180 | 0.190 | 0.193 | 0.198 | 0.210 | 0.227 | 0.243 |
| 0.16 | 0.196 | 0.222 | 0.234 | 0.236 | 0.243 | 0.256 | 0.276 | 0.293 |
| 0.18 | 0.236 | 0.265 | 0.278 | 0.281 | 0.288 | 0.302 | 0.325 | 0.344 |
| 0.20 | 0.277 | 0.310 | 0.323 | 0.327 | 0.334 | 0.349 | 0.374 | 0.394 |
| 0.22 | 0.319 | 0.354 | 0.368 | 0.372 | 0.380 | 0.396 | 0.422 | 0.442 |
| 0.24 | 0.361 | 0.398 | 0.413 | 0.417 | 0.424 | 0.442 | 0.468 | 0.490 |
| 0.26 | 0.403 | 0.441 | 0.457 | 0.461 | 0.469 | 0.486 | 0.513 | 0.536 |
| 0.28 | 0.444 | 0.484 | 0.499 | 0.503 | 0.511 | 0.528 | 0.556 | 0.579 |
| 0.30 | 0.485 | 0.525 | 0.540 | 0.544 | 0.553 | 0.570 | 0.597 | 0.619 |
| 0.35 | 0.583 | 0.622 | 0.636 | 0.640 | 0.648 | 0.664 | 0.689 | 0.710 |
| 0.40 | 0.672 | 0.707 | 0.720 | 0.723 | 0.730 | 0.744 | 0.766 | 0.784 |
| 0.45 | 0.750 | 0.780 | 0.791 | 0.794 | 0.799 | 0.810 | 0.829 | 0.844 |
| 0.50 | 0.817 | 0.842 | 0.849 | 0.851 | 0.856 | 0.863 | 0.877 | 0.888 |
| 0.55 | 0.873 | 0.890 | 0.894 | 0.896 | 0.899 | 0.904 | 0.912 | 0.920 |
| 0.60 | 0.917 | 0.927 | 0.928 | 0.929 | 0.931 | 0.932 | 0.936 | 0.940 |
| 0.65 | 0.949 | 0.953 | 0.952 | 0.952 | 0.952 | 0.951 | 0.950 | 0.950 |
| 0.70 | 0.972 | 0.969 | 0.965 | 0.965 | 0.963 | 0.960 | 0.955 | 0.952 |
| 0.75 | 0.984 | 0.976 | 0.970 | 0.970 | 0.967 | 0.961 | 0.953 | 0.947 |
| 0.80 | 0.988 | 0.974 | 0.968 | 0.967 | 0.963 | 0.956 | 0.945 | 0.937 |
| 0.9 | 0.974 | 0.952 | 0.945 | 0.943 | 0.938 | 0.929 | 0.914 | 0.903 |
| 1.0 | 0.937 | 0.913 | 0.903 | 0.901 | 0.896 | 0.885 | 0.869 | 0.856 |
| 1.1 | 0.883 | 0.858 | 0.850 | 0.847 | 0.842 | 0.832 | 0.816 | 0.802 |
| 1.2 | 0.818 | 0.796 | 0.788 | 0.786 | 0.782 | 0.773 | 0.758 | 0.745 |
| 1.3 | 0.748 | 0.729 | 0.724 | 0.721 | 0.718 | 0.712 | 0.700 | 0.687 |
| 1.4 | 0.675 | 0.662 | 0.658 | 0.656 | 0.654 | 0.649 | 0.640 | 0.630 |
| 1.5 | 0.604 | 0.595 | 0.594 | 0.593 | 0.591 | 0.588 | 0.582 | 0.575 |
| 1.6 | 0.535 | 0.532 | 0.532 | 0.532 | 0.531 | 0.531 | 0.528 | 0.523 |
| 1.8 | 0.411 | 0.418 | 0.421 | 0.421 | 0.422 | 0.426 | 0.428 | 0.428 |
| 2.0 | 0.308 | 0.322 | 0.327 | 0.328 | 0.331 | 0.336 | 0.343 | 0.347 |
| 2.2 | 0.226 | 0.244 | 0.250 | 0.252 | 0.256 | 0.262 | 0.272 | 0.279 |
| 2.4 | 0.163 | 0.184 | 0.190 | 0.191 | 0.195 | 0.202 | 0.214 | 0.222 |
| 2.6 | 0.116 | 0.137 | 0.143 | 0.144 | 0.148 | 0.155 | 0.168 | 0.176 |
| 2.8 | 0.082 | 0.102 | 0.107 | 0.108 | 0.111 | 0.118 | 0.130 | 0.139 |
| 3.0 | 0.057 | 0.075 | 0.080 | 0.081 | 0.084 | 0.089 | 0.100 | 0.110 |
| 3.2 | 0.039 | 0.055 | 0.059 | 0.060 | 0.063 | 0.067 | 0.077 | 0.086 |
| 3.4 | 0.027 | 0.041 | 0.044 | 0.045 | 0.047 | 0.050 | 0.059 | 0.067 |
| 3.6 | 0.018 | 0.030 | 0.032 | 0.033 | 0.035 | 0.037 | 0.044 | 0.052 |
| 3.8 | 0.012 | 0.022 | 0.024 | 0.024 | 0.026 | 0.028 | 0.034 | 0.041 |
| 4.0 | 0.008 | 0.016 | 0.018 | 0.018 | 0.019 | 0.021 | 0.026 | 0.032 |
| 4.2 | 0.006 | 0.012 | 0.013 | 0.013 | 0.015 | 0.016 | 0.020 | 0.025 |
| 4.4 | 0.004 | 0.009 | 0.010 | 0.010 | 0.011 | 0.012 | 0.015 | 0.020 |
| 4.6 | 0.003 | 0.007 | 0.007 | 0.007 | 0.008 | 0.008 | 0.011 | 0.016 |
| 4.8 | 0.002 | 0.005 | 0.005 | 0.005 | 0.006 | 0.006 | 0.009 | 0.012 |
| 5.0 | 0.001 | 0.003 | 0.004 | 0.004 | 0.004 | 0.005 | 0.007 | 0.009 |

**Table A5. Reduced $(2p)$ radial wave functions**
**Atoms with incomplete $L$ shells**

| $s = r/\bar{r}$ | $Ne^{+2}$ $(2p)^4$ $^3P$ | $O^{+2}$ $(2p)^2$ $^3P$ | $O^{+}$ $(2p)^3$ $^4S$ | $O^0$ $(2p)^4$ $^3P$ | $N^0$ $(2p)^3$ $^4S$ | $C^0$ $(2p)^2$ $^3P$ | $O^-$ $(2p)^5$ $^2P$ | $N^-$ $(2p)^4$ $^3P$ |
|---|---|---|---|---|---|---|---|---|
| 0.00 | 0 | 0 | 0 | 0 | 0 | 0 | 0 | 0 |
| 0.02 | 0.007 | 0.006 | 0.007 | 0.009 | 0.009 | 0.009 | 0.012 | 0.013 |
| 0.04 | 0.026 | 0.024 | 0.026 | 0.033 | 0.031 | 0.030 | 0.044 | 0.045 |
| 0.06 | 0.054 | 0.050 | 0.055 | 0.067 | 0.063 | 0.064 | 0.088 | 0.090 |
| 0.08 | 0.088 | 0.082 | 0.091 | 0.108 | 0.103 | 0.102 | 0.141 | 0.143 |
| 0.10 | 0.128 | 0.119 | 0.131 | 0.155 | 0.147 | 0.147 | 0.200 | 0.201 |
| 0.12 | 0.172 | 0.160 | 0.175 | 0.205 | 0.195 | 0.195 | 0.259 | 0.262 |
| 0.14 | 0.217 | 0.202 | 0.221 | 0.257 | 0.245 | 0.243 | 0.320 | 0.323 |
| 0.16 | 0.264 | 0.247 | 0.268 | 0.309 | 0.295 | 0.291 | 0.381 | 0.382 |
| 0.18 | 0.311 | 0.292 | 0.316 | 0.360 | 0.345 | 0.340 | 0.440 | 0.440 |
| 0.20 | 0.359 | 0.338 | 0.363 | 0.411 | 0.394 | 0.389 | 0.496 | 0.496 |
| 0.22 | 0.406 | 0.384 | 0.409 | 0.461 | 0.442 | 0.436 | 0.549 | 0.549 |
| 0.24 | 0.451 | 0.428 | 0.455 | 0.508 | 0.489 | 0.482 | 0.598 | 0.598 |
| 0.26 | 0.495 | 0.471 | 0.499 | 0.553 | 0.533 | 0.526 | 0.644 | 0.643 |
| 0.28 | 0.538 | 0.513 | 0.541 | 0.596 | 0.574 | 0.567 | 0.687 | 0.685 |
| 0.30 | 0.578 | 0.553 | 0.582 | 0.636 | 0.614 | 0.607 | 0.725 | 0.723 |
| 0.35 | 0.672 | 0.647 | 0.673 | 0.725 | 0.704 | 0.697 | 0.807 | 0.805 |
| 0.40 | 0.751 | 0.728 | 0.752 | 0.796 | 0.778 | 0.771 | 0.867 | 0.865 |
| 0.45 | 0.815 | 0.796 | 0.816 | 0.852 | 0.837 | 0.831 | 0.910 | 0.906 |
| 0.50 | 0.866 | 0.852 | 0.866 | 0.894 | 0.882 | 0.877 | 0.936 | 0.934 |
| 0.55 | 0.906 | 0.895 | 0.904 | 0.924 | 0.915 | 0.911 | 0.949 | 0.948 |
| 0.60 | 0.933 | 0.927 | 0.932 | 0.941 | 0.936 | 0.934 | 0.952 | 0.951 |
| 0.65 | 0.950 | 0.947 | 0.949 | 0.949 | 0.948 | 0.947 | 0.947 | 0.946 |
| 0.70 | 0.958 | 0.961 | 0.957 | 0.949 | 0.951 | 0.952 | 0.936 | 0.935 |
| 0.75 | 0.959 | 0.965 | 0.957 | 0.942 | 0.948 | 0.950 | 0.920 | 0.919 |
| 0.80 | 0.952 | 0.961 | 0.951 | 0.930 | 0.938 | 0.941 | 0.899 | 0.899 |
| 0.9 | 0.924 | 0.938 | 0.923 | 0.894 | 0.905 | 0.910 | 0.850 | 0.851 |
| 1.0 | 0.881 | 0.897 | 0.880 | 0.846 | 0.860 | 0.865 | 0.796 | 0.798 |
| 1.1 | 0.828 | 0.844 | 0.827 | 0.793 | 0.806 | 0.811 | 0.740 | 0.743 |
| 1.2 | 0.769 | 0.784 | 0.768 | 0.736 | 0.750 | 0.755 | 0.686 | 0.687 |
| 1.3 | 0.708 | 0.721 | 0.707 | 0.680 | 0.692 | 0.696 | 0.633 | 0.634 |
| 1.4 | 0.647 | 0.657 | 0.646 | 0.624 | 0.635 | 0.638 | 0.583 | 0.585 |
| 1.5 | 0.588 | 0.594 | 0.587 | 0.571 | 0.579 | 0.581 | 0.537 | 0.538 |
| 1.6 | 0.531 | 0.534 | 0.530 | 0.521 | 0.525 | 0.528 | 0.494 | 0.494 |
| 1.8 | 0.427 | 0.424 | 0.427 | 0.428 | 0.429 | 0.428 | 0.415 | 0.417 |
| 2.0 | 0.338 | 0.331 | 0.339 | 0.349 | 0.346 | 0.344 | 0.350 | 0.352 |
| 2.2 | 0.265 | 0.254 | 0.266 | 0.283 | 0.277 | 0.273 | 0.296 | 0.296 |
| 2.4 | 0.206 | 0.194 | 0.206 | 0.228 | 0.220 | 0.217 | 0.250 | 0.250 |
| 2.6 | 0.158 | 0.146 | 0.159 | 0.182 | 0.174 | 0.170 | 0.212 | 0.212 |
| 2.8 | 0.121 | 0.108 | 0.122 | 0.146 | 0.137 | 0.132 | 0.179 | 0.179 |
| 3.0 | 0.092 | 0.080 | 0.092 | 0.116 | 0.107 | 0.103 | 0.152 | 0.151 |
| 3.2 | 0.069 | 0.059 | 0.070 | 0.092 | 0.084 | 0.080 | 0.128 | 0.128 |
| 3.4 | 0.052 | 0.043 | 0.053 | 0.073 | 0.065 | 0.061 | 0.109 | 0.109 |
| 3.6 | 0.039 | 0.032 | 0.040 | 0.058 | 0.050 | 0.047 | 0.093 | 0.092 |
| 3.8 | 0.029 | 0.023 | 0.030 | 0.046 | 0.039 | 0.036 | 0.079 | 0.079 |
| 4.0 | 0.022 | 0.017 | 0.022 | 0.036 | 0.031 | 0.027 | 0.067 | 0.067 |
| 4.2 | 0.016 | 0.012 | 0.016 | 0.028 | 0.024 | 0.021 | 0.057 | 0.057 |
| 4.4 | 0.012 | 0.019 | 0.012 | 0.022 | 0.019 | 0.016 | 0.049 | 0.049 |
| 4.6 | 0.009 | 0.007 | 0.009 | 0.017 | 0.014 | 0.013 | 0.042 | 0.042 |
| 4.8 | 0.007 | 0.004 | 0.006 | 0.010 | 0.008 | 0.008 | 0.031 | 0.031 |

**Table A6. Reduced (3s)(3p) radial wave functions**
**Atoms with complete (3s)(3p) groups**

| $s = r/\bar{r}$ | $P^*(3s; s)$ | | | | | $P^*(3p; s)$ | | | | |
|---|---|---|---|---|---|---|---|---|---|---|
| | $Cu^+$ | $Mn^{+4}$ | $Ca^{+2}$ | $K^+$ | $Ar^0$ | $Cu^+$ | $Mn^{+2}$ | $Ca^{+2}$ | $K^+$ | $Ar^0$ |
| 0.00 | 0 | 0 | 0 | 0 | 0 | 0 | 0 | 0 | 0 | 0 |
| 0.02 | 0.279 | 0.269 | 0.266 | 0.264 | 0.259 | 0.042 | 0.043 | 0.045 | 0.049 | 0.054 |
| 0.04 | 0.333 | 0.322 | 0.299 | 0.291 | 0.269 | 0.134 | 0.138 | 0.143 | 0.152 | 0.162 |
| 0.06 | 0.260 | 0.252 | 0.209 | 0.186 | 0.159 | 0.244 | 0.246 | 0.251 | 0.260 | 0.275 |
| 0.08 | 0.125 | 0.121 | 0.064 | 0.036 | 0.003 | 0.348 | 0.349 | 0.350 | 0.358 | 0.368 |
| 0.10 | − 0.033 | − 0.031 | − 0.093 | − 0.122 | − 0.155 | 0.436 | 0.434 | 0.429 | 0.431 | 0.434 |
| 0.12 | − 0.187 | − 0.180 | − 0.240 | − 0.265 | − 0.292 | 0.501 | 0.497 | 0.484 | 0.478 | 0.470 |
| 0.14 | − 0.323 | − 0.312 | − 0.362 | − 0.381 | − 0.400 | 0.542 | 0.535 | 0.513 | 0.499 | 0.478 |
| 0.16 | − 0.433 | − 0.419 | − 0.455 | − 0.466 | − 0.474 | 0.560 | 0.549 | 0.519 | 0.495 | 0.461 |
| 0.18 | − 0.513 | − 0.498 | − 0.519 | − 0.520 | − 0.516 | 0.554 | 0.542 | 0.504 | 0.471 | 0.423 |
| 0.20 | − 0.585 | − 0.548 | − 0.552 | − 0.542 | − 0.528 | 0.529 | 0.516 | 0.471 | 0.429 | 0.370 |
| 0.22 | − 0.587 | − 0.572 | − 0.558 | − 0.540 | − 0.514 | 0.487 | 0.472 | 0.423 | 0.373 | 0.304 |
| 0.24 | − 0.585 | − 0.570 | − 0.542 | − 0.514 | − 0.479 | 0.430 | 0.415 | 0.363 | 0.306 | 0.228 |
| 0.26 | − 0.557 | − 0.548 | − 0.504 | − 0.469 | − 0.425 | 0.362 | 0.348 | 0.293 | 0.231 | 0.146 |
| 0.28 | − 0.514 | − 0.507 | − 0.450 | − 0.409 | − 0.358 | 0.286 | 0.272 | 0.218 | 0.151 | 0.060 |
| 0.30 | − 0.454 | − 0.450 | − 0.383 | − 0.337 | − 0.281 | 0.204 | 0.192 | 0.138 | 0.068 | − 0.027 |
| 0.35 | − 0.257 | − 0.261 | − 0.180 | − 0.125 | − 0.069 | − 0.015 | − 0.024 | − 0.074 | − 0.146 | − 0.242 |
| 0.40 | − 0.023 | − 0.036 | + 0.049 | + 0.105 | + 0.171 | − 0.235 | − 0.240 | − 0.281 | − 0.349 | − 0.439 |
| 0.45 | + 0.213 | + 0.196 | 0.276 | 0.329 | 0.389 | − 0.438 | − 0.440 | − 0.470 | − 0.533 | − 0.611 |
| 0.50 | 0.435 | 0.415 | 0.484 | 0.530 | 0.582 | − 0.615 | − 0.614 | − 0.636 | − 0.688 | − 0.752 |
| 0.55 | 0.628 | 0.608 | 0.664 | 0.702 | 0.744 | − 0.761 | − 0.758 | − 0.774 | − 0.814 | − 0.863 |
| 0.60 | 0.786 | 0.771 | 0.812 | 0.841 | 0.873 | − 0.877 | − 0.872 | − 0.882 | − 0.912 | − 0.946 |
| 0.65 | 0.912 | 0.900 | 0.928 | 0.948 | 0.970 | − 0.964 | − 0.958 | − 0.964 | − 0.982 | − 1.004 |
| 0.70 | 1.005 | 0.998 | 1.013 | 1.025 | 1.037 | − 1.024 | − 1.020 | − 1.021 | − 1.030 | − 1.039 |
| 0.75 | 1.067 | 1.065 | 1.070 | 1.075 | 1.079 | − 1.060 | − 1.057 | − 1.057 | − 1.057 | − 1.056 |
| 0.80 | 1.101 | 1.106 | 1.103 | 1.102 | 1.099 | − 1.077 | − 1.075 | − 1.074 | − 1.069 | − 1.057 |
| 0.9 | 1.113 | 1.124 | 1.111 | 1.101 | 1.088 | − 1.065 | − 1.066 | − 1.066 | − 1.050 | − 1.028 |
| 1.0 | 1.064 | 1.080 | 1.063 | 1.050 | 1.032 | − 1.011 | − 1.016 | − 1.015 | − 0.997 | − 0.970 |
| 1.1 | 0.983 | 0.999 | 0.981 | 0.968 | 0.951 | − 0.935 | − 0.940 | − 0.942 | − 0.923 | − 0.895 |
| 1.2 | 0.884 | 0.898 | 0.884 | 0.872 | 0.858 | − 0.847 | − 0.853 | − 0.856 | − 0.839 | − 0.813 |
| 1.3 | 0.782 | 0.791 | 0.782 | 0.772 | 0.761 | − 0.756 | − 0.763 | − 0.765 | − 0.752 | − 0.731 |
| 1.4 | 0.680 | 0.685 | 0.681 | 0.675 | 0.668 | − 0.668 | − 0.674 | − 0.676 | − 0.667 | − 0.653 |
| 1.5 | 0.585 | 0.585 | 0.586 | 0.583 | 0.580 | − 0.585 | − 0.590 | − 0.590 | − 0.586 | − 0.578 |
| 1.6 | 0.500 | 0.495 | 0.499 | 0.499 | 0.500 | − 0.508 | − 0.512 | − 0.511 | − 0.511 | − 0.510 |
| 1.8 | 0.358 | 0.345 | 0.353 | 0.359 | 0.366 | − 0.379 | − 0.381 | − 0.376 | − 0.383 | − 0.392 |
| 2.0 | 0.251 | 0.234 | 0.244 | 0.253 | 0.263 | − 0.279 | − 0.278 | − 0.271 | − 0.282 | − 0.297 |
| 2.2 | 0.173 | 0.156 | 0.166 | 0.175 | 0.186 | − 0.203 | − 0.199 | − 0.192 | − 0.206 | − 0.223 |
| 2.4 | 0.119 | 0.101 | 0.111 | 0.120 | 0.131 | − 0.147 | − 0.141 | − 0.134 | − 0.147 | − 0.166 |
| 2.6 | 0.081 | 0.065 | 0.073 | 0.082 | 0.092 | − 0.106 | − 0.099 | − 0.093 | − 0.105 | − 0.124 |
| 2.8 | 0.055 | 0.041 | 0.048 | 0.055 | 0.064 | − 0.078 | − 0.068 | − 0.064 | − 0.074 | − 0.092 |
| 3.0 | 0.037 | 0.026 | 0.031 | 0.036 | 0.044 | − 0.054 | − 0.046 | − 0.043 | − 0.052 | − 0.067 |
| 3.2 | 0.025 | 0.016 | 0.020 | 0.024 | 0.030 | − 0.039 | − 0.032 | − 0.030 | − 0.036 | − 0.049 |
| 3.4 | 0.017 | 0.009 | 0.012 | 0.016 | 0.021 | − 0.028 | − 0.022 | − 0.020 | − 0.026 | − 0.036 |
| 3.6 | 0.011 | 0.005 | 0.008 | 0.011 | 0.014 | − 0.020 | − 0.015 | − 0.014 | − 0.018 | − 0.026 |
| 3.8 | 0.008 | 0.002 | 0.005 | 0.007 | 0.010 | − 0.014 | − 0.010 | − 0.009 | − 0.012 | − 0.019 |
| 4.0 | 0.005 | 0.001 | 0.003 | 0.005 | 0.007 | − 0.010 | − 0.007 | − 0.006 | − 0.008 | − 0.014 |
| 4.2 | 0.003 | 0.001 | 0.002 | 0.003 | 0.005 | − 0.006 | − 0.005 | − 0.004 | − 0.006 | − 0.010 |
| 4.4 | 0.002 | | 0.001 | 0.002 | 0.003 | − 0.004 | − 0.003 | − 0.003 | − 0.004 | − 0.007 |
| 4.6 | 0.001 | | 0.001 | 0.001 | 0.002 | − 0.003 | − 0.002 | − 0.002 | − 0.003 | − 0.005 |

## Table A7. Reduced (3$d$) radial wave functions

| $s = r/\bar{r}$ | H | $Mn^{+4}$ $(3d)^3\ {}^4F$ | $Zn^{+2}$ $(3d)^{10}\ {}^1S$ | $Mn^{+2}$ $(3d)^5\ {}^6S$ | $V^{+2}$ $(3d)^3\ {}^4F$ | $Cu^+$ $(3d)^{10}\ {}^1S$ | $Mn^+$ $(3d)^6\ {}^5D$ | $Ti^+$ $(3d)^3\ {}^4F$ | $Ca^+$ $(3d)^1\ {}^2D$ |
|---|---|---|---|---|---|---|---|---|---|
| 0.00 | 0 | 0 | 0 | 0 | 0 | 0 | 0 | 0 | 0 |
| 0.02 | 0.000 | 0.001 | 0.001 | 0.001 | 0.001 | 0.002 | 0.003 | 0.003 | 0.004 |
| 0.04 | 0.002 | 0.006 | 0.007 | 0.007 | 0.009 | 0.010 | 0.011 | 0.013 | 0.022 |
| 0.06 | 0.006 | 0.017 | 0.022 | 0.022 | 0.025 | 0.028 | 0.031 | 0.034 | 0.054 |
| 0.08 | 0.013 | 0.034 | 0.047 | 0.044 | 0.049 | 0.057 | 0.060 | 0.067 | 0.100 |
| 0.10 | 0.024 | 0.059 | 0.080 | 0.074 | 0.080 | 0.095 | 0.099 | 0.110 | 0.155 |
| 0.12 | 0.038 | 0.089 | 0.119 | 0.111 | 0.119 | 0.141 | 0.146 | 0.158 | 0.215 |
| 0.14 | 0.057 | 0.124 | 0.163 | 0.153 | 0.162 | 0.193 | 0.197 | 0.211 | 0.276 |
| 0.16 | 0.079 | 0.163 | 0.212 | 0.199 | 0.209 | 0.249 | 0.252 | 0.267 | 0.338 |
| 0.18 | 0.105 | 0.206 | 0.264 | 0.247 | 0.260 | 0.306 | 0.310 | 0.324 | 0.399 |
| 0.20 | 0.134 | 0.251 | 0.317 | 0.297 | 0.311 | 0.365 | 0.368 | 0.382 | 0.457 |
| 0.22 | 0.167 | 0.297 | 0.371 | 0.348 | 0.362 | 0.424 | 0.425 | 0.439 | 0.512 |
| 0.24 | 0.202 | 0.345 | 0.425 | 0.399 | 0.414 | 0.481 | 0.480 | 0.492 | 0.565 |
| 0.26 | 0.239 | 0.393 | 0.479 | 0.449 | 0.465 | 0.536 | 0.534 | 0.544 | 0.613 |
| 0.28 | 0.279 | 0.440 | 0.531 | 0.498 | 0.514 | 0.589 | 0.585 | 0.594 | 0.656 |
| 0.30 | 0.319 | 0.486 | 0.580 | 0.546 | 0.561 | 0.638 | 0.634 | 0.640 | 0.696 |
| 0.35 | 0.426 | 0.596 | 0.689 | 0.654 | 0.670 | 0.748 | 0.740 | 0.742 | 0.777 |
| 0.40 | 0.534 | 0.695 | 0.782 | 0.748 | 0.762 | 0.834 | 0.823 | 0.821 | 0.835 |
| 0.45 | 0.638 | 0.778 | 0.857 | 0.824 | 0.836 | 0.898 | 0.887 | 0.879 | 0.874 |
| 0.50 | 0.735 | 0.848 | 0.912 | 0.884 | 0.894 | 0.941 | 0.931 | 0.919 | 0.899 |
| 0.55 | 0.821 | 0.903 | 0.948 | 0.928 | 0.935 | 0.967 | 0.959 | 0.946 | 0.913 |
| 0.60 | 0.895 | 0.943 | 0.970 | 0.958 | 0.964 | 0.979 | 0.972 | 0.958 | 0.919 |
| 0.65 | 0.955 | 0.971 | 0.980 | 0.974 | 0.980 | 0.980 | 0.973 | 0.960 | 0.918 |
| 0.70 | 1.001 | 0.987 | 0.980 | 0.980 | 0.985 | 0.972 | 0.967 | 0.956 | 0.912 |
| 0.75 | 1.034 | 0.993 | 0.972 | 0.977 | 0.980 | 0.956 | 0.954 | 0.944 | 0.903 |
| 0.80 | 1.053 | 0.990 | 0.957 | 0.966 | 0.970 | 0.935 | 0.936 | 0.928 | 0.890 |
| 0.9 | 1.056 | 0.963 | 0.914 | 0.931 | 0.931 | 0.884 | 0.887 | 0.885 | 0.858 |
| 1.0 | 0.021 | 0.917 | 0.860 | 0.881 | 0.880 | 0.825 | 0.832 | 0.833 | 0.819 |
| 1.1 | 0.958 | 0.859 | 0.798 | 0.823 | 0.821 | 0.765 | 0.774 | 0.778 | 0.777 |
| 1.2 | 0.876 | 0.793 | 0.735 | 0.760 | 0.758 | 0.706 | 0.716 | 0.723 | 0.731 |
| 1.3 | 0.785 | 0.725 | 0.674 | 0.697 | 0.695 | 0.648 | 0.660 | 0.669 | 0.684 |
| 1.4 | 0.691 | 0.657 | 0.616 | 0.636 | 0.633 | 0.594 | 0.606 | 0.615 | 0.636 |
| 1.5 | 0.599 | 0.591 | 0.562 | 0.577 | 0.574 | 0.544 | 0.555 | 0.565 | 0.587 |
| 1.6 | 0.512 | 0.528 | 0.510 | 0.522 | 0.517 | 0.498 | 0.507 | 0.519 | 0.540 |
| 1.8 | 0.362 | 0.414 | 0.419 | 0.421 | 0.415 | 0.416 | 0.422 | 0.431 | 0.449 |
| 2.0 | 0.247 | 0.319 | 0.344 | 0.337 | 0.329 | 0.347 | 0.350 | 0.354 | 0.368 |
| 2.2 | 0.163 | 0.242 | 0.277 | 0.267 | 0.257 | 0.[illegible]88 | 0.289 | 0.289 | 0.296 |
| 2.4 | 0.105 | 0.182 | 0.222 | 0.209 | 0.200 | 0.240 | 0.238 | 0.234 | 0.236 |
| 2.6 | 0.066 | 0.135 | 0.179 | 0.162 | 0.155 | 0.199 | 0.195 | 0.188 | 0.185 |
| 2.8 | 0.041 | 0.099 | 0.142 | 0.124 | 0.119 | 0.165 | 0.159 | 0.150 | 0.144 |
| 3.0 | 0.025 | 0.072 | 0.114 | 0.095 | 0.091 | 0.138 | 0.130 | 0.120 | 0.111 |
| 3.2 | 0.015 | 0.052 | 0.091 | 0.073 | 0.069 | 0.113 | 0.106 | 0.096 | 0.084 |
| 3.4 | 0.009 | 0.038 | 0.073 | 0.056 | 0.052 | 0.093 | 0.086 | 0.075 | 0.064 |
| 3.6 | 0.005 | 0.027 | 0.058 | 0.043 | 0.039 | 0.077 | 0.069 | 0.060 | 0.048 |
| 3.8 | 0.003 | 0.020 | 0.045 | 0.033 | 0.029 | 0.063 | 0.055 | 0.048 | 0.036 |
| 4.0 | 0.002 | 0.014 | 0.037 | 0.025 | 0.022 | 0.052 | 0.046 | 0.038 | 0.027 |
| 4.2 | 0.001 | 0.009 | 0.029 | 0.019 | 0.017 | 0.043 | 0.037 | 0.030 | 0.020 |
| 4.4 | | 0.006 | 0.023 | 0.014 | 0.013 | 0.035 | 0.030 | 0.023 | 0.015 |
| 4.6 | | 0.004 | 0.018 | 0.011 | 0.010 | 0.029 | 0.024 | 0.018 | 0.011 |
| 4.8 | | 0.003 | 0.014 | 0.009 | 0.008 | 0.024 | 0.020 | 0.015 | 0.008 |
| 5.0 | | 0.002 | 0.012 | 0.007 | 0.006 | 0.020 | 0.016 | 0.012 | 0.005 |

# APPENDIX 3

## Addenda

This appendix has been added (October, 1956) in proof. Its purpose is to refer briefly to developments in the subject of this book since the main text was written.

On the general theory of the approximate treatment of systems of many interacting particles are three papers by Löwdin[1] and on the more specific topic mentioned in § 6.7 there is the paper by Pratt to which reference is there given.

Miss C. Froese[2] has carried out calculations, with exchange, of the functions $Q$ and the limiting screening constants $\sigma_0$ of § 7.6 for configurations up to $(1s)^2$ $(2s)^2$ $(2p)^6$ $(3s)^2$ $(3p)^6$ $(3d)^{10}$ with not more than one incomplete group. For a full table of results, reference should be made to her paper; the following results, for configurations of closed groups, are given here:

| Configuration | Values of Limiting Screening $\sigma_0$ | | | | |
|---|---|---|---|---|---|
| | $(2s)$ | $(2p)$ | $(3s)$ | $(3p)$ | $(3d)$ |
| $(1s)^2$ $(2s)^2$ $(2p)^6$ | 3.28 | 4.35 | | | |
| $(1s)^2$ $(2s)^2$ $(2p)^6$ $(3s)^2$ $(3p)^6$ | 3.84 | 4.89 | 7.52 | 9.02 | |
| $(1s)^2$ $(2s)^2$ $(2p)^6$ $(3s)^2$ $(3p)^6$ $(3d)^{10}$ | 4.77 | 5.88 | 10.80 | 12.60 | 14.53 |

These results, combined with those derived from calculations for finite values of the atomic number (see Appendix 2, Table A1) show that *for a given configuration* the screening number $\sigma$ is nearly linear in $\bar{r}$ right from $\bar{r} = 0$ to the singly ionized atoms, and, where such results are available, even to neutral atoms and negative ions.

A simplified form of the method of § 7.4 for interpolating wave functions with respect to atomic number has been devised[3] which makes it unnecessary to use plots of the reduced wave function $P^*(nl; s)$ against $\bar{r}$ for each value of $s$ for which it is required to interpolate $P^*(nl; s)$.

A complete solution of the equations of the relativistic self-consistent field without exchange for $Hg^{+2}$ has been carried out by D. F. Mayers.[4] This atom is much heavier than $Cu^+$, the only one for which (as far as I know) relativistic calculations had previously been carried out (see § 9.3) and relativistic effects are correspondingly much more marked. In this work the equations used were those derived from § 9.2 (7), (8) and (9), (10) by use of $\log r$ as

[1] P.-O. Löwdin, *Phys. Rev.*, **97**, 1474, 1490, and 1509 (1955). See also P.-O. Löwdin and H. Shull, *Phys. Rev.*, **101**, 1730 (1956).

[2] C. Froese, *Proc. Roy. Soc.*, (in press).

[3] C. Froese and D. R. Hartree, *Proc. Cambridge Phil. Soc.* (in press).

[4] In preparation for publication.

independent variable, these equations being integrated outwards and inwards and matched, by adjustment of $\varepsilon(= -2E)$, at an intermediate radius $r_0$; the matching is done in terms of the ratio $Q/P$ for the two integrations. Mayers found that for the pair of first-order equations § 9.2 (7), (8) or (9), (10) there is a formula similar to § 5.3.1 (4) for estimating $\Delta\varepsilon$ from the degree of mismatch at $r_0$ between the solutions obtained by outward and inward integration. With a digital computer, this enables the determination of $\varepsilon$ to be made quite automatic, as in the nonrelativistic case.

The results show that relativistic effects on all $s$ and $p$ wave functions are appreciable, although, except for those with $n = 1$ and 2, the relativistic terms in the equations are small over most of the range of $r$ for which the wave functions are appreciable. The effect of these terms is to shift the phase of the oscillation of $P(r)$ with $r$; this phase shift persists in the outward integration, and ultimately affects the matching with the solution which tends to 0 as $r \to \infty$.

The following are addenda to Appendix 1. Calculations of wave functions with exchange have been carried out for $Ne^{+4}$ and results for $Ne^{+3}$ obtained by interpolation,[3] results for $Al^{+1}$ and $Fe^{+14}$ are included in reference 28 of Appendix 1. Calculations have also been done for $Fe^{+13}$ by Miss Froese[5] and for $Mn^{+4}$ by Piper,[6] and without exchange, for the $(3d)^7$ $(4s)$ and $(3d)^8$ configurations of $Fe^0$ by Stern,[7] and for $Ur^{+6}$ and $Ur^{+5}$ by Mrs. Ridley.[5] Some results derived from wave functions not yet published at the time of writing are included in Fig. 7.6 and Table A1. For $Ne^{+4}$, the values of $\bar{r}$ and $\sigma$, for addition to Table A1, are:

| | | | $\bar{r}_{2s}$ | $\sigma_{2s}$ | $\bar{r}_{2p}$ | $\sigma_{2p}$ |
|---|---|---|---|---|---|---|
| $Ne^{+4}$ | $(2p)^2$ | $^3P$ | $0.766_3$ | 2.17 | $0.699_7$ | 2.85 |

[5] In preparation for publication.

[6] W. W. Piper and J. S. Prener, *Phys. Rev.*, **100**, 1250 (1955). Calculations for the 28-electron sequence $Zn^{+2}$ to $Br^{+7}$ have also been carried out by Piper.

[7] F. Stern, *Phys. Rev.*, **98**, 1552 (1955).

# NAME INDEX

*Note:* References to Appendix 1 are not included in this Index.

# SUBJECT INDEX